Everyman, I will go with thee, and be thy guide,
In thy most need to go by thy side.

This is No. 958 of Everyman's Library

EVERYMAN'S LIBRARY

Founded 1906 by J. M. Dent (d. 1926)
Edited by Ernest Rhys (d. 1946)

ESSAYS & BELLES-LETTRES

STORIES, ESSAYS, AND POEMS
BY D. H. LAWRENCE SELECTED
WITH AN INTRODUCTION BY
DESMOND HAWKINS

DAVID HERBERT LAWRENCE, born on 11th September 1885 at Eastwood, Notts, the son of a coal miner. Educated at Nottingham High School and Nottingham University College, he became a teacher and settled in London. Much of his later life spent abroad. Died at Vence on 2nd March 1930.

STORIES, ESSAYS, AND POEMS

D. H. LAWRENCE

LONDON: J. M. DENT & SONS LTD

J. M. DENT & SONS LTD.
Aldine House · Bedford St. · London

Made in Great Britain
by
The Temple Press · Letchworth · Herts
This collection first published in 1939
Last reprinted 1949

INTRODUCTION

WHEN Byron died, young men wore a band of crape on their hats, and Jane Welsh wrote to Carlyle: 'If they had said the sun or the moon had gone out of the heavens, it could not have struck me with the idea of a more awful and dreary blank in the creation than the words: Byron is dead.' The sudden news, in March 1930, of the death of D. H. Lawrence at the early age of forty-four, had—as Rebecca West recorded in her *Elegy*—a similar effect. If the young wore no crape on their hats, it was only because they probably wore no hats either. The devotion and the sense of personal loss cannot be disputed: Lawrence was as eagerly championed, as warmly defended, as industriously imitated, as was Byron by contemporary admirers. During the twenties and early thirties, the prophetic voice which aroused the greatest enthusiasm among the post-War generation was Lawrence's.

The comparison with Byron is more than a chance resemblance, for Lawrence also was a man of great *personal* genius and of revolutionary significance. There is a kind of poet who lives his own poetry, so that his life and his works are scarcely to be separated. Of such, Byron is perhaps the supreme example. The young men who wore black crape for Byron were mourning, not only a poet, but a man whose way with life had seemed to initiate a revolt and to foreshadow an emancipation. And so it was with those who felt that Lawrence's death removed a protagonist who in some way focused and represented their own hopes and efforts.

In *Lady Chatterley's Lover* Lawrence wrote:

It is the way our sympathy flows and recoils that really determines our lives. And here lies the vast importance of the novel, properly handled. It can inform and lead into new places the flow of our sympathetic consciousness, and it can lead our sympathy away in recoil from things gone dead.

Increasingly Lawrence became an explorer of the 'flow and recoil' in the world about him. Ridiculing the Fabian belief in progressive intellectualism, Lawrence maintained that in Europe an excessive mental refinement had impoverished the blood, the vital 'flow and recoil' of emotion. He believed that Christian civilization was in ultimate decay, and that we were waiting for new gods to appear and initiate a fresh cycle: a belief which has much in common with the theory of Yeats. Accordingly Lawrence turned away from Europe and began his travels, exploring people and places throughout the world with such sensitivity to the spirit of place as only genius can display. Lawrence saw, not only the living people, but the ghosts that stand behind them: the vestiges of old religions, the special 'presence' of the Australian bush, the burden of the past in the American Indian. This ability to evoke the deepest reality of a place is one of Lawrence's greatest gifts. I have included the *Letter from Germany*, written in 1924, as a brilliant, topical, and astonishingly clairvoyant example; and there are masterly little sketches, of England in war-time, of the Red Sea, of pre-War Germany, in some of the letters which I have selected.

'The visible world is not true. The invisible world is true and real. One must live and work from that,' Lawrence wrote in a letter to Lady Cynthia Asquith. He was, for all that, a great lover of the visible world; and particularly a lover of flowers, ever since his childhood days in a Nottinghamshire mining village. The letters from Italy and Germany, on Lawrence's first journey abroad, are filled with delighted descriptions; and 'Flowery Tuscany' is surely unsurpassed, of its kind, by any writer in this century. But Lawrence, like Donne and Wordsworth and Blake, read the invisible world in the visible: the early exquisite portrayals of country life gave place to the voice of prophecy, and Lawrence increasingly devoted himself to calling a vulgar, mechanical, and insensitive world to repentance and reverence. In spite of his repudiations, he never broke away from his natural roots in Europe and England, and he admitted it. Even the bitterest of his attacks is interspersed with the playful malice of familiarity, the teasing and the underlying affection of kinship.

The poems and stories and sketches in this volume flower directly out of a life spent in a passionately experienced exploration of the 'flow and recoil' of sympathy. Even the slightest piece is stamped with the vivid and personal quality of Lawrence's vision. In a letter to Edward Garnett, his early adviser, Lawrence protested that he was not aiming to create more 'characters' within the traditional moral scheme of the European novel. Instead he endeavoured to penetrate through the dramas of the mental will to the elemental pattern of behaviour, the direct intuitive response. 'It is always interesting,' he wrote, in a letter to Lady Ottoline Morrell, 'to see the original self in man being modified by a big universal idea. One has to recover the original self now.' Lawrence's sympathy recoiled from most of the stock relationships and sentiments of the modern world. He felt, as other great writers have felt, that our sense of community—our at-oneness, as man to man—had been lost, and our individual relationships largely falsified by arbitrary 'feelings.' If I am to name Lawrence's most distinctive gift, I choose his insight into the obscure origins of human relationships. In one sense, all his stories and many of his poems are studies of the least articulate and most decisive movements of sympathy and antipathy between people. Lawrence's judgment is concentrated on our integrity, our reverence, our tenderness, our insouciance, and our recoil from 'things gone dead.' In the light of these standards he reviews contemporary society and transforms it in a new vision. The Lovely Lady (in the story of that title), the married couple in 'Things,' the hero of 'England, my England' — how differently they would have been presented in a Galsworthy novel or a Shaw play! They are familiar, easily recognizable characters; but the fineness and quickness of Lawrence's eye seizes an unexpected view of them, and our sympathy begins to recoil from a newly discovered evil in them, and to flow in a new way.

It is for that unique vision that we honour Lawrence. He has enriched our literature with a fresh idiom of human relationships, a new way of discerning and evaluating experience. He is one of the originators, one of the principal sources, of our time; there are few subsequent writers who do not acknowledge their indebtedness to Lawrence's previous explorations. He bequeaths to us a whole world of the imagination, a doctrine and an interpretation of life, rendered with the depth and vividness and powerful evocation of a great poet. He stands in vehement protest against our inhumanity, against the coldness of our hearts, against 'the iron of Idea and Ideal,' against pomposity and the scheming mental will. He is in the true succession of the Romantic prophets chastening a Philistine world; a worthy descendant of Blake and Whitman, a dominating figure in the literature of this century.

BIOGRAPHICAL NOTE

David Herbert Lawrence was born on 11th September 1885, the son of a collier, in the mining village of Eastwood in Nottinghamshire. Having qualified as a school-teacher, he took up a post in Croydon and remained there for two years. He had begun writing at an early age, and he resigned from the Croydon school when the publication of *The White Peacock* and the favourable reception of his poems made it plain that he had a different vocation. Encouraged by Edward Garnett, Ford Madox Ford, and Edward Marsh, Lawrence rapidly established himself as a distinguished and versatile new-comer, with remarkable gifts as a poet, a novelist, and a playwright. At this time Lawrence fell in love with a Mrs W—— and they left the country to live together in Germany and Italy. After Mrs W——'s divorce they were married, in July 1914.

In his early work Lawrence confined himself to mining themes and to descriptions of his native countryside, drawn with a delicate and sensitive touch. The escape from workaday Croydon to freedom in Europe, the adventure of marriage, the tonic of literary recognition, and then the outbreak of war, brought Lawrence rapidly to maturity. The inevitable rupture with Garnett occurred, and Lawrence destroyed his chances as a fashionable novelist with *The Rainbow*, a landmark in English fiction which was promptly banned. The singularity and courage of Lawrence's attitude to the War is revealed in his letters. Associated with Middleton Murry and Bertrand Russell, constantly forming groups to migrate and found a new civilization, Lawrence turned increasingly to the formulation of his personal philosophy. A ludicrous act of official buffoonery led to Lawrence's expulsion from Cornwall, under suspicion of being a spy; in the adversity of circumstances he came to see himself as an outlaw, against 'this social whole as it exists.' When the War ended, Lawrence left England and never again returned except as a passing visitor. In the decade following the War his fame spread widely. No other contemporary except Gandhi could inspire such fascinated bewilderment and sublime idiocies in the gutter-press; nor had Swinburne or Havelock Ellis had to contend with such vilification and such magisterial low comedy. Popularly Lawrence epitomized the subversive influences which seemed to menace the old order, and as such he was reviled and eulogized with equal vehemence.

Meanwhile, the tuberculosis which he had contracted in early life was beyond cure. In spite of it he maintained his prolific output of poems, pamphlets, and stories until his death at Vence in 1930. A vast body of memoirs, by his wife, his sister, and most of his friends, has since accumulated and gives an impressive testimony to Lawrence's magnetic and captivating personality.

The text of this volume is taken without abridgment (except in the Letters) from the editions published by William Heinemann Ltd, to whom, and to Mrs D. H. Lawrence, I am indebted for permission to avail myself with complete freedom of whatever I required for this selection. If there are lamentable omissions (and what selection is ever guiltless?) the fault is mine, and the excuse is the inevitable pressure of space. My primary aim has been to ensure that every phase and category of Lawrence's writing is adequately represented.

DESMOND HAWKINS.

BIBLIOGRAPHY

The following is a list of Lawrence's chief works with the date of their first appearance in book form:

Novels: *The White Peacock*, 1911; *The Trespasser*, 1912; *Sons and Lovers*, 1913; *The Rainbow*, 1915; *Women in Love*, 1920; *The Lost Girl*, 1920; *Aaron's Rod*, 1922; *Kangaroo*, 1923; *The Boy in the Bush* (with M. L. Skinner), 1924; *The Plumed Serpent*, 1926; *Lady Chatterley's Lover*, 1928; *The Virgin and the Gipsy*, 1930.

Shorter fiction: *The Prussian Officer*, 1914; *England, my England*, 1922; *The Ladybird*, 1923; *St Mawr (and The Princess)*, 1925; *Sun*, 1926 (unexpurgated edition, 1928); *Glad Ghosts*, 1926; *Rawdon's Roof*, 1928; *The Woman who rode away*, 1928; *The Escaped Cock*, 1929; *Love among the Haystacks*, 1930; *The Man who died*, 1931; *The Tales of D. H. Lawrence* (his collected shorter fiction), 1934; *A Modern Lover*, 1934.

Poetry: *Love Poems and Others*, 1913; *Amores*, 1916; *Look! We have come through*, 1917; *New Poems*, 1918; *Bay*, 1919; *Tortoises*, 1922; *Birds, Beasts, and Flowers*, 1923; *Collected Poems*, 1928 and 1932; *Pansies*, 1929; *Nettles*, 1930; *The Triumph of the Machine*, 1930; *Last Poems*, 1933.

Drama: *The Widowing of Mrs Holroyd*, 1914; *Touch and Go*, 1920; *David*, 1926; *Plays*, 1933; *A Collier's Friday Night*, 1934.

Essays, and other miscellaneous prose works: *Twilight in Italy*, 1916; *Sea and Sardinia*, 1921; *Psycho-analysis and the Unconscious*, 1921; *Movements in European History*, 1921; *Fantasia of the Unconscious*, 1923; *Studies in Classic American Literature*, 1923; *Reflections on the Death of a Porcupine*, 1925; *Mornings in Mexico*, 1927; *Sex locked out*, 1928; *My Skirmish with Jolly Roger*, 1929; *Pornography and Obscenity*, 1929; *Assorted Articles*, 1930; *Apropos of Lady Chatterley's Lover*, 1930; *Apocalypse*, 1931; *Letters*, 1932; *Etruscan Places*, 1932; *Phoenix*, 1936.

Lawrence also translated three volumes of Giovanni Verga (1923, 1925, and 1928) and *The Story of Dr Mamente* by A. F. Grazzini, 1929. A volume of his paintings was published in 1929.

Lives and studies of Lawrence include those by H. J. Seligmann, 1924; Richard Aldington, 1927 and 1930; Rebecca West, 1930; Stephen Potter, 1930; J. M. Murry (*Son of Woman*), 1931; Ada Lawrence and G. Stuart Gelder (*Early Life of D. H. Lawrence*), 1932; C. Carswell (*The Savage Pilgrimage*), 1932; E. and A. Brewster (*Reminiscences and Correspondence*), 1934; Frieda Lawrence—Lawrence's wife—(*Not I but the Wind . . .*), 1935; E. T. (*D. H. Lawrence—A Personal Record*), 1935. A bibliography was compiled by Edward D. McDonald in 1925 and a supplement was issued in 1931.

CONTENTS

STORIES

ODOUR OF CHRYSANTHEMUMS

I

THE small locomotive engine, Number 4, came clanking, stumbling down from Selston with seven full wagons. It appeared round the corner with loud threats of speed, but the colt that it startled from among the gorse, which still flickered indistinctly in the raw afternoon, outdistanced it at a canter. A woman, walking up the railway line to Underwood, drew back into the hedge, held her basket aside, and watched the footplate of the engine advancing. The trucks thumped heavily past, one by one, with slow inevitable movement, as she stood insignificantly trapped between the jolting black wagons and the hedge; then they curved away towards the coppice where the withered oak leaves dropped noiselessly, while the birds, pulling at the scarlet hips beside the track, made off into the dusk that had already crept into the spinney. In the open, the smoke from the engine sank and cleaved to the rough grass. The fields were dreary and forsaken, and in the marshy strip that led to the whimsey, a reedy pit-pond, the fowls had already abandoned their run among the alders, to roost in the tarred fowl-house. The pit-bank loomed up beyond the pond, flames like red sores licking its ashy sides, in the afternoon's stagnant light. Just beyond rose the tapering chimneys and the clumsy black headstocks of Brinsley Colliery. The two wheels were spinning fast up against the sky, and the winding-engine rapped out its little spasms. The miners were being turned up.

The engine whistled as it came into the wide bay of railway lines beside the colliery, where rows of trucks stood in harbour.

Miners, single, trailing, and in groups, passed like shadows diverging home. At the edge of the ribbed level of sidings squat a low cottage, three steps down from the cinder track. A large bony vine clutched at the house, as if to claw down the tiled roof. Round the bricked yard grew a few wintry primroses. Beyond, the long garden sloped down to a bush-covered brook course. There were some twiggy apple-trees, winter-crack trees, and ragged cabbages. Beside the path hung dishevelled pink chrysanthemums, like pink cloths hung on bushes. A woman came stooping out of the felt-covered fowl-house, half-way down the garden. She closed and pad-locked the door, then drew herself erect, having brushed some bits from her white apron.

She was a tall woman of imperious mien, handsome, with definite black eyebrows. Her smooth black hair was parted exactly. For a few moments she stood steadily watching the miners as they passed along the railway: then she turned towards the brook course. Her face was calm and set, her mouth was closed with disillusionment. After a moment she called:

'John!' There was no answer. She waited, and then said distinctly:

'Where are you?'

'Here!' replied a child's sulky voice from among the bushes. The woman looked piercingly through the dusk.

'Are you at that brook?' she asked sternly.

For answer the child showed himself before the rasp-berry canes that rose like whips. He was a small, sturdy boy of five. He stood quite still, defiantly.

'Oh!' said the mother, conciliated. 'I thought you were down at that wet brook—and you remember what I told you——'

The boy did not move or answer.

'Come, come on in,' she said more gently, 'it's getting dark. There's your grandfather's engine coming down the line!'

The lad advanced slowly, with resentful, taciturn movement. He was dressed in trousers and waistcoat of cloth that was too thick and hard for the size of the garments. They were evidently cut down from a man's clothes.

As they went slowly towards the house he tore at the ragged wisps of chrysanthemums and dropped the petals in handfuls along the path.

'Don't do that—it does look nasty,' said his mother. He refrained, and she, suddenly pitiful, broke off a twig with three or four wan flowers and held them against her face. When mother and son reached the yard her hand hesitated, and instead of laying the flower aside, she pushed it in her apron-band. The mother and son stood at the foot of the three steps looking across the bay of lines at the passing home of the miners. The trundle of the small train was imminent. Suddenly the engine loomed past the house and came to a stop opposite the gate.

The engine-driver, a short man with round grey beard, leaned out of the cab high above the woman.

'Have you got a cup of tea?' he said in a cheery, hearty fashion.

It was her father. She went in, saying she would mash. Directly, she returned.

'I didn't come to see you on Sunday,' began the little grey-bearded man.

'I didn't expect you,' said his daughter.

The engine-driver winced; then, reassuming his cheery, airy manner, he said:

'Oh, have you heard then? Well, and what do you think——?'

'I think it is soon enough,' she replied.

At her brief censure the little man made an impatient gesture, and said coaxingly, yet with dangerous coldness:

'Well, what 's a man to do? It 's no sort of life for a man of my years, to sit at my own hearth like a stranger. And if I 'm going to marry again it may as well be soon as late—what does it matter to anybody?'

The woman did not reply, but turned and went into the house. The man in the engine-cab stood assertive, till she returned with a cup of tea and a piece of bread and butter on a plate. She went up the steps and stood near the footplate of the hissing engine.

'You needn't 'a' brought me bread an' butter,' said

her father. 'But a cup of tea'—he sipped appreciatively—'it's very nice.' He sipped for a moment or
two, then: 'I hear as Walter's got another bout on,'
he said.

'When hasn't he?' said the woman bitterly.

'I heered tell of him in the "Lord Nelson" braggin' as
he was going to spend that b—— afore he went: half a
sovereign that was.'

'When?' asked the woman.

'A' Sat'day night—I know that's true.'

'Very likely,' she laughed bitterly. 'He gives me
twenty-three shillings.'

'Ay, it's a nice thing, when a man can do nothing
with his money but make a beast of himself!' said the
grey-whiskered man. The woman turned her head
away. Her father swallowed the last of his tea and
handed her the cup.

'Ay,' he sighed, wiping his mouth. 'It's a settler,
it is——'

He put his hand on the lever. The little engine
strained and groaned, and the train rumbled towards
the crossing. The woman again looked across the metals.
Darkness was settling over the spaces of the railway and
trucks: the miners, in grey sombre groups, were still
passing home. The winding-engine pulsed hurriedly,
with brief pauses. Elizabeth Bates looked at the
dreary flow of men, then she went indoors. Her husband
did not come.

The kitchen was small and full of firelight; red coals
piled glowing up the chimney mouth. All the life of
the room seemed in the white, warm hearth and the
steel fender reflecting the red fire. The cloth was laid
for tea; cups glinted in the shadows. At the back,
where the lowest stairs protruded into the room, the
boy sat struggling with a knife and a piece of whitewood.
He was almost hidden in the shadow. It was half-past
four. They had but to await the father's coming to
begin tea. As the mother watched her son's sullen
little struggle with the wood, she saw herself in his
silence and pertinacity; she saw the father in her child's

indifference to all but himself. She seemed to be occupied by her husband. He had probably gone past his home, slung past his own door, to drink before he came in, while his dinner spoiled and wasted in waiting. She glanced at the clock, then took the potatoes to strain them in the yard. The garden and fields beyond the brook were closed in uncertain darkness. When she rose with the saucepan, leaving the drain steaming into the night behind her, she saw the yellow lamps were lit along the high road that went up the hill away beyond the space of the railway lines and the field.

Then again she watched the men trooping home, fewer now and fewer.

Indoors the fire was sinking and the room was dark red. The woman put her saucepan on the hob, and set a batter pudding near the mouth of the oven. Then she stood unmoving. Directly, gratefully, came quick young steps to the door. Someone hung on the latch a moment, then a little girl entered and began pulling off her outdoor things, dragging a mass of curls, just ripening from gold to brown, over her eyes with her hat.

Her mother chid her for coming late from school, and said she would have to keep her at home the dark winter days.

'Why, mother, it's hardly a bit dark yet. The lamp's not lighted, and my father's not home.'

'No, he isn't. But it's a quarter to five. Did you see anything of him?'

The child became serious. She looked at her mother with large, wistful blue eyes.

'No, mother, I've never seen him. Why? Has he come up an' gone past, to Old Brinsley? He hasn't, mother, 'cos I never saw him.'

'He'd watch that,' said the mother bitterly, 'he'd take care as you didn't see him. But you may depend upon it, he's seated in the "Prince o' Wales." He wouldn't be this late.'

The girl looked at her mother piteously.

'Let's have our teas, mother, should we?' said she.

The mother called John to table. She opened the

door once more and looked out across the darkness of the
lines. All was deserted: she could not hear the winding-
engines.

'Perhaps,' she said to herself, 'he's stopped to get
some ripping done.'

They sat down to tea. John, at the end of the table
near the door, was almost lost in the darkness. Their
faces were hidden from each other. The girl crouched
against the fender slowly moving a thick piece of bread
before the fire. The lad, his face a dusky mark on the
shadow, sat watching her who was transfigured in the
red glow.

'I do think it's beautiful to look in the fire,' said the
child.

'Do you?' said her mother. 'Why?'

'It's so red, and full of little caves—and feels so nice
and you can fair smell it.'

'It'll want mending directly,' replied her mother, 'and
then if your father comes he'll carry on and say there
never is a fire when a man comes home sweating from
the pit. A public-house is always warm enough.'

There was silence till the boy said complainingly:
'Make haste, our Annie.'

'Well, I am doing! I can't make the fire do it no
faster, can I?'

'She keeps wafflin' it about so's to make 'er slow,'
grumbled the boy.

'Don't have such an evil imagination, child,' replied
the mother.

Soon the room was busy in the darkness with the crisp
sound of crunching. The mother ate very little. She
drank her tea determinedly, and sat thinking. When
she rose her anger was evident in the stern unbending
of her head. She looked at the pudding in the fender,
and broke out:

'It is a scandalous thing as a man can't even come
home to his dinner! If it's crozzled up to a cinder I
don't see why I should care. Past his very door he
goes to get to a public-house, and here I sit with his
dinner waiting for him——'

She went out. As she dropped piece after piece of coal on the red fire, the shadows fell on the walls, till the room was almost in total darkness.

'I canna see,' grumbled the invisible John. In spite of herself, the mother laughed.

'You know the way to your mouth,' she said. She set the dustpan outside the door. When she came again like a shadow on the hearth, the lad repeated, complaining sulkily:

'I canna see.'

'Good gracious!' cried the mother irritably, 'you 're as bad as your father if it 's a bit dusk!'

Nevertheless she took a paper spill from a sheaf on the mantelpiece and proceeded to light the lamp that hung from the ceiling in the middle of the room. As she reached up, her figure displayed itself just rounding with maternity.

'Oh, mother——!' exclaimed the girl.

'What?' said the woman, suspended in the act of putting the lamp glass over the flame. The copper reflector shone handsomely on her, as she stood with up-lifted arm, turning to face her daughter.

'You 've got a flower in your apron!' said the child, in a little rapture at this unusual event.

'Goodness me!' exclaimed the woman, relieved. 'One would think the house was afire.' She replaced the glass and waited a moment before turning up the wick. A pale shadow was seen floating vaguely on the floor.

'Let me smell!' said the child, still rapturously, coming forward and putting her face to her mother's waist.

'Go along, silly!' said the mother, turning up the lamp. The light revealed their suspense so that the woman felt it almost unbearable. Annie was still bending at her waist. Irritably, the mother took the flowers out from her apron-band.

'Oh, mother—don't take them out!' Annie cried, catching her hand and trying to replace the sprig.

'Such nonsense!' said the mother, turning away.

The child put the pale chrysanthemums to her lips, murmuring:

'Don't they smell beautiful!'

Her mother gave a short laugh.

'No,' she said, 'not to me. It was chrysanthemums when I married him, and chrysanthemums when you were born, and the first time they ever brought him home, drunk, he'd got brown chrysanthemums in his button-hole.'

She looked at the children. Their eyes and their parted lips were wondering. The mother sat rocking in silence for some time. Then she looked at the clock.

'Twenty minutes to six!' In a tone of fine bitter carelessness she continued: 'Eh, he'll not come now till they bring him. There he'll stick! But he needn't come rolling in here in his pit-dirt, for *I* won't wash him. He can lie on the floor—— Eh, what I fool I've been, what a fool! And this is what I came here for, to this dirty hole, rats and all, for him to slink past his very door. Twice last week—he's begun now——'

She silenced herself, and rose to clear the table.

While for an hour or more the children played, sub-duedly intent, fertile of imagination, united in fear of the mother's wrath, and in dread of their father's home-coming, Mrs Bates sat in her rocking-chair making a 'singlet' of thick cream-coloured flannel, which gave a dull wounded sound as she tore off the grey edge. She worked at her sewing with energy, listening to the children, and her anger wearied itself, lay down to rest, opening its eyes from time to time and steadily watching, its ears raised to listen. Sometimes even her anger quailed and shrank, and the mother suspended her sewing, tracing the footsteps that thudded along the sleepers outside; she would lift her head sharply to bid the children 'hush,' but she recovered herself in time, and the footsteps went past the gate, and the children were not flung out of their play-world.

But at last Annie sighed, and gave in. She glanced at her wagon of slippers, and loathed the game. She turned plaintively to her mother.

'Mother!'—but she was inarticulate.

John crept out like a frog from under the sofa. His mother glanced up.

'Yes,' she said, 'just look at those shirt-sleeves!'

The boy held them out to survey them, saying nothing. Then somebody called in a hoarse voice away down the line, and suspense bristled in the room, till two people had gone by outside, talking.

'It is time for bed,' said the mother.

'My father hasn't come,' wailed Annie plaintively. But her mother was primed with courage.

'Never mind. They'll bring him when he does come—like a log.' She meant there would be no scene. 'And he may sleep on the floor till he wakes himself. I know he'll not go to work to-morrow after this!'

The children had their hands and faces wiped with a flannel. They were very quiet. When they had put on their nightdresses, they said their prayers, the boy mumbling. The mother looked down at them, at the brown silken bush of intertwining curls in the nape of the girl's neck, at the little black head of the lad, and her heart burst with anger at their father who caused all three such distress. The children hid their faces in her skirts for comfort.

When Mrs Bates came down, the room was strangely empty, with a tension of expectancy. She took up her sewing and stitched for some time without raising her head. Meantime her anger was tinged with fear.

II

The clock struck eight and she rose suddenly, dropping her sewing on her chair. She went to the stairfoot door, opened it, listening. Then she went out, locking the door behind her.

Something scuffled in the yard, and she started, though she knew it was only the rats with which the place was overrun. The night was very dark. In the great bay of railway lines, bulked with trucks, there was no trace of light, only away back she could see a few

yellow lamps at the pit-top, and the red smear of the
burning pit-bank on the night. She hurried along the
edge of the track, then, crossing the converging lines,
came to the stile by the white gates, whence she emerged
on the road. Then the fear which had led her shrank.
People were walking up to New Brinsley; she saw the
lights in the houses; twenty yards further on were the
broad windows of the 'Prince of Wales,' very warm
and bright, and the loud voices of men could be heard
distinctly. What a fool she had been to imagine that
anything had happened to him! He was merely drinking over there at the 'Prince of Wales.' She faltered.
She had never yet been to fetch him, and she never
would go. So she continued her walk towards the long
straggling line of houses, standing blank on the highway.
She entered a passage between the dwellings.

'Mr Rigley?—Yes! Did you want him? No, he's
not in at this minute.'

The raw-boned woman leaned forward from her dark
scullery and peered at the other, upon whom fell a dim
light through the blind of the kitchen window.

'Is it Mrs Bates?' she asked in a tone tinged with
respect.

'Yes. I wondered if your master was at home.
Mine hasn't come yet.'

''Asn't 'e! Oh, Jack's been 'ome an' 'ad 'is dinner
an' gone out. 'E's just gone for 'alf an hour afore
bedtime. Did you call at the "Prince of Wales"?'

'No——'

'No, you didn't like——! It's not very nice.' The
other woman was indulgent. There was an awkward
pause. 'Jack never said nothink about—about your
mester,' she said.

'No!—I expect he's stuck in there!'

Elizabeth Bates said this bitterly, and with recklessness. She knew that the woman across the yard was
standing at her door listening, but she did not care.
As she turned:

'Stop a minute! I'll just go an' ask Jack if 'e knows
anythink,' said Mrs Rigley.

'Oh, no—I wouldn't like to put—— !'

'Yes, I will, if you'll just step inside an' see as th' childer doesn't come downstairs and set theirselves afire.'

Elizabeth Bates, murmuring a remonstrance, stepped inside. The other woman apologized for the state of the room.

The kitchen needed apology. There were little frocks and trousers and childish undergarments on the squab and on the floor, and a litter of playthings everywhere. On the black American cloth of the table were pieces of bread and cake, crusts, slops, and a teapot with cold tea.

'Eh, ours is just as bad,' said Elizabeth Bates, looking at the woman, not at the house. Mrs Rigley put a shawl over her head and hurried out, saying:

'I shanna be a minute.'

The other sat, noting with faint disapproval the general untidiness of the room. Then she fell to counting the shoes of various sizes scattered over the floor. There were twelve. She sighed and said to herself: 'No wonder!'—glancing at the litter. There came the scratching of two pairs of feet on the yard, and the Rigleys entered. Elizabeth Bates rose. Rigley was a big man, with very large bones. His head looked particularly bony. Across his temple was a blue scar, caused by a wound got in the pit, a wound in which the coal-dust remained blue like tattooing.

''Asna 'e come whoam yit?' asked the man, without any form of greeting, but with deference and sympathy. 'I couldna say wheer he is—'e 's non ower theer!'—he jerked his head to signify the 'Prince of Wales.'

''E 's 'appen gone up to th' "Yew,"' said Mrs Rigley.

There was another pause. Rigley had evidently something to get off his mind:

'Ah left 'im finishin' a stint,' he began. 'Loose-all 'ad bin gone about ten minutes when we com'n away, an' I shouted: "Are ter comin', Walt?" an' 'e said: "Go on, Ah shanna be but a' ef a minnit," so we com'n ter th' bottom, me an' Bowers, thinkin' as 'e wor just behint, an' 'ud come up i' the' next bantle——'

He stood perplexed, as if answering a charge of

deserting his mate. Elizabeth Bates, now again certain of disaster, hastened to reassure him:

'I expect 'e's gone up to th' "Yew Tree," as you say. It's not the first time. I've fretted myself into a fever before now. He'll come home when they carry him.'

'Ay, isn't it too bad!' deplored the other woman.

'I'll just step up to Dick's an' see if 'e *is* theer,' offered the man, afraid of appearing alarmed, afraid of taking liberties.

'Oh, I wouldn't think of bothering you that far,' said Elizabeth Bates, with emphasis, but he knew she was glad of his offer.

As they stumbled up the entry, Elizabeth Bates heard Rigley's wife run across the yard and open her neighbour's door. At this, suddenly all the blood in her body seemed to switch away from her heart.

'Mind!' warned Rigley. 'Ah 've said many a time as Ah 'd fill up them ruts in this entry, sumb'dy 'll be breakin' their legs yit.'

She recovered herself and walked quickly along with the miner.

'I don't like leaving the children in bed, and nobody in the house,' she said.

'No, you dunna!' he replied courteously. They were soon at the gate of the cottage.

'Well, I shanna be many minnits. Dunna you be frettin' now, 'e 'll be all right,' said the butty.

'Thank you very much, Mr Rigley,' she replied.

'You're welcome!' he stammered, moving away. 'I shanna be many minnits.'

The house was quiet. Elizabeth Bates took off her hat and shawl, and rolled back the rug. When she had finished, she sat down. It was a few minutes past nine. She was startled by the rapid chuff of the winding-engine at the pit, and the sharp whirr of the brakes on the rope as it descended. Again she felt the painful sweep of her blood, and she put her hand to her side, saying aloud: 'Good gracious!—it's only the nine o'clock deputy going down,' rebuking herself.

She sat still, listening. Half an hour of this, and she was wearied out.

'What am I working myself up like this for?' she said pitiably to herself, 'I s'll only be doing myself some damage.'

She took out her sewing again.

At a quarter to ten there were footsteps. One person! She watched for the door to open. It was an elderly woman, in a black bonnet and a black woollen shawl—his mother. She was about sixty years old, pale, with blue eyes, and her face all wrinkled and lamentable. She shut the door and turned to her daughter-in-law peevishly.

'Eh, Lizzie, whatever shall we do, whatever shall we do!' she cried.

Elizabeth drew back a little, sharply.

'What is it, mother?' she said.

The elder woman seated herself on the sofa.

'I don't know, child, I can't tell you!'—she shook her head slowly. Elizabeth sat watching her, anxious and vexed.

'I don't know,' replied the grandmother, sighing very deeply. 'There's no end to my troubles, there isn't. The things I've gone through, I'm sure it's enough——' She wept without wiping her eyes, the tears running.

'But, mother,' interrupted Elizabeth, 'what do you mean? What is it?'

The grandmother slowly wiped her eyes. The fountains of her tears were stopped by Elizabeth's directness. She wiped her eyes slowly.

'Poor child! Eh, you poor thing!' she moaned. 'I don't know what we're going to do, I don't—and you as you are—it's a thing, it is indeed!'

Elizabeth waited.

'Is he dead?' she asked, and at the words her heart swung violently, though she felt a slight flush of shame at the ultimate extravagance of the question. Her words sufficiently frightened the old lady, almost brought her to herself.

'Don't say so, Elizabeth! We'll hope it's not as

bad as that; no, may the Lord spare us that, Elizabeth. Jack Rigley came just as I was sittin' down to a glass afore going to bed, an' 'e said, "'Appen you 'll go down th' line, Mrs Bates. Walt 's had an accident. 'Appen you 'll go an' sit wi' 'er till we can get him home." I hadn't time to ask him a word afore he was gone. An' I put my bonnet on an' come straight down, Lizzie. I thought to myself: "Eh, that poor blessed child, if anybody should come an' tell her of a sudden, there 's no knowin' what 'll 'appen to 'er." You mustn't let it upset you, Lizzie—or you know what to expect. How long is it, six months—or is it five, Lizzie? Ay!'—the old woman shook her head—'time slips on, it slips on! Ay!'

Elizabeth's thoughts were busy elsewhere. If he was killed—would she be able to manage on the little pension and what she could earn?—she counted up rapidly. If he was hurt—they wouldn't take him to the hospital —how tiresome he would be to nurse!—but perhaps she 'd be able to get him away from the drink and his hateful ways. She would—while he was ill. The tears offered to come to her eyes at the picture. But what sentimental luxury was this she was beginning? She turned to consider the children. At any rate she was absolutely necessary for them. They were her business.

'Ay!' repeated the old woman, 'it seems but a week or two since he brought me his first wages. Ay—he was a good lad, Elizabeth, he was, in his way. I don't know why he got to be such a trouble, I don't. He was a happy lad at home, only full of spirits. But there 's no mistake he 's been a handful of trouble, he has! I hope the Lord 'll spare him to mend his ways. I hope so, I hope so. You 've had a sight o' trouble with him, Elizabeth, you have indeed. But he was a jolly enough lad wi' me, he was, I can assure you. I don't know how it is. . . .'

The old woman continued to muse aloud, a monotonous irritating sound, while Elizabeth thought concentratedly, startled once, when she heard the winding-engine chuff quickly, and the brakes skirr with a shriek. Then she heard the engine more slowly, and the brakes made no sound. The old woman did not notice. Elizabeth waited in suspense. The mother-in-law talked, with lapses into silence.

'But he wasn't your son, Lizzie, an' it makes a difference. Whatever he was, I remember him when he was little, an' I learned to understand him and to make allowances. You've got to make allowances for them——'

It was half-past ten, and the old woman was saying: 'But it's trouble from beginning to end; you're never too old for trouble, never too old for that——' when the gate banged back, and there were heavy feet on the steps.

'I'll go, Lizzie, let me go,' cried the old woman, rising. But Elizabeth was at the door. It was a man in pit-clothes.

'They're bringin' 'im, missis,' he said. Elizabeth's heart halted a moment. Then it surged on again, almost suffocating her.

'Is he—is it bad?' she asked.

The man turned away, looking at the darkness:

'The doctor says 'e'd been dead hours. 'E saw 'im i' th' lamp-cabin.'

The old woman, who stood just behind Elizabeth, dropped into a chair, and folded her hands, crying: 'Oh, my boy, my boy!'   . .

'Hush!' said Elizabeth, with a sharp twitch of a frown. 'Be still, mother, don't waken th' children: I wouldn't have them down for anything!'

The old woman moaned softly, rocking herself. The man was drawing away. Elizabeth took a step forward.

'How was it?' she asked.

'Well, I couldn't say for sure,' the man replied, very ill at ease. ''E wor finishin' a stint an' th' butties 'ad gone, an' a lot o' stuff come down atop 'n 'im.'

'And crushed him?' cried the widow, with a shudder.

'No,' said the man, 'it fell at th' back of 'im. 'E wor under th' face, an' it niver touched 'im. It shut 'im in. It seems 'e wor smothered.'

Elizabeth shrank back. She heard the old woman behind her cry:

'What?—what did 'e say it was?'

The man replied, more loudly: ''E wor smothered.'

Then the old woman wailed aloud, and this relieved Elizabeth.

'Oh, mother,' she said, putting her hand on the old woman, 'don't waken th' children, don't waken th' children.'

She wept a little, unknowing, while the old mother rocked herself and moaned. Elizabeth remembered that they were bringing him home, and she must be ready. 'They.'ll lay him in the parlour,' she said to herself, standing a moment pale and perplexed.

Then she lighted a candle and went into the tiny room. The air was cold and damp, but she could not make a fire, there was no fire-place. She set down the candle and looked round. The candlelight glittered on the lustre-glasses, on the two vases that held some of the pink chrysanthemums, and on the dark mahogany. There was a cold, deathly smell of chrysanthemums in the room. Elizabeth stood looking at the flowers. She turned away, and calculated whether there would be room to lay him on the floor, between the couch and the chiffonier. She pushed the chairs aside. There would be room to lay him down and to step round him. Then she fetched the old red tablecloth, and another old cloth, spreading them down to save her bit of carpet. She shivered on leaving the parlour; so, from the dresser-drawer she took a clean shirt and put it at the fire to air. All the time her mother-in-law was rocking herself in the chair and moaning.

'You'll have to move from there, mother,' said Elizabeth. 'They'll be bringing him in. Come in the rocker.'

The old mother rose mechanically, and seated herself by the fire, continuing to lament. Elizabeth went into the pantry for another candle, and there, in the little penthouse under the naked tiles, she heard them coming. She stood still in the pantry doorway, listening. She heard them pass the end of the house, and come awkwardly down the three steps, a jumble of shuffling footsteps and muttering voices. The old woman was silent. The men were in the yard.

Then Elizabeth heard Matthews, the manager of the pit, say: 'You go in first, Jim. Mind!'

The door came open, and the two women saw a collier backing into the room, holding one end of a stretcher, on which they could see the nailed pit-boots of the dead man. The two carriers halted, the man at the head stooping to the lintel of the door.

'Wheer will you have him?' asked the manager, a short, white-bearded man.

Elizabeth roused herself and came from the pantry carrying the unlighted candle.

'In the parlour,' she said.

'In there, Jim!' pointed the manager, and the carriers backed round into the tiny room. The coat with which they had covered the body fell off as they awkwardly turned through the two doorways, and the women saw their man, naked to the waist, lying stripped for work. The old woman began to moan in a low voice of horror.

'Lay th' stretcher at th' side,' snapped the manager, 'an' put 'im on th' cloths. Mind now, mind! Look you now——'

One of the men had knocked off a vase of chrysanthemums. He stared awkwardly, then they set down the stretcher. Elizabeth did not look at her husband. As soon as she could get in the room, she went and picked up the broken vase and the flowers.

'Wait a minute!' she said.

The three men waited in silence while she mopped up the water with a duster.

'Eh, what a job, to be sure!' the manager was saying, rubbing his brow with trouble and perplexity. 'Never knew such a thing in my life, never! He'd no business to ha' been left. I never knew such a thing in my life! Fell over him clean as a whistle, an' shut him in. Not four foot of space, there wasn't—yet it scarce bruised him.'

He looked down at the dead man, lying prone, half naked, all grimed with coal-dust.

'"'Sphyxiated," the doctor said. It *is* the most terrible job I 've ever known. Seems as if it was done o' purpose. Clean over him, an' shut 'im in, like a mouse-trap'—he made a sharp, descending gesture with his hand.

The colliers standing by jerked aside their heads in hopeless comment.

The horror of the thing bristled upon them all.

Then they heard the girl's voice upstairs calling shrilly: 'Mother, mother—who is it? Mother, who is it?'

Elizabeth hurried to the foot of the stairs and opened the door:

'Go to sleep!' she commanded sharply. 'What are you shouting about? Go to sleep at once—there 's nothing——'

Then she began to mount the stairs. They could hear her on the boards, and on the plaster floor of the little bedroom. They could hear her distinctly:

'What 's the matter now?—what 's the matter with you, silly thing?'—her voice was much agitated, with an unreal gentleness.

'I thought it was some men come,' said the plaintive voice of the child. 'Has he come?'

'Yes, they 've brought him. There 's nothing to make a fuss about. Go to sleep now, like a good child.'

They could hear her voice in the bedroom, they waited whilst she covered the children under the bedclothes.

'Is he drunk?' asked the girl, timidly, faintly.

'No! No—he 's not! He—he 's asleep.'

'Is he asleep downstairs?'

'Yes—and don't make a noise.'

There was silence for a moment, then the men heard the frightened child again:

'What 's that noise?'

'It 's nothing, I tell you, what are you bothering for?'

The noise was the grandmother moaning. She was oblivious of everything, sitting on her chair rocking and moaning. The manager put his hand on her arm and bade her 'Sh—ssh!'

The old woman opened her eyes and looked at him. She was shocked by this interruption, and seemed to wonder.

'What time is it?' The plaintive thin voice of the child, sinking back unhappily into sleep, asked this last question.

'Ten o'clock,' answered the mother more softly. Then she must have bent down and kissed the children.

Matthews beckoned to the men to come away. They put on their caps and took up the stretcher. Stepping over the body, they tiptoed out of the house. None of them spoke till they were far from the wakeful children.

When Elizabeth came down she found her mother alone on the parlour floor, leaning over the dead man, the tears dropping on him.

'We must lay him out,' the wife said. She put on the kettle, then returning knelt at the feet, and began to unfasten the knotted leather laces. The room was clammy and dim with only one candle, so that she had to bend her face almost to the floor. At last she got off the heavy boots and put them away.

'You must help me now,' she whispered to the old woman. Together they stripped the man.

When they arose, saw him lying in the naïve dignity of death, the women stood arrested in fear and respect. For a few moments they remained still, looking down, the old mother whimpering. Elizabeth felt countermanded. She saw him, how utterly inviolable he lay in himself. She had nothing to do with him. She could not accept it. Stooping, she laid her hand on him, in claim. He was still warm, for the mine was hot where he had died. His mother had his face between her hands, and was murmuring incoherently. The old tears fell in succession as drops from wet leaves; the mother was not weeping, merely her tears flowed. Elizabeth embraced the body of her husband, with cheek and lips. She seemed to be listening, inquiring, trying to get some

connection. But she could not. She was driven away.
He was impregnable.

She rose, went into the kitchen, where she poured
warm water into a bowl, brought soap and flannel and a
soft towel.

'I must wash him,' she said.

Then the old mother rose stiffly, and watched Elizabeth as she carefully washed his face, carefully brushing
the big blond moustache from his mouth with the
flannel. She was afraid with a bottomless fear, so she
ministered to him. The old woman, jealous, said:

'Let me wipe him!'—and she kneeled on the other side
drying slowly as Elizabeth washed, her big black bonnet
sometimes brushing the dark head of her daughter-in-
law. They worked thus in silence for a long time. They
never forgot it was death, and the touch of the man's
dead body gave them strange emotions, different in each
of the women; a great dread possessed them both, the
mother felt the lie was given to her womb, she was
denied; the wife felt the utter isolation of the human
soul, the child within her was a weight apart from her.

At last it was finished. He was a man of handsome
body, and his face showed no traces of drink. He was
blond, full-fleshed, with fine limbs. But he was dead.

'Bless him,' whispered his mother, looking always
at his face, and speaking out of sheer terror. 'Dear
lad—bless him!' She spoke in a faint, sibilant ecstasy
of fear and mother love.

Elizabeth sank down again to the floor, and put her
face against his neck, and trembled and shuddered.
But she had to draw away again. He was dead, and her
living flesh had no place against his. A great dread and
weariness held her: she was so unavailing. Her life
was gone like this.

'White as milk he is, clear as a twelve-month baby,
bless him, the darling!' the old mother murmured to
herself. 'Not a mark on him, clear and clean and white,
beautiful as ever a child was made,' she murmured with
pride. Elizabeth kept her face hidden.

'He went peaceful, Lizzie—peaceful as sleep. Isn't

he beautiful, the lamb? Ay, he must ha' made his peace, Lizzie. 'Appen he made it all right, Lizzie, shut in there. He'd have time. He wouldn't look like this if he hadn't made his peace. The lamb, the dear lamb. Eh, but he had a hearty laugh. I loved to hear it. He had the heartiest laugh, Lizzie, as a lad——'

Elizabeth looked up. The man's mouth was fallen back, slightly open under the cover of the moustache. The eyes, half shut, did not show glazed in the obscurity. Life with its smoky burning gone from him, had left him apart and utterly alien to her. And she knew what a stranger he was to her. In her womb was ice of fear, because of this separate stranger with whom she had been living as one flesh. Was this what it all meant— utter, intact, separateness, obscured by heat of living? In dread she turned her face away. The fact was too deadly. There had been nothing between them, and yet they had come together, exchanging their nakedness repeatedly. Each time he had taken her, they had been two isolated beings, far apart as now. He was no more responsible than she. The child was like ice in her womb. For as she looked at the dead man, her mind, cold and detached, said clearly: 'Who am I? What have I been doing? I have been fighting a husband who did not exist. *He* existed all the time. What wrong have I done? What was that I have been living with? There lies the reality, this man.' And her soul died in her for fear: she knew she had never seen him, he had never seen her, they had met in the dark, and had fought in the dark, not knowing whom they met nor whom they fought. And now she saw, and turned silent in seeing. For she had been wrong. She had said he was something he was not; she had felt familiar with him. Whereas he was apart all the while, living as she never lived, feeling as she never felt.

In fear and shame she looked at his naked body, that she had known falsely. And he was the father of her children. Her soul was torn from her body and stood apart. She looked at his naked body and was ashamed, as if she had denied it. After all, it was itself. It seemed awful to her. She looked at his face, and she turned her own face to the wall. For his look was other than hers, his way was not her way. She had denied him what he was—she saw it now. She had refused him as himself. And this had been her life, and his life. She was grateful to death, which restored the truth. And she knew she was not dead.

And all the while her heart was bursting with grief and pity for him. What had he suffered? What stretch of horror for this helpless man! She was rigid with agony. She had not been able to help him. He had been cruelly injured, this naked man, this other being, and she could make no reparation. There were the children—but the children belonged to life. This dead man had nothing to do with them. He and she were only channels through which life had flowed to issue in the children. She was a mother—but how awful she knew it now to have been a wife. And he, dead now, knew how awful he must have felt it to be a husband. She felt that in the next world he would be a stranger to her. If they met there, in the beyond, they would only be ashamed of what had been before. The children had come, for some mysterious reason, out of both of them. But the children did not unite them. Now he was dead, she knew how eternally he was apart from her, how eternally he had nothing more to do with her. She saw this episode of her life closed. They had denied each other in life. Now he had withdrawn. An anguish came over her. It was finished then: it had become hopeless between them long before he died. Yet he had been her husband. But how little!

'Have you got his shirt, 'Lizabeth?'

Elizabeth turned without answering, though she strove to weep and behave as her mother-in-law expected. But she could not, she was silenced. She went into the kitchen and returned with the garment.

'It is aired,' she said, griping the cotton shirt here and there to try. She was almost ashamed to handle him; what right had she or any one to lay hands on him? but her touch was humble on his body. It was hard work to clothe him. He was so heavy and inert. A terrible dread gripped her all the while: that he could be so heavy and utterly inert, unresponsive, apart. The horror of the distance between them was almost too much for her—it was so infinite a gap she must look across.

At last it was finished. They covered him with a sheet and left him lying, with his face bound. And she fastened the door of the little parlour, lest the children should see what was lying there. Then, with peace sunk heavy on her heart, she went about making tidy the kitchen. She knew she submitted to life, which was her immediate master. But from death, her ultimate master, she winced with fear and shame.

THE WHITE STOCKING

I

'I 'M getting up, Teddilinks,' said Mrs Whiston, and she sprang out of bed briskly.

'What the Hanover 's got you?' asked Whiston.

'Nothing. Can't I get up?' she replied animatedly.

It was about seven o'clock, scarcely light yet in the cold bedroom. Whiston lay still and looked at his wife. She was a pretty little thing, with her fleecy, short black hair all tousled. He watched her as she dressed quickly, flicking her small, delightful limbs, throwing her clothes about her. Her slovenliness and untidiness did not trouble him. When she picked up the edge of her petticoat, ripped off a torn string of white lace, and flung it on the dressing-table, her careless abandon made his spirit glow. She stood before the mirror and roughly scrambled together her profuse little mane of hair. He watched the quickness and softness of her young shoulders, calmly, like a husband, and appreciatively.

'Rise up,' she cried, turning to him with a quick wave of her arm—'and shine forth.'

They had been married two years. But still, when she had gone out of the room, he felt as if all his light and warmth were taken away, he became aware of the raw, cold morning. So he rose himself, wondering casually what had roused her so early. Usually she lay in bed as late as she could.

Whiston fastened a belt round his loins and went downstairs in shirt and trousers. He heard her singing in her snatchy fashion. The stairs creaked under his weight. He passed down the narrow little passage, which she called a hall, of the seven-and-sixpenny house which was his first home.

He was a shapely young fellow of about twenty-eight, sleepy now and easy with well-being. He heard the water drumming into the kettle, and she began to whistle. He loved the quick way she dodged the supper cups under the tap to wash them for breakfast. She looked an untidy minx, but she was quick and handy enough.

'Teddilinks,' she cried.

'What?'

'Light a fire, quick.'

She wore an old, sack-like dressing-jacket of black silk pinned across her breast. But one of the sleeves, coming unfastened, showed some delightful pink upper-arm.

'Why don't you sew your sleeve up?' he said, suffering from the sight of the exposed soft flesh.

'Where?' she cried, peering round. 'Nuisance,' she said, seeing the gap, then with light fingers went on drying the cups.

The kitchen was of fair size, but gloomy. Whiston poked out the dead ashes.

Suddenly a thud was heard at the door down the passage.

'I'll go,' cried Mrs Whiston, and she was gone down the hall.

The postman was a ruddy-faced man who had been a soldier. He smiled broadly, handing her some packages.

'They've not forgot you,' he said impudently.

'No—lucky for them,' she said, with a toss of the head. But she was interested only in her envelopes this morning. The postman waited inquisitively, smiling in an ingratiating fashion. She slowly, abstractedly, as if she did not know any one was there, closed the door in his face, continuing to look at the addresses on her letters.

She tore open the thin envelope. There was a long, hideous, cartoon valentine. She smiled briefly and dropped it on the floor. Struggling with the string of a packet, she opened a white cardboard box, and there lay a white silk handkerchief packed neatly under the paper lace of the box, and her initial, worked in heliotrope, fully displayed. She smiled pleasantly, and gently put the box aside. The third envelope contained another white packet—apparently a cotton handkerchief neatly folded. She shook it out. It was a long white stocking, but there was a little weight in the toe. Quickly, she thrust down her arm, wriggling her fingers into the toe of the stocking, and brought out a small box. She peeped inside the box, then hastily opened a door on her left hand, and went into the little, cold sitting-room. She had her lower lip caught earnestly between her teeth.

With a little flash of triumph, she lifted a pair of pearl ear-rings from the small box, and she went to the mirror. There, earnestly, she began to hook them through her ears, looking at herself sideways in the glass. Curiously concentrated and intent she seemed as she fingered the lobes of her ears, her head bent on one side.

Then the pearl ear-rings dangled under her rosy, small ears. She shook her head sharply, to see the swing of the drops. They went chill against her neck, in little, sharp touches. Then she stood still to look at herself, bridling her head in the dignified fashion. Then she simpered at herself. Catching her own eye, she could not help winking at herself and laughing.

She turned to look at the box. There was a scrap of paper with this posy:

> Pearls may be fair, but thou art fairer.
> Wear these for me, and I'll love the wearer.

She made a grimace and a grin. But she was drawn to the mirror again, to look at her ear-rings.

Whiston had made the fire burn, so he came to look for her. When she heard him, she started round quickly, guiltily. She was watching him with intent blue eyes when he appeared.

He did not see much, in his morning-drowsy warmth. He gave her, as ever, a feeling of warmth and slowness. His eyes were very blue, very kind, his manner simple. 'What ha' you got?' he asked.

'Valentines,' she said briskly, ostentatiously turning to show him the silk handkerchief. She thrust it under his nose. 'Smell how good,' she said.

'Who's that from?' he replied, without smelling.

'It 's a valentine,' she cried. 'How do I know who it 's from?'

'I 'll bet you know,' he said.

'Ted!—I don't!' she cried, beginning to shake her head, then stopping because of the ear-rings.

He stood still a moment, displeased.

'They 've no right to send you valentines, now,' he said.

'Ted!—Why not? You 're not jealous, are you? I haven't the least idea who it 's from. Look—there 's my initial'—she pointed with an emphatic finger at the heliotrope embroidery—

'E for Elsie,
Nice little gelsie,'

she sang.

'Get out,' he said. 'You know who it 's from.'

'Truth, I don't,' she cried.

He looked round, and saw the white stocking lying on a chair.

'Is this another?' he said.

'No, that 's a sample,' she said. 'There 's only a comic.' And she fetched in the long cartoon.

He stretched it out and looked at it solemnly.

'Fools!' he said, and went out of the room.

She flew upstairs and took off the ear-rings. When she returned, he was crouched before the fire blowing the coals. The skin of his face was flushed, and slightly pitted, as if he had had small-pox. But his neck was white and smooth and goodly. She hung her arms round his neck as he crouched there, and clung to him. He balanced on his toes.

'This fire 's a slow-coach,' he said.

'And who else is a slow-coach?' she said.

'One of us two, I know,' he said, and he rose carefully. She remained clinging round his neck, so that she was lifted off her feet.

'Ha!—swing me,' she cried.

He lowered his head, and she hung in the air, swinging from his neck, laughing. Then she slipped off.

'The kettle is singing,' she sang, flying for the teapot.

He bent down again to blow the fire. The veins in his neck stood out, his shirt collar seemed too tight.

> 'Doctor Wyer,
> Blow the fire,
> Puff! puff! puff!'

she sang, laughing.

He smiled at her.

She was so glad because of her pearl ear-rings.

Over the breakfast she grew serious. He did not notice. She became portentous in her gravity. Almost it penetrated through his steady good-humour to irritate him.

'Teddy!' she said at last.

'What?' he asked.

'I told you a lie,' she said, humbly tragic.

His soul stirred uneasily.

'Oh ay?' he said casually.

She was not satisfied. He ought to be more moved.

'Yes,' she said.

He cut a piece of bread.

'Was it a good one?' he asked.

She was piqued. Then she considered—*was* it a good one? Then she laughed.

'No,' she said, 'it wasn't up to much.'

'Ah!' he said easily, but with a steady strength of fondness for her in his tone. 'Get it out then.'

It became a little more difficult.

'You know that white stocking,' she said earnestly. 'I told you a lie. It wasn't a sample. It was a valentine.'

A little frown came on his brow.

'Then what did you invent it as a sample for?' he said. But he knew this weakness of hers. The touch of anger in his voice frightened her.

'I was afraid you'd be cross,' she said pathetically.

'I'll bet you were vastly afraid,' he said.

'I *was*, Teddy.'

There was a pause. He was resolving one or two things in his mind.

'And who sent it?' he asked.

'I can guess,' she said, 'though there wasn't a word with it—except——'

She ran to the sitting-room and returned with a slip of paper.

> Pearls may be fair, but thou art fairer.
> Wear these for me, and I'll love the wearer.

He read it twice, then a dull red flush came on his face.

'And *who* do you guess it is?' he asked, with a ringing of anger in his voice.

'I suspect it's Sam Adams,' she said, with a little virtuous indignation.

Whiston was silent for a moment.

'Fool!' he said. 'An' what's it got to do with pearls? —and how can he say "wear these for me" when there's only one? He hasn't got the brain to invent a proper verse.'

He screwed the slip of paper into a ball and flung it into the fire.

'I suppose he thinks it'll make a pair with the one last year,' she said.

'Why, did he send one then?'

'Yes. I thought you'd be wild if you knew.'

His jaw set rather sullenly.

Presently he rose, and went to wash himself, rolling back his sleeves and pulling open his shirt at the breast. It was as if his fine, clear-cut temples and steady eyes were degraded by the lower, rather brutal part of his face. But she loved it. As she whisked about, clearing the table, she loved the way in which he stood washing himself. He was such a man. She liked to see his neck glistening with water as he swilled it. It amused her and pleased her and thrilled her. He was so sure, so permanent, he had her so utterly in his power. It gave her a delightful, mischievous sense of liberty. Within his grasp, she could dart about excitingly.

He turned round to her, his face red from the cold water, his eyes fresh and very blue.

'You haven't been seeing anything of him, have you?' he asked roughly.

'Yes,' she answered, after a moment, as if caught guilty. 'He got into the tram with me, and he asked me to drink a coffee and a Benedictine in the Royal.'

'You've got it off fine and glib,' he said sullenly. 'And did you?'

'Yes,' she replied, with the air of a traitor before the rack.

The blood came up into his neck and face, he stood motionless, dangerous.

'It was cold, and it was such fun to go into the Royal,' she said.

'You'd go off with a nigger for a packet of chocolate,' he said, in anger and contempt, and some bitterness. Queer how he drew away from her, cut her off from him.

'Ted—how beastly!' she cried. 'You know quite well——' She caught her lip, flushed, and the tears came to her eyes.

He turned away, to put on his necktie. She went about her work, making a queer pathetic little mouth, down which occasionally dripped a tear.

He was ready to go. With his hat jammed down on his head, and his overcoat buttoned up to his chin, he came to kiss her. He would be miserable all the day if he went without. She allowed herself to be kissed. Her cheek was wet under his lips, and his heart burned. She hurt him so deeply. And she felt aggrieved, and did not quite forgive him.

In a moment she went upstairs to her ear-rings. Sweet they looked nestling in the little drawer—sweet! She examined them with voluptuous pleasure, she threaded them in her ears, she looked at herself, she posed and postured and smiled and looked sad and tragic and winning and appealing, all in turn before the mirror. And she was happy, and very pretty.

She wore her ear-rings all morning, in the house. She was self-conscious, and quite brilliantly winsome, when the baker came, wondering if he would notice. All the tradesmen left her door with a glow in them, feeling elated, and unconsciously favouring the delightful little creature, though there had been nothing to notice in her behaviour.

She was stimulated all the day. She did not think about her husband. He was the permanent basis from which she took these giddy little flights into nowhere. At night, like chickens and curses, she would come home to him, to roost.

Meanwhile Whiston, a traveller and confidential support of a small firm, hastened about his work, his heart all the while anxious for her, yearning for surety, and kept tense by not getting it.

II

She had been a warehouse girl in Adams's lace factory before she was married. Sam Adams was her employer. He was a bachelor of forty, growing stout, a man well dressed and florid, with a large brown moustache and thin hair. From the rest of his well-groomed, showy appearance, it was evident his baldness was a chagrin to him. He had a good presence, and some Irish blood in his veins.

His fondness for the girls, or the fondness of the girls for him, was notorious. And Elsie, quick, pretty, almost witty little thing—she *seemed* witty, although, when her sayings were repeated, they were entirely trivial—she had a great attraction for him. He would come into the warehouse dressed in a rather sporting reefer coat, of fawn colour, and trousers of fine black-and-white check, a cap with a big peak and scarlet carnation in his button-hole, to impress her. She was only half impressed. He was too loud for her good taste. Instinctively perceiving this, he sobered down to navy blue. Then a well-built man, florid, with large brown whiskers, smart navy blue suit, fashionable boots, and manly hat, he was the irreproachable. Elsie was impressed.

But meanwhile Whiston was courting her, and she made splendid little gestures, before her bedroom mirror, of the constant-and-true sort:

True, true till death——

That was her song. Whiston was made that way, so there was no need to take thought for him.

Every Christmas Sam Adams gave a party at his house, to which he invited his superior workpeople—not factory hands and labourers but those above. He was a generous man in his way, with a real warm feeling for giving pleasure.

Two years ago Elsie had attended this Christmas party for the last time. Whiston had accompanied her. At that time he worked for Sam Adams.

She had been very proud of herself, in her close-fitting, full-skirted dress of blue silk. Whiston called for her. Then she tripped beside him, holding her large cashmere shawl across her breast. He strode with long strides, his trousers handsomely strapped under his boots, and her silk shoes bulging the pockets of his full-skirted overcoat.

They passed through the park gates, and her spirits rose. Above them the Castle Rock loomed grandly in the night, the naked trees stood still and dark in the frost along the boulevard.

They were rather late. Agitated with anticipation, in the cloak-room she gave up her shawl, donned her silk shoes, and looked at herself in the mirror. The loose bunches of curls on either side her face danced prettily, her mouth smiled.

She hung a moment in the door of the brilliantly lighted room. Many people were moving within the blaze of lamps, under the crystal chandeliers, the full skirts of the women balancing and floating, the side-whiskers and white cravats of the men bowing above. Then she entered the light.

In an instant Sam Adams was coming forward, lifting both his arms in boisterous welcome. There was a constant red laugh on his face.

'Come late, would you,' he shouted, 'like royalty?'

He seized her hands and led her forward. He opened his mouth wide when he spoke, and the effect of the warm, dark opening behind the brown whiskers was disturbing. But she was floating into the throng on his arm. He was very gallant.

'Now then,' he said, taking her card to write down the dances, 'I've got *carte blanche*, haven't I?'

'Mr Whiston doesn't dance,' she said.

'I am a lucky man!' he said, scribbling his initials. 'I was born with an *amourette* in my mouth.'

He wrote on, quietly. She blushed and laughed, not knowing what it meant.

'Why, what is that?' she said.

'It's you, even littler than you are, dressed in little wings,' he said.

'I should have to be pretty small to get in your mouth,' she said.

'You think you're too big, do you!' he said easily.

He handed her her card, with a bow.

'Now I'm set up, my darling, for this evening,' he said.

Then, quick, always at his ease, he looked over the room. She waited in front of him. He was ready. Catching the eye of the band, he nodded. In a moment, the music began. He seemed to relax, giving himself up.

'Now then, Elsie,' he said, with a curious caress in his voice that seemed to lap the outside of her body in a warm glow, delicious. She gave herself to it. She liked it.

He was an excellent dancer. He seemed to draw her close in to him by some male warmth of attraction, so that she became all soft and pliant to him, flowing to his form, whilst he united her with him and they lapsed along in one movement. She was just carried in a kind of strong, warm flood, her feet moved of themselves, and only the music threw her away from him, threw her back to him, to his clasp, in his strong form moving against her, rhythmically, deliciously.

When it was over, he was pleased and his eyes had a curious gleam which thrilled her and yet had nothing to do with her. Yet it held her. He did not speak to her. He only looked straight into her eyes with a curious gleaming look that disturbed her fearfully and deliciously. But also there was in his look some of the automatic irony of the *roué*. It left her partly cold. She **was** not carried away.

She went, driven by an opposite, heavier impulse, to Whiston. He stood looking gloomy, trying to admit that she had a perfect right to enjoy herself apart from him. He received her with rather grudging kindliness.

'Aren't you going to play whist?' she asked.

'Ay,' he said. 'Directly.'

'I do wish you could dance.'

'Well, I can't,' he said. 'So you enjoy yourself.'

'But I should enjoy it better if I could dance with you.'

'Nay, you 're all right,' he said. 'I 'm not made that way.'

'Then you ought to be!' she cried.

'Well, it 's my fault, not yours. You enjoy yourself,' he bade her. Which she proceeded to do, a little bit irked.

She went with anticipation to the arms of Sam Adams, when the time came to dance with him. It *was* so gratifying, irrespective of the man. And she felt a little grudge against Whiston, soon forgotten when her host was holding her near to him, in a delicious embrace. And she watched his eyes, to meet the gleam in them, which gratified her.

She was getting warmed right through, the glow was penetrating into her, driving away everything else. Only in her heart was a little tightness, like conscience.

When she got a chance, she escaped from the dancing-room to the card-room. There, in a cloud of smoke, she found Whiston playing cribbage. Radiant, roused, animated, she came up to him and greeted him. She was too strong, too vibrant a note in the quiet room. He lifted his head, and a frown knitted his gloomy forehead.

'Are you playing cribbage? Is it exciting? How are you getting on?' she chattered.

He looked at her. None of these questions needed answering, and he did not feel in touch with her. She turned to the cribbage-board.

'Are you white or red?' she asked.

'He 's red,' replied the partner.

'Then you 're losing,' she said, still to Whiston. And she lifted the red peg from the board. 'One—two

— three — four — five — six — seven — eight —— Right up there you ought to jump——'

'Now put it back in its right place,' said Whiston.

'Where was it?' she asked gaily, knowing her transgression. He took the little red peg away from her and stuck it in its hole.

The cards were shuffled.

'What a shame you're losing!' said Elsie.

'You'd better cut for him,' said the partner.

She did so, hastily. The cards were dealt. She put her hand on his shoulder, looking at his cards.

'It's good,' she cried, 'isn't it?'

He did not answer, but threw down two cards. It moved him more strongly than was comfortable, to have her hand on his shoulder, her curls dangling and touching his ears, whilst she was roused to another man. It made the blood flame over him.

At that moment Sam Adams appeared, florid and boisterous, intoxicated more with himself, with the dancing, than with wine. In his eye the curious, impersonal light gleamed.

'I thought I should find you here, Elsie,' he cried boisterously, a disturbing, high note in his voice.

'What made you think so?' she replied, the mischief rousing in her.

The florid, well-built man narrowed his eyes to a smile.

'I should never look for you among the ladies,' he said, with a kind of intimate, animal call to her. He laughed, bowed, and offered her his arm.

'Madam, the music waits.'

She went almost helplessly, carried along with him, unwilling, yet delighted.

That dance was an intoxication to her. After the first few steps, she felt herself slipping away from herself. She almost knew she was going, she did not even want to go. Yet she must have chosen to go. She lay in the arm of the steady, close man with whom she was dancing, and she seemed to swim away out of contact with the room, into him. She had passed into another, denser element of him, an essential privacy. The room was all vague around her, like an atmosphere, like under sea, with a flow of ghostly, dumb movements. But she herself was held real against her partner, and it seemed she was connected with him, as if the movements of his body and limbs were her own movements, yet not her own movements—and oh, delicious! He also was given up, oblivious, concentrated, into the dance. His eye was unseeing. Only his large, voluptuous body gave off a subtle activity. His fingers seemed to search into her flesh. Every moment, and every moment, she felt she would give way utterly, and sink molten: the fusion point was coming when she would fuse down into perfect unconsciousness at his feet and knees. But he bore her round the room in the dance, and he seemed to sustain all her body with his limbs, his body, and his warmth seemed to come closer into her, nearer, till it would fuse right through her, and she would be as liquid to him, as an intoxication only.

It was exquisite. When it was over, she was dazed, and was scarcely breathing. She stood with him in the middle of the room as if she were alone in a remote place. He bent over her. She expected his lips on her bare shoulder, and waited. Yet they were not alone, they were not alone. It was cruel.

''Twas good, wasn't it, my darling?' he said to her, low and delighted. There was a strange impersonality about his low, exultant call that appealed to her irresistibly. Yet why was she aware of some part shut off in her? She pressed his arm, and he led her towards the door.

She was not aware of what she was doing, only a little grain of resistant trouble was in her. The man, possessed, yet with a superficial presence of mind, made way to the dining-room, as if to give her refreshment, cunningly working to his own escape with her. He was molten hot, filmed over with presence of mind, and bottomed with cold disbelief. In the dining-room was Whiston, carrying coffee to the plain, neglected ladies. Elsie saw him but felt as if he could not see her. She was beyond his reach and ken. A sort of fusion existed between her and the large man at her side. She ate her custard, but an incomplete fusion all the while sustained and contained her within the being of her employer.

But she was growing cooler. Whiston came up. She looked at him, and saw him with different eyes. She saw his slim, young man's figure real and enduring before her. That was he. But she was in the spell with the other man, fused with him, and she could not be taken away.

'Have you finished your cribbage?' she asked, with hasty evasion of him.

'Yes,' he replied. 'Aren't you getting tired of dancing?'

'Not a bit,' she said.

'Not she,' said Adams heartily. 'No girl with any spirit gets tired of dancing. Have something else, Elsie. Come—sherry. Have a glass of sherry with us, Whiston.'

Whilst they sipped the wine, Adams watched Whiston almost cunningly, to find his advantage.

'We'd better be getting back—there's the music,' he said. 'See the women get something to eat, Whiston, will you, there's a good chap.'

And he began to draw away. Elsie was drifting helplessly with him. But Whiston put himself beside them, and went along with them. In silence they passed through to the dancing-room. There Adams hesitated, and looked round the room. It was as if he could not see.

A man came hurrying forward, claiming Elsie, and Adams went to his other partner. Whiston stood watching during the dance. She was conscious of him standing there observant of her, like a ghost, or a judgment, or a guardian angel. She was also conscious, much more intimately and impersonally, of the body of the other man moving somewhere in the room. She still belonged to him, but a feeling of distraction possessed her, and helplessness. Adams danced on, adhering to Elsie, waiting his time, with the persistence of cynicism.

The dance was over. Adams was detained. Elsie found herself beside Whiston. There was something shapely about him as he sat, about his knees and his distinct figure, that she clung to. It was as if he had enduring form. She put her hand on his knee.

'Are you enjoying yourself?' he asked.

'*Ever* so,' she replied, with a fervent, yet detached tone.

'It's going on for one o'clock,' he said.

'Is it?' she answered. It meant nothing to her.

'Should we be going?' he said.

She was silent. For the first time for an hour or more an inkling of her normal consciousness returned. She resented it.

'What for?' she said.

'I thought you might have had enough,' he said.

A slight soberness came over her, an irritation at being frustrated of her illusion.

'Why?' she said.

'We've been here since nine,' he said.

That was no answer, no reason. It conveyed nothing to her. She sat detached from him. Across the room Sam Adams glanced at her. She sat there exposed for him.

'You don't want to be too free with Sam Adams,' said Whiston cautiously, suffering. 'You know what he is.'

'How, free?' she asked.

'Why—you don't want to have too much to do with him.'

She sat silent. He was forcing her into consciousness of her position. But he could not get hold of her feelings, to change them. She had a curious, perverse desire that he should not.

'I like him,' she said.

'What do you find to like in him?' he said, with a hot heart.

'I don't know—but I like him,' she said.

She was immutable. He sat feeling heavy and dulled with rage. He was not clear as to what he felt. He sat there unliving whilst she danced. And she, distracted, lost to herself between the opposing forces of the two men, drifted. Between the dances, Whiston kept near to her. She was scarcely conscious. She glanced repeatedly at her card, to see when she would dance again with Adams, half in desire, half in dread. Sometimes she met his steady, glaucous eye as she passed him in the dance. Sometimes she saw the steadiness of his flank as he danced. And it was always as if she rested on his arm, were borne along, upborne by him, away from herself. And always there was present the other's antagonism. She was divided.

The time came for her to dance with Adams. Oh, the delicious closing of contact with him, of his limbs touching her limbs, his arm supporting her. She seemed to resolve. Whiston had not made himself real to her. He was only a heavy place in her consciousness.

But she breathed heavily, beginning to suffer from the closeness of strain. She was nervous. Adams also was constrained. A tightness, a tension was coming over them all, And he was exasperated, feeling something counteracting physical magnetism, feeling a will stronger with her than his own, intervening in what was becoming a vital necessity to him.

Elsie was almost lost to her own control. As she went forward with him to take her place at the dance, she stooped for her pocket-handkerchief. The music sounded for quadrilles. Everybody was ready. Adams stood with his body near her, exerting his attraction over her. He was tense and fighting. She stooped for her pocket-handkerchief, and shook it as she rose. It shook out and fell from her hand. With agony, she saw she had taken a white stocking instead of a handkerchief. For a second it lay on the floor, a twist of white stocking. Then, in an instant, Adams picked it up, with a little, surprised laugh of triumph.

'That 'll do for me,' he whispered—seeming to take possession of her. And he stuffed the stocking in his trousers pocket, and quickly offered her his handkerchief.

The dance began. She felt weak and faint, as if her will were turned to water. A heavy sense of loss came over her. She could not help herself any more. But it was peace.

When the dance was over, Adams yielded her up. Whiston came to her.

'What was it as you dropped?' Whiston asked.

'I thought it was my handkerchief—I'd taken a stocking by mistake,' she said, detached and muted.

'And he's got it?'

'Yes.'

'What does he mean by that?'

She lifted her shoulders.

'Are you going to let him keep it?' he asked.

'I don't let him.'

There was a long pause.

'Am I to go and have it out with him?' he asked, his face flushed, his blue eyes going hard with opposition.

'No,' she said, pale.

'Why?'

'No—I don't want you to say anything about it.'

He sat exasperated and nonplussed.

'You'll let him keep it, then?' he asked.

She sat silent and made no form of answer.

'What do you mean by it?' he said, dark with fury. And he started up.

'No!' she cried. 'Ted!' And she caught hold of him, sharply detaining him.

It made him black with rage.

'Why?' he said.

The something about her mouth was pitiful to him. He did not understand, but he felt she must have her reasons.

'Then I'm not stopping here,' he said. 'Are you coming with me?'

She rose mutely, and they went out of the room. Adams had not noticed.

In a few moments they were in the street.

'What the hell do you mean?' he said, in a black fury.

She went at his side, in silence, neutral.

'That great hog, an' all,' he added.

Then they went a long time in silence through the frozen, deserted darkness of the town. She felt she could not go indoors. They were drawing near her house.

'I don't want to go home,' she suddenly cried in distress and anguish. 'I don't want to go home.'

He looked at her.

'Why don't you?' he said.

'I don't want to go home,' was all she could sob.

He heard somebody coming.

'Well, we can walk a bit farther,' he said.

She was silent again. They passed out of the town into the fields. He held her by the arm — they could not speak.

'What's a-matter?' he asked at length, puzzled.

She began to cry again.

At last he took her in his arms to soothe her. She sobbed by herself, almost unaware of him.

'Tell me what's a-matter, Elsie,' he said. 'Tell me what's a-matter—my dear—tell me, then——'

He kissed her wet face, and caressed her. She made no response. He was puzzled and tender and miserable.

At length she became quiet. Then he kissed her, and she put her arms round him, and clung to him very tight, as if for fear and anguish. He held her in his arms, wondering.

'Ted!' she whispered, frantic. 'Ted!'

'What, my love?' he answered, becoming also afraid.

'Be good to me,' she cried. 'Don't be cruel to me.'

'No, my pet,' he said, amazed and grieved. 'Why?'

'Oh, be good to me,' she sobbed.

And he held her very safe, and his heart was white-hot with love for her. His mind was amazed. He could only hold her against his chest that was white-hot with love and belief in her. So she was restored at last.

III

She refused to go to her work at Adams's any more. Her father had to submit and she sent in her notice—she was not well. Sam Adams was ironical. But he had a curious patience. He did not fight.

In a few weeks she and Whiston were married. She loved him with passion and worship, a fierce little abandon of love that moved him to the depths of his being, and gave him a permanent surety and sense of realness in himself. He did not trouble about himself any more; he felt he was fulfilled and now he had only the many things in the world to busy himself about. Whatever troubled him, at the bottom was surety. He had found himself in this love.

They spoke once or twice of the white stocking.

'Ah!' Whiston exclaimed. 'What does it matter?'

He was impatient and angry, and could not bear to consider the matter. So it was left unresolved.

She was quite happy at first, carried away by her adoration of her husband. Then gradually she got used to him. He always was the ground of her happiness, but she got used to him, as to the air she breathed. He never got used to her in the same way.

Inside of marriage she found her liberty. She was rid of the responsibility of herself. Her husband must look after that. She was free to get what she could out of her time.

So that when, after some months, she met Sam Adams, she was not quite as unkind to him as she might have been. With a young wife's new and exciting knowledge of men, she perceived he was in love with her, she knew he had always kept an unsatisfied desire for her. And, sportive, she could not help playing a little with this, though she cared not one jot for the man himself.

When Valentine's day came, which was near the first anniversary of her wedding day, there arrived a white stocking with a little amethyst brooch. Luckily Whiston did not see it, so she said nothing of it to him.

She had not the faintest intention of having anything to do with Sam Adams, but once a little brooch was in her possession, it was hers, and she did not trouble her head for a moment how she had come by it. She kept it.

Now she had the pearl ear-rings. They were a more valuable and a more conspicuous present. She would have to ask her mother to give them to her, to explain their presence. She made a little plan in her head. And she was extraordinarily pleased. As for Sam Adams, even if he saw her wearing them, he would not give her away. What fun, if he saw her wearing his ear-rings! She would pretend she had inherited them from her grandmother, her mother's mother. She laughed to herself as she went down town in the afternoon, the pretty drops dangling in front of her curls. But she saw no one of importance.

Whiston came home tired and depressed. All day the male in him had been uneasy, and this had fatigued him. She was curiously against him, inclined, as she sometimes was nowadays, to make mock of him and jeer at him and cut him off. He did not understand this, and it angered him deeply. She was uneasy before him.

She knew he was in a state of suppressed irritation. The veins stood out on the backs of his hands, his brow was drawn stiffly. Yet she could not help goading him.

'What did you do wi' that white stocking?' he asked, out of a gloomy silence, his voice strong and brutal.

'I put it in a drawer—why?' she replied flippantly.

'Why didn't you put it on the fire-back?' he said harshly. 'What are you hoarding it up for?'

'I 'm not hoarding it up,' she said. 'I 've got a pair.'

He relapsed into gloomy silence. She, unable to move him, ran away upstairs, leaving him smoking by the fire. Again she tried on the ear-rings. Then another little inspiration came to her. She drew on the white stockings, both of them.

Presently she came down in them. Her husband still sat immovable and glowering by the fire.

'Look!' she said. 'They 'll do beautifully.'

And she picked up her skirts to her knees, and twisted round, looking at her pretty legs in the neat stockings.

He filled with unreasonable rage, and took the pipe from his mouth.

'Don't they look nice?' she said. 'One from last year and one from this, they just do. Save you buying a pair.'

And she looked over her shoulders at her pretty calves, and at the dangling frills of her knickers.

'Put your skirts down and don't make a fool of yourself,' he said.

'Why a fool of myself?' she asked.

And she began to dance slowly round the room, kicking up her feet half reckless, half jeering, in a ballet-dancer's fashion. Almost fearfully, yet in defiance, she kicked up her legs at him, singing as she did so. She resented him.

'You little fool, ha' done with it,' he said. 'And you 'll backfire them stockings, I 'm telling you.' He was angry. His face flushed dark, he kept his head bent. She ceased to dance.

'I shan't,' she said. 'They 'll come in very useful.'

He lifted his head and watched her, with lighted, dangerous eyes.

'You 'll put 'em on the fire-back, I tell you,' he said.

It was a war now. She bent forward, in a ballet-dancer's fashion, and put her tongue between her teeth.

'I shan't backfire them stockings,' she sang, repeating his words, 'I shan't, I shan't, I shan't.'

And she danced round the room doing a high kick to the tune of her words. There was a real biting indifference in her behaviour.

'We 'll see whether you will or not,' he said, 'trollops! You 'd like Sam Adams to know you was wearing 'em, wouldn't you? That 's what would please you.'

'Yes, I 'd like him to see how nicely they fit me, he might give me some more then.'

And she looked down at her pretty legs.

He knew somehow that she *would* like Sam Adams to see how pretty her legs looked in the white stockings. It made his anger go deep, almost to hatred.

'Yer nasty trolley,' he cried. 'Put yer petticoats down, and stop being so foul-minded.'

'I'm not foul-minded,' she said. 'My legs are my own. And why shouldn't Sam Adams think they're nice?'

There was a pause. He watched her with eyes glittering to a point.

'Have you been havin' owt to do with him?' he asked.

'I've just spoken to him when I've seen him,' she said. 'He's not as bad as you would make out.'

'Isn't he?' he cried, a certain wakefulness in his voice. 'Them who has anything to do wi' him is too bad for me, I tell you.'

'Why, what are you frightened of him for?' she mocked.

She was rousing all his uncontrollable anger. He sat glowering. Every one of her sentences stirred him up like a red-hot iron. Soon it would be too much. And she was afraid herself; but she was neither conquered nor convinced.

A curious little grin of hate came on his face. He had a long score against her.

'What am I frightened of him for?' he repeated automatically. 'What am I frightened of him for? Why, for you, you stray-running little bitch.'

She flushed. The insult went deep into her, right home.

'Well, if you're so dull——' she said, lowering her eyelids, and speaking coldly, haughtily.

'If I'm so dull I'll break your neck the first word you speak to him,' he said, tense.

'Pf!' she sneered. 'Do you think I'm frightened of you?' She spoke coldly, detached.

She was frightened, for all that, white round the mouth.

His heart was getting hotter.

'You *will* be frightened of me, the next time you have anything to do with him,' he said.

'Do you think *you*'d ever be told—ha!'

Her jeering scorn made him go white-hot, molten.

He knew he was incoherent, scarcely responsible for what he might do. Slowly, unseeing, he rose and went out of doors, stifled, moved to kill her.

He stood leaning against the garden fence, unable either to see or hear. Below him, far off, fumed the lights of the town. He stood still, unconscious with a black storm of rage, his face lifted to the night.

Presently, still unconscious of what he was doing, he went indoors again. She stood, a small, stubborn figure with tight-pressed lips and big, sullen, childish eyes, watching him, white with fear. He went heavily across the floor and dropped into his chair.

There was silence.

'*You*'re not going to tell me everything I shall do, and everything I shan't,' she broke out at last.

He lifted his head.

'I tell you *this*,' he said, low and intense. 'Have anything to do with Sam Adams, and I'll break your neck.'

She laughed, shrill and false.

'How I hate your word "break your neck,"' she said, with a grimace of the mouth. 'It sounds so common and beastly. Can't you say something else——'

There was a dead silence.

'And besides,' she said, with a queer chirrup of mocking laughter, 'what do you know about anything? He sent me an amethyst brooch and a pair of pearl ear-rings.'

'He what?' said Whiston, in a suddenly normal voice. His eyes were fixed on her.

'Sent me a pair of pearl ear-rings, and an amethyst brooch,' she repeated, mechanically, pale to the lips.

And her big, black, childish eyes watched him, fascinated, held in her spell.

He seemed to thrust his face and his eyes forward at her, as he rose slowly and came to her. She watched transfixed in terror. Her throat made a small sound, as she tried to scream.

Then, quick as lightning, the back of his hand struck her with a crash across the mouth, and she was flung back blinded against the wall. The shock shook a

queer sound out of her. And then she saw him still
coming on, his eyes holding her, his fist drawn back,
advancing slowly. At any instant the blow might
crash into her.

Mad with terror, she raised her hands with a queer
clawing movement to cover her eyes and her temples,
opening her mouth in a dumb shriek. There was no
sound. But the sight of her slowly arrested him. He
hung before her, looking at her fixedly, as she stood
crouched against the wall with open, bleeding mouth,
and wide-staring eyes, and two hands clawing over her
temples. And his lust to see her bleed, to break her and
destroy her, rose from an old source against her. It
carried him. He wanted satisfaction.

But he had seen her standing there, a piteous, horrified
thing, and he turned his face aside in shame and nausea.
He went and sat heavily in his chair, and a curious ease,
almost like sleep, came over his brain.

She walked away from the wall towards the fire, dizzy,
white to the lips, mechanically wiping her small, bleeding mouth. He sat motionless. Then, gradually, her
breath began to hiss, she shook, and was sobbing silently,
in grief for herself. Without looking, he saw. It made
his mad desire to destroy her come back.

At length he lifted his head. His eyes were glowing
again, fixed on her.

'And what did he give them you for?' he asked, in a
steady, unyielding voice.

Her crying dried up in a second. She also was tense.

'They came as valentines,' she replied, still not
subjugated, even if beaten.

'When, to-day?'

'The pearl ear-rings to-day—the amethyst brooch
last year.'

'You've had it a year?'

'Yes.'

She felt that now nothing would prevent him if he
rose to kill her. She could not prevent him any more.
She was yielded up to him. They both trembled in the
balance, unconscious.

'What have you had to do with him?' he asked, in a barren voice.

'I've not had anything to do with him,' she quavered.

'You just kept 'em because they were jewellery?' he said.

A weariness came over him. What was the worth of speaking any more of it? He did not care any more. He was dreary and sick.

She began to cry again, but he took no notice. She kept wiping her mouth on her handkerchief. He could see it, the blood-mark. It made him only more sick and tired of the responsibility of it, the violence, the shame.

When she began to move about again, he raised his head once more from his dead, motionless position.

'Where are the things?' he said.

'They are upstairs,' she quavered. She knew the passion had gone down in him.

'Bring them down,' he said.

'I won't,' she wept, with rage. 'You're not going to bully me and hit me like that on the mouth.'

And she sobbed again. He looked at her in contempt and compassion and in rising anger.

'Where are they?' he said.

'They're in the little drawer under the looking-glass,' she sobbed.

He went slowly upstairs, struck a match, and found the trinkets. He brought them downstairs in his hand.

'These?' he said, looking at them as they lay in his palm.

She looked at them without answering. She was not interested in them any more.

He looked at the little jewels. They were pretty.

'It's none of their fault,' he said to himself.

And he searched round slowly, persistently, for a box. He tied the things up and addressed them to Sam Adams. Then he went out in his slippers to post the little package.

When he came back she was still sitting crying.

'You'd better go to bed,' he said.

She paid no attention.   He sat by the fire.   She still cried.

'I 'm sleeping down here,' he said.   'Go you to bed.'

In a few moments she lifted her tear-strained, swollen face and looked at him with eyes all forlorn and pathetic. A great flash of anguish went over his body.   He went over, slowly, and very gently took her in his hands. She let herself be taken.   Then as she lay against his shoulder, she sobbed aloud:

'I never meant——'

'My love—my little love——' he cried, in anguish of spirit, holding her in his arms.

ENGLAND, MY ENGLAND

HE was working on the edge of the common, beyond the
small brook that ran in the dip at the bottom of the
garden, carrying the garden path in continuation from
the plank bridge on to the common. He had cut the
rough turf and bracken, leaving the grey, dryish soil
bare. But he was worried because he could not get
the path straight, there was a pleat between his brows.
He had set up his sticks, and taken the sights between
the big pine-trees, but for some reason everything seemed
wrong. He looked again, straining his keen blue eyes,
that had a touch of the Viking in them, through the
shadowy pine-trees as through a doorway, at the green-
grassed garden path rising from the shadow of alders
by the log bridge up to the sunlit flowers. Tall white
and purple columbines, and the butt-end of the old
Hampshire cottage that crouched near the earth amid
flowers, blossoming in the bit of shaggy wildness round
about.

There was a sound of children's voices calling and
talking: high, childish, girlish voices, slightly didactic
and tinged with domineering: 'If you don't come quick,
nurse, I shall run out there to where there are snakes.'
And nobody had the sang-froid to reply: 'Run then,
little fool.' It was always: 'No, darling. Very well,
darling. In a moment, darling. Darling, you *must*
be patient.'

His heart was hard with disillusion: a continual gnawing and resistance. But he worked on. What was
there to do but submit!

The sunlight blazed down upon the earth, there was a
vividness of flamy vegetation, of fierce seclusion amid the
savage peace of the commons. Strange how the savage
England lingers in patches: as here, amid these shaggy
gorse commons, and marshy, snake-infested places near

the foot of the south downs. The spirit of place lingering on primeval, as when the Saxons came, so long ago.

Ah, how he had loved it! The green garden path,
the tufts of flowers, purple and white columbines, and
great oriental red poppies with their black chaps and
mulleins tall and yellow: this flamy garden which had
been a garden for a thousand years, scooped out in the
little hollow among the snake-infested commons. He
had made it flame with flowers, in a sun cup under its
hedges and trees. So old, so old a place! And yet he
had re-created it.

The timbered cottage with its sloping, cloak-like roof
was old and forgotten. It belonged to the old England
of hamlets and yeoman. Lost all alone on the edge
of the common, at the end of a wide, grassy, brier-
entangled lane shaded with oak, it had never known the
world of to-day. Not till Egbert came with his bride.
And he had come to fill it with flowers.

The house was ancient and very uncomfortable. But
he did not want to alter it. Ah, marvellous to sit there
in the wide, black, time-old chimney, at night when the
wind roared overhead, and the wood which he had
chopped himself sputtered on the hearth! Himself on
one side the angle, and Winifred on the other.

Ah, how he had wanted her: Winifred! She was
young and beautiful and strong with life, like a flame
in sunshine. She moved with a slow grace of energy
like a blossoming, red-flowered bush in motion. She,
too, seemed to come out of the old England, ruddy,
strong, with a certain crude, passionate quiescence and a
hawthorn robustness. And he, he was tall and slim
and agile, like an English archer with his long supple
legs and fine movements. Her hair was nut-brown and
all in energic curls and tendrils. Her eyes were nut-
brown, too, like a robin's for brightness. And he was
white-skinned with fine, silky hair that had darkened
from fair, and a slightly arched nose of an old country
family. They were a beautiful couple.

The house was Winifred's. Her father was a man of
energy, too. He had come from the north poor. Now

he was moderately rich. He had bought this fair stretch of inexpensive land, down in Hampshire. Not far from the tiny church of the almost extinct hamlet stood his own house, a commodious old farm-house standing back from the road across a bare grassed yard. On one side of this quadrangle was the long, long barn or shed which he had made into a cottage for his youngest daughter Priscilla. One saw little blue-and-white check curtains at the long windows, and inside, overhead, the grand old timbers of the high-pitched shed. This was Prissy's house. Fifty yards away was the pretty little new cottage which he had built for his daughter Magdalen, with the vegetable garden stretching away to the oak copse. And then away beyond the lawns and rose-trees of the house-garden went the track across a shaggy, wild grass space, towards the ridge of tall black pines that grew on a dike-bank, through the pines and above the sloping little bog, under the wide, desolate oak-trees, till there was Winifred's cottage crouching unexpectedly in front, so much alone, and so primitive.

It was Winifred's own house, and the gardens and the bit of common and the boggy slope were hers: her tiny domain. She had married just at the time when her father had bought the estate, about ten years before the war, so she had been able to come to Egbert with this for a marriage portion. And who was more delighted, he or she, it would be hard to say. She was only twenty at the time, and he was only twenty-one. He had about a hundred and fifty pounds a year of his own— and nothing else but his very considerable personal attractions. He had no profession: he earned nothing. But he talked of literature and music, he had a passion for old folk-music, collecting folk-songs and folk-dances, studying the Morris-dance and the old customs. Of course, in time he would make money in these ways.

Meanwhile youth and health and passion and promise. Winifred's father was always generous: but still, he was a man from the north with a hard head and a hard skin too, having received a good many knocks. At home he kept the hard head out of sight, and played at poetry and romance with his literary wife and his sturdy, passionate girls. He was a man of courage, not given to complaining, bearing his burdens by himself. No, he did not let the world intrude far into his home. He had a delicate, sensitive wife whose poetry won some fame in the narrow world of letters. He himself, with his tough old barbarian fighting spirit, had an almost child-like delight in verse, in sweet poetry, and in the delightful game of a cultured home. His blood was strong even to coarseness. But that only made the home more vigorous, more robust and Christmasy. There was always a touch of Christmas about him, now he was well off. If there was poetry after dinner, there were also chocolates, and nuts, and good little out-of-the-way things to be munching.

Well then, into this family came Egbert. He was made of quite a different paste. The girls and the father were strong-limbed, thick-blooded people, true English, as holly-trees and hawthorn are English. Their culture was grafted on to them, as one might perhaps graft a common pink rose on to a thorn-stem. It flowered oddly enough, but it did not alter their blood.

And Egbert was a born rose. The age-long breeding had left him with a delightful spontaneous passion. He was not clever, nor even 'literary.' No, but the intonation of his voice, and the movement of his supple, handsome body, and the fine texture of his flesh and his hair, the slight arch of his nose, the quickness of his blue eyes would easily take the place of poetry. Winifred loved him, loved him, this southerner, as a higher being. A *higher* being, mind you. Not a deeper. And as for him, he loved her in passion with every fibre of him. She was the very warm stuff of life to him.

Wonderful then, those days at Crockham Cottage, the first days, all alone save for the woman who came to work in the mornings. Marvellous days, when she had all his tall, supple, fine-fleshed youth to herself, for herself, and he had her like a ruddy fire into which he could cast himself for rejuvenation. Ah, that it might never end, this passion, this marriage! The flame of their two

bodies burnt again into that old cottage, that was
haunted already by so much bygone physical desire.
You could not be in the dark room for an hour without
the influences coming over you. The hot blood-desire
of bygone yeomen, there in this old den where they had
lusted and bred for so many generations. The silent
house, dark, with thick, timbered walls and the big
black chimney-place, and the sense of secrecy. Dark,
with low, little windows, sunk into the earth. Dark,
like a lair where strong beasts had lurked and mated,
lonely at night and lonely by day, left to themselves and
their own intensity for so many generations. It seemed
to cast a spell on the two young people. They became
different. There was a curious secret glow about
them, a certain slumbering flame hard to understand,
that enveloped them both. They too felt that they did
not belong to the London world any more. Crockham
had changed their blood: the sense of the snakes that
lived and slept even in their own garden, in the sun,
so that he, going forward with the spade, would see a
curious coiled brownish pile on the black soil, which
suddenly would start up, hiss, and dazzle rapidly away,
hissing. One day Winifred heard the strangest scream
from the flower-bed under the low window of the living-
room: ah, the strangest scream, like the very soul of the
dark past crying aloud. She ran out, and saw a long
brown snake on the flower-bed, and in its flat mouth the one
hind leg of a frog that was striving to escape, and screaming its strange, tiny, bellowing scream. She looked at
the snake, and from its sullen flat head it looked at her,
obstinately. She gave a cry, and it released the frog
and slid angrily away.

That was Crockham. The spear of modern invention
had not passed through it, and it lay there secret,
primitive, savage as when the Saxons first came. And
Egbert and she were caught there, caught out of the world.

He was not idle, nor was she. There were plenty of
things to be done, the house to be put into final repair
after the workmen had gone, cushions and curtains to
sew, the paths to make, the water to fetch and attend

to, and then the slope of the deep-soiled, neglected garden to level, to terrace with little terraces and paths, and to fill with flowers. He worked away, in his shirt sleeves, worked all day intermittently doing this thing and the other. And she, quiet and rich in herself, seeing him stooping and labouring away by himself, would come to help him, to be near him. He, of course, was an amateur —a born amateur. He worked so hard, and did so little, and nothing he ever did would hold together for long. If he terraced the garden, he held up the earth with a couple of long narrow planks that soon began to bend with the pressure from behind, and would not need many years to rot through and break and let the soil slither all down again in a heap towards the stream-bed. But there you are. He had not been brought up to come to grips with anything, and he thought it would do. Nay, he did not think there was anything else except little temporary contrivances possible, he who had such a passion for his old enduring cottage, and for the old enduring things of the bygone England. Curious that the sense of permanency in the past had such a hold over him, whilst in the present he was all amateurish and sketchy.

Winifred could not criticize him. Town-bred, everything seemed to her splendid, and the very digging and shovelling itself seemed romantic. But neither Egbert nor she yet realized the difference between work and romance.

Godfrey Marshall, her father, was at first perfectly pleased with the *ménage* down at Crockham Cottage. He thought Egbert was wonderful, the many things he accomplished, and he was gratified by the glow of physical passion between the two young people. To the man who in London still worked hard to keep steady his modest fortune, the thought of this young couple digging away and loving one another down at Crockham Cottage, buried deep among the commons and marshes, near the pale-showing bulk of the downs, was like a chapter of living romance. And they drew the sustenance for their fire of passion from him, from the old man.

It was he who fed their flame. He triumphed secretly in the thought. And it was to her father that Winifred still turned, as the one source of all surety and life and support. She loved Egbert with passion. But behind her was the power of her father. It was the power of her father she referred to, whenever she needed to refer. It never occurred to her to refer to Egbert, if she were in difficulty or doubt. No, in all the *serious* matters she depended on her father.

For Egbert had no intention of coming to grips with life. He had no ambition whatsoever. He came from a decent family, from a pleasant country home, from delightful surroundings. He should, of course, have had a profession. He should have studied law or entered business in some way. But no—that fatal three pounds a week would keep him from starving as long as he lived, and he did not want to give himself into bondage. It was not that he was idle. He was always doing something, in his amateurish way. But he had no desire to give himself to the world, and still less had he any desire to fight his way in the world. No, no, the world wasn't worth it. He wanted to ignore it, to go his own way apart, like a casual pilgrim down the forsaken side-tracks. He loved his wife, his cottage, and garden. He would make his life there, as a sort of epicurean hermit. He loved the past, the old music and dances and customs of old England. He would try and live in the spirit of these, not in the spirit of the world of business.

But often Winifred's father called her to London: for he loved to have his children round him. So Egbert and she must have a tiny flat in town, and the young couple must transfer themselves from time to time from the country to the city. In town Egbert had plenty of friends, of the same ineffectual sort as himself, tampering with the arts, literature, painting, sculpture, music. He was not bored.

Three pounds a week, however, would not pay for all this. Winifred's father paid. He liked paying. He made her only a very small allowance, but he often gave her ten pounds—or gave Egbert ten pounds. So they both looked on the old man as the mainstay. Egbert didn't mind being patronized and paid for. Only when he felt the family was a little *too* condescending, on account of money, he began to get huffy.

Then, of course, children came: a lovely little blonde daughter with a head of thistle-down. Everybody adored the child. It was the first exquisite blonde thing that had come into the family, a little mite with the white, slim, beautiful limbs of its father, and as it grew up the dancing, dainty movement of a wild little daisy-spirit. No wonder the Marshalls all loved the child: they called her Joyce. They themselves had their own grace, but it was slow, rather heavy. They had every one of them strong, heavy limbs and darkish skins, and they were short in stature. And now they had for one of their own this light little cowslip child. She was like a little poem in herself.

But nevertheless she brought a new difficulty. Winifred must have a nurse for her. Yes, yes, there must be a nurse. It was the family decree. Who was to pay for the nurse? The grandfather—seeing the father himself earned no money. Yes, the grandfather would pay, as he had paid all the lying-in expenses. There came a slight sense of money-strain. Egbert was living on his father-in-law.

After the child was born it was never quite the same between him and Winifred. The difference was at first hardly perceptible. But it was there. In the first place Winifred had a new centre of interest. She was not going to adore her child. But she had what the modern mother so often has in the place of spontaneous love: a profound sense of duty towards her child. Winifred appreciated her darling little girl, and felt a deep sense of duty towards her. Strange, that this sense of duty should go deeper than the love for her husband. But so it was. And so it often is. The responsibility of motherhood was the prime responsibility in Winifred's heart: the responsibility of wifehood came a long way second.

Her child seemed to link up again in a circuit with her own family. Her father and mother, herself, and her child, that was the human trinity for her. Her husband——? Yes, she loved him still. But that was like play. She had an almost barbaric sense of duty and of family. Till she married, her first human duty had been towards her father: he was the pillar, the source of life, the everlasting support. Now another link was added to the chain of duty: her father, herself, and her child.

Egbert was out of it. Without anything happening, he was gradually, unconsciously excluded from the circle. His wife still loved him, physically. But, but—he was *almost* the unnecessary party in the affair. He could not complain of Winifred. She still did her duty towards him. She still had a physical passion for him, that physical passion on which he had put all his life and soul. But—but——

It was for a long while an ever-recurring *but*. And then, after the second child, another blonde, winsome, touching little thing, not so proud and flame-like as Joyce—after Annabel came, then Egbert began truly to realize how it was. His wife still loved him. But —and now the but had grown enormous—her physical love for him was of secondary importance to her. It became ever less important. After all, she had had it, this physical passion, for two years now. It was not this that one lived from. No, no—something sterner, realer.

She began to resent her own passion for Egbert— just a little she began to despise it. For, after all, there he was, he was charming, he was lovable, he was terribly desirable. But—but—oh, the awful looming cloud of that *but*!—he did not stand firm in the landscape of her life like a tower of strength, like a great pillar of significance. No, he was like a cat one has about the house, which will one day disappear and leave no trace. He was like a flower in the garden, trembling in the wind of life, and then gone, leaving nothing to show. As an adjunct, as an accessary, he was perfect. Many a

woman would have adored to have him about her all
her life, the most beautiful and desirable of all her
possessions. But Winifred belonged to another school.

The years went by, and instead of coming more to
grips with life, he relaxed more. He was of a subtle,
sensitive, passionate nature. But he simply *would* not
give himself to what Winifred called life, *Work*. No,
he would not go into the world and work for money.
No, he just would not. If Winifred liked to live beyond
their small income—well, it was her look out.

And Winifred did not really want him to go out into
the world to work for money. Money became, alas, a
word like a firebrand between them, setting them both
aflame with anger. But that is because we must talk
in symbols. Winifred did not really care about money.
She did not care whether he earned or did not earn
anything. Only she knew she was dependent on her
father for three-fourths of the money spent for herself
and her children, that she let that be the *casus belli*,
the drawn weapon between herself and Egbert.

What did she want—what did she want? Her mother
once said to her, with that characteristic touch of irony:
'Well, dear, if it is your fate to consider the lilies, that
toil not, neither do they spin, that is one destiny among
many others, and perhaps not so unpleasant as most.
Why do you take it amiss, my child?'

The mother was subtler than her children, they very
rarely knew how to answer her. So Winifred was only
more confused. It was not a question of lilies. At
least, if it were a question of lilies, then her children
were the little blossoms. They at least *grew*. Doesn't
Jesus say: 'Consider the lilies *how they grow*'? Good
then, she had her growing babies. But as for that other
tall, handsome flower of a father of theirs, he was full
grown already, so she did not want to spend her life
considering him in the flower of his days.

No, it was not that he didn't earn money. It was not
that he was idle. He was *not* idle. He was always
doing something, always working away, down at Crockham, doing little jobs. But, oh dear, the little jobs—

the garden paths—the gorgeous flowers—the chairs to mend, old chairs to mend!

It was that he stood for nothing. If he had done something unsuccessfully, and *lost* what money they had! If he had but striven with something. Nay, even if he had been wicked, a waster, she would have been more free. She would have had something to resist, at least. A waster stands for something, really. He says: 'No, I will not aid and abet society in this business of increase and hanging together, I will upset the apple-cart as much as I can, in my small way.' Or else he says: 'No, I will *not* bother about others. If I have lusts, they are my own, and I prefer them to other people's virtues.' So, a waster, a scamp, takes a sort of stand. He exposes himself to opposition and final castigation: at any rate in story-books.

But Egbert! What are you to do with a man like Egbert? He had no vices. He was really kind, nay generous. And he was not weak. If he had been weak Winifred could have been kind to him. But he did not even give her that consolation. He was not weak, and he did not want her consolation or her kindness. No, thank you. He was of a fine passionate temper, and of a rarer steel than she. He knew it, and she knew it. Hence she was only the more baffled and maddened, poor thing. He, the higher, the finer, in his way the stronger, played with his garden, and his old folk-songs and Morris-dances, just played, and let her support the pillars of the future on her own heart.

And he began to get bitter, and a wicked look began to come on his face. He did not give in to her; not he. There were seven devils inside his long, slim, white body. He was healthy, full of restrained life. Yes, even he himself had to lock up his own vivid life inside himself, now she would not take it from him. Or rather, now that she only took it occasionally. For she had to yield at times. She loved him so, she desired him so, he was so exquisite to her, the fine creature that he was, finer than herself. Yes, with a groan she had to give in to her own unquenched passion for him. And he came to her then—ah, terrible, ah, wonderful, sometimes she wondered how either of them could live after the terror of the passion that swept between them. It was to her as if pure lightning, flash after flash, went through every fibre of her, till extinction came.

But it is the fate of human beings to live on. And it is the fate of clouds that seem nothing but bits of vapour slowly to pile up, to pile up and fill the heavens and blacken the sun entirely.

So it was. The love came back, the lightning of passion flashed tremendously between them. And there was blue sky and gorgeousness for a little while. And then, as inevitably, as inevitably, slowly the clouds began to edge up again above the horizon, slowly, slowly to lurk about the heavens, throwing an occasional cold and hateful shadow: slowly, slowly to congregate, to fill the empyrean space.

And as the years passed, the lightning cleared the sky more and more rarely, less and less the blue showed. Gradually the grey lid sank down upon them, as if it would be permanent.

Why didn't Egbert do something, then? Why didn't he come to grips with life? Why wasn't he like Winifred's father, a pillar of society, even if a slender, exquisite column? Why didn't he go into harness of some sort? Why didn't he take *some* direction?

Well, you can bring an ass to the water, but you cannot make him drink. The world was the water and Egbert was the ass. And he wasn't having any. He couldn't: he just couldn't. Since necessity did not force him to work for his bread and butter, he would not work for work's sake. You can't make the columbine flowers nod in January, nor make the cuckoo sing in England at Christmas. Why? It isn't his season. He doesn't want to. Nay, he *can't* want to.

And there it was with Egbert. He couldn't link up with the world's work, because the basic desire was absent from him. Nay, at the bottom of him he had an even stronger desire: to hold aloof. To hold aloof. To do nobody any damage. But to hold aloof. It was not his season.

Perhaps he should not have married and had children. But you can't stop the waters flowing.

Which held true for Winifred, too. She was not made to endure aloof. Her family tree was a robust vegetation that had to be stirring and believing. In one direction or another her life *had* to go. In her own home she had known nothing of this diffidence which she found in Egbert, and which she could not understand, and which threw her into such dismay. What was she to do, what was she to do, in face of this terrible diffidence?

It was all so different in her own home. Her father may have had his own misgivings, but he kept them to himself. Perhaps he had no very profound belief in this world of ours, this society which we have elaborated with so much effort, only to find ourselves elaborated to death at last. But Godfrey Marshall was of tough, rough fibre, not without a vein of healthy cunning through it all. It was for him a question of winning through, and leaving the rest to heaven. Without having many illusions to grace him, he still *did* believe in heaven. In a dark and unquestioning way, he had a sort of faith: an acrid faith like the sap of some not-to-be-exterminated tree. Just a blind acrid faith as sap is blind and acrid, and yet pushes on in growth and in faith. Perhaps he was unscrupulous, but only as a striving tree is unscrupulous, pushing its single way in a jungle of others.

In the end, it is only this robust, sap-like faith which keeps man going. He may live on for many generations inside the shelter of the social establishment which he has erected for himself, as pear-trees and currant bushes would go on bearing fruit for many seasons, inside a walled garden, even if the race of man were suddenly exterminated. But bit by bit the wall fruit-trees would gradually pull down the very walls that sustained them. Bit by bit every establishment collapses, unless it is renewed or restored by living hands, all the while.

Egbert could not bring himself to any more of this restoring or renewing business. He was not aware of

the fact; but awareness doesn't help much, anyhow.
He just couldn't. He had the stoic and epicurean
quality of his old, fine breeding. His father-in-law,
however, though he was not one bit more of a fool than
Egbert, realized that since we are here we may as well
live. And so he applied himself to his own tiny section
of the social work, and to doing the best for his family,
and to leave the rest to the ultimate will of heaven.
A certain robustness of blood made him able to go on.
But sometimes even from him spurted a sudden gall of
bitterness against the world and its make-up. And yet
—he had his own will-to-succeed, and this carried him
through. He refused to ask himself what the success
would amount to. It amounted to the estate down in
Hampshire, and his children lacking for nothing, and
himself of some importance in the world: and *basta !*
—*Basta! Basta!*

Nevertheless do not let us imagine that he was a
common pusher. He was not. He knew as well as
Egbert what disillusion meant. Perhaps in his soul he
had the same estimation of success. But he had a
certain acrid courage, and a certain will-to-power. In
his own small circle he would emanate power, the single
power of his own blind self. With all his spoiling of his
children, he was still the father of the old English type.
He was too wise to make laws and to domineer in the
abstract. But he had kept, and all honour to him, a
certain primitive dominion over the souls of his children,
the old, almost magic prestige of paternity. There it
was, still burning in him, the old smoky torch of paternal
godhead.

And in the sacred glare of this torch his children had
been brought up. He had given the girls every liberty,
at last. But he had never really let them go beyond his
power. And they, venturing out into the hard white
light of our fatherless world, learned to see with the
eyes of the world. They learned to criticize their father,
even, from some effulgence of worldly white light, to
see him as inferior. But this was all very well in the
head. The moment they forgot their tricks of criticism,

the old red glow of his authority came over them again. He was not to be quenched.

Let the psycho-analyst talk about father complex. It is just a word invented. Here was a man who had kept alive the old red flame of fatherhood, fatherhood that had even the right to sacrifice the child to God, like Isaac. Fatherhood that had life-and-death authority over the children: a great natural power. And till his children could be brought under some other great authority as girls; or could arrive at manhood and become themselves centres of the same power, continuing the same male mystery as men; until such time, willy-nilly, Godfrey Marshall would keep his children.

It had seemed as if he might lose Winifred. Winifred had *adored* her husband, and looked up to him as to something wonderful. Perhaps she had expected in him another great authority, a male authority greater, finer than her father's. For having once known the glow of male power, she would not easily turn to the cold white light of feminine independence. She would hunger, hunger all her life for the warmth and shelter of true male strength.

And hunger she might, for Egbert's power lay in the abnegation of power. He was himself the living negative of power. Even of responsibility. For the negation of power at last means the negation of responsibility. As far as these things went, he would confine himself to himself. He would try to confine his own *influence* even to himself. He would try, as far as possible, to abstain from influencing his children by assuming any responsibility for them. 'A little child shall lead them——' His child should lead, then. He would try not to make it go in any direction whatever. He would abstain from influencing it. Liberty!——

Poor Winifred was like a fish out of water in this liberty, gasping for the denser element which should contain her. Till her child came. And then she knew that she must be responsible for it, that she must have authority over it.

But here Egbert, silently and negatively, stepped in.

Silently, negatively, but fatally he neutralized her authority over her children.

There was a third little girl born. And after this Winifred wanted no more children. Her soul was turning to salt.

So she had charge of the children, they were her responsibility. The money for them had come from her father. She would do her very best for them, and have command over their life and death. But no! Egbert would not take the responsibility. He would not even provide the money. But he would not let her have her way. Her dark, silent, passionate authority he would not allow. It was a battle between them, the battle between liberty and the old blood-power. And, of course, he won. The little girls loved him and adored him. 'Daddy! Daddy!' They could do as they liked with him. Their mother would have ruled them. She would have ruled them passionately, with indulgence, with the old dark magic of parental authority, something looming and unquestioned and, after all, divine: if we believe in divine authority. The Marshalls did, being Catholic.

And Egbert, he turned her old dark, Catholic blood-authority into a sort of tyranny. He would not leave her her children. He stole them from her, and yet without assuming responsibility for them. He stole them from her, in emotion and spirit, and left her only to command their behaviour. A thankless lot for a mother. And her children adored him, adored him, little knowing the empty bitterness they were preparing for themselves when they too grew up to have husbands: husbands such as Egbert, adorable and null.

Joyce, the eldest, was still his favourite. She was now a quicksilver little thing of six years old. Barbara, the youngest, was a toddler of two years. They spent most of their time down at Crockham, because he wanted to be there. And even Winifred loved the place really. But now, in her frustrated and blinded state, it was full of menace for her children. The adders, the poison-berries, the brook, the marsh, the water that might not be pure—one thing and another. From mother and nurse it was a guerrilla gunfire of commands, and blithe, quicksilver disobedience from the three blonde, never-still little girls. Behind the girls was the father, against mother and nurse. And so it was.

'If you don't come quick, nurse, I shall run out there to where there are snakes.'

'Joyce, you *must* be patient. I'm just changing Annabel.'

There you are. There it was: always the same. Working away on the common across the brook he heard it. And he worked on, just the same.

Suddenly he heard a shriek, and he flung the spade from him and started for the bridge, looking up like a startled deer. Ah, there was Winifred—Joyce had hurt herself. He went on up the garden.

'What is it?'

The child was still screaming—now it was: 'Daddy! Daddy! Oh—oh, daddy!' And the mother was saying:

'Don't be frightened, darling. Let mother look.'

But the child only cried:

'Oh, daddy, daddy, daddy!'

She was terrified by the sight of the blood running from her own knee. Winifred crouched down, with her child of six in her lap, to examine the knee. Egbert bent over also.

'Don't make such a noise, Joyce,' he said irritably. 'How did she do it?'

'She fell on that sickle thing which you left lying about after cutting the grass,' said Winifred, looking into his face with bitter accusation as he bent near.

He had taken his handkerchief and tied it round the knee. Then he lifted the still sobbing child in his arms, and carried her into the house and upstairs to her bed. In his arms she became quiet. But his heart was burning with pain and with guilt. He had left the sickle there lying on the edge of the grass, and so his first-born child whom he loved so dearly had come to hurt. But then it was an accident—it was an accident. Why should he feel guilty? It would probably be nothing, better in two or three days.   Why take it to heart, why worry?   He put it aside.

The child lay on the bed in her little summer frock, her face very white now after the shock.   Nurse had come carrying the youngest child: and little Annabel stood holding her skirt.   Winifred, terribly serious and wooden-seeming, was bending over the knee, from which she had taken his blood-soaked handkerchief.   Egbert bent forward, too, keeping more sang-froid in his face than in his heart.   Winifred went all of a lump of seriousness, so he had to keep some reserve.   The child moaned and whimpered.

The knee was still bleeding profusely—it was a deep cut right in the joint.

'You'd better go for the doctor, Egbert,' said Winifred bitterly.

'Oh, no!   Oh, no!' cried Joyce in a panic.

'Joyce, my darling, don't cry!' said Winifred, suddenly catching the little girl to her breast in a strange tragic anguish, the *Mater Dolorata*.   Even the child was frightened into silence.   Egbert looked at the tragic figure of his wife with the child at her breast, and turned away.   Only Annabel started suddenly to cry: 'Joycey, Joycey, don't have your leg bleeding!'

Egbert rode four miles to the village for the doctor. He could not help feeling that Winifred was laying it on rather.   Surely the knee itself wasn't hurt!   Surely not.   It was only a surface cut.

The doctor was out.   Egbert left the message and came cycling swiftly home, his heart pinched with anxiety.   He dropped sweating off his bicycle and went into the house, looking rather small, like a man who is at fault.   Winifred was upstairs sitting by Joyce, who was looking pale and important in bed, and was eating some tapioca pudding.   The pale, small, scared face of his child went to Egbert's heart.

'Doctor Wing was out.   He'll be here about half-past two,' said Egbert.

'I don't want him to come,' whimpered Joyce.

'Joyce, dear, you must be patient and quiet,' said

Winifred. 'He won't hurt you. But he will tell us
what to do to make your knee better quickly. That is
why he must come.'

Winifred always explained carefully to her little girls:
and it always took the words off their lips for the moment.

'Does it bleed yet?' said Egbert.

Winifred moved the bedclothes carefully aside.

'I think not,' she said.

Egbert stooped also to look.

'No, it doesn't,' he said. Then he stood up with a
relieved look on his face. He turned to the child.

'Eat your pudding, Joyce,' he said. 'It won't be
anything. You've only got to keep still for a few
days.'

'You haven't had your dinner, have you, daddy?'

'Not yet.'

'Nurse will give it to you,' said Winifred.

'You'll be all right, Joyce,' he said, smiling to the
child and pushing the blonde hair aside off her brow.
She smiled back winsomely into his face.

He went downstairs and ate his meal alone. Nurse
served him. She liked waiting on him. All women
liked him and liked to do things for him.

The doctor came—a fat country practitioner, pleasant
and kind.

'What, little girl, been tumbling down, have you?
There's a thing to be doing, for a smart little lady like
you! What! And cutting your knee! Tut-tut-tut!
That *wasn't* clever of you, now was it? Never mind,
never mind, soon be better. Let us look at it. Won't
hurt you. Not the least in life. Bring a bowl with a
little warm water, nurse. Soon have it all right again,
soon have it all right.'

Joyce smiled at him with a pale smile of faint
superiority. This was *not* the way in which she was used
to being talked to.

He bent down, carefully looking at the little, thin,
wounded knee of the child. Egbert bent over him.

'Oh, dear, oh, dear! Quite a deep little cut. Nasty
little cut. Nasty little cut. But, never mind. Never

mind, little lady. We'll soon have it better. Soon have it better, little lady. What's your name?'

'My name is Joyce,' said the child distinctly.

'Oh, really!' he replied. 'Oh, really! Well, that's a fine name too, in my opinion. Joyce, eh?—And how old might Miss Joyce be? Can she tell me that?'

'I'm six,' said the child, slightly amused and very condescending.

'Six! There now. Add up and count as far as six, can you? Well, that's a clever little girl, a clever little girl. And if she has to drink a spoonful of medicine, she won't make a murmur, I'll be bound. Not like *some* little girls. What? Eh?'

'I take it if mother wishes me to,' said Joyce.

'Ah, there now! That's the style! That's what I like to hear from a little lady in bed because she's cut her knee. That's the style——'

The comfortable and prolix doctor dressed and bandaged the knee and recommended bed and a light diet for the little lady. He thought a week or a fortnight would put it right. No bones or ligatures damaged —fortunately. Only a flesh cut. He would come again in a day or two.

So Joyce was reassured and stayed in bed and had all her toys up. Her father often played with her. The doctor came the third day. He was fairly pleased with the knee. It was healing. It was healing—yes—yes. Let the child continue in bed. He came again after a day or two. Winifred was a trifle uneasy. The wound seemed to be healing on the top, but it hurt the child too much. It didn't look quite right. She said so to Egbert.

'Egbert, I'm sure Joyce's knee isn't healing properly.'

'I think it is,' he said. 'I think it's all right.'

'I'd rather Doctor Wing came again—I don't feel satisfied.'

'Aren't you trying to imagine it worse than it really is?'

'You would say so, of course. But I shall write a post card to Doctor Wing now.'

The doctor came next day. He examined the knee. Yes, there was inflammation. Yes, there *might* be a little septic poisoning—there might. There might. Was the child feverish?

So a fortnight passed by, and the child *was* feverish, and the knee was more inflamed and grew worse and was painful, painful. She cried in the night, and her mother had to sit up with her. Egbert still insisted it was nothing, really—it would pass. But in his heart he was anxious.

Winifred wrote again to her father. On Saturday the elderly man appeared. And no sooner did Winifred see the thick, rather short figure in its grey suit than a great yearning came over her.

'Father, I'm not satisfied with Joyce. I'm not satisfied with Doctor Wing.'

'Well, Winnie, dear, if you're not satisfied we must have further advice, that is all.'

The sturdy, powerful, elderly man went upstairs, his voice sounding rather grating through the house, as if it cut upon the tense atmosphere.

'How are you, Joyce, darling?' he said to the child. 'Does your knee hurt you? Does it hurt you, dear?'

'It does sometimes.' The child was shy of him, cold towards him.

'Well, dear, I'm sorry for that. I hope you try to bear it, and not trouble mother too much.'

There was no answer. He looked at the knee. It was red and stiff.

'Of course,' he said, 'I think we must have another doctor's opinion. And if we're going to have it, we had better have it at once. Egbert, do you think you might cycle in to Bingham for Doctor Wayne? I found him *very* satisfactory for Winnie's mother.'

'I can go if you think it necessary,' said Egbert.

'Certainly I think it necessary. Even if there *is* nothing, we can have peace of mind. Certainly I think it necessary. I should like Doctor Wayne to come this evening if possible.'

So Egbert set off on his bicycle through the wind, like a boy sent on an errand, leaving his father-in-law a pillar of assurance, with Winifred.

Doctor Wayne came, and looked grave. Yes, the knee was certainly taking the wrong way. The child might be lame for life.

Up went the fire of fear and anger in every heart. Doctor Wayne came again the next day for a proper examination. And, yes, the knee had really taken bad ways. It should be X-rayed. It was very important.

Godfrey Marshall walked up and down the lane with the doctor, beside the standing motor-car: up and down, up and down in one of those consultations of which he had had so many in his life.

As a result he came indoors to Winifred.

'Well, Winnie, dear, the best thing to do is to take Joyce up to London, to a nursing home where she can have proper treatment. Of course this knee has been allowed to go wrong. And apparently there is a risk that the child may even lose her leg. What do you think, dear? You agree to our taking her up to town and putting her under the best care?'

'Oh, father, you *know* I would do anything on earth for her.'

'I know you would, Winnie darling. The pity is that there has been this unfortunate delay already. I can't think what Doctor Wing was doing. Apparently the child is in danger of losing her leg. Well, then if you will have everything ready, we will take her up to town to-morrow. I will order the large car from Denley's to be here at ten. Egbert, will you take a telegram at once to Doctor Jackson? It is a small nursing home for children and for surgical cases, not far from Baker Street. I'm sure Joyce will be all right there.'

'Oh, father, can't I nurse her myself?'

'Well, darling, if she is to have proper treatment, she had best be in a home. The X-ray treatment, and the electric treatment, and whatever is necessary.'

'It will cost a great deal——' said Winifred.

'We can't think of cost, if the child's leg is in danger —or even her life. No use speaking of cost,' said the elder man impatiently.

And so it was. Poor Joyce, stretched out on a bed

in the big closed motor-car—the mother sitting by her head, the grandfather in his short grey beard and a bowler hat, sitting by her feet, thick, and implacable in his responsibility—they rolled slowly away from Crockham, and from Egbert who stood there bareheaded and a little ignominious, left behind. He was to shut up the house and bring the rest of the family back to town, by train, the next day.

Followed a dark and bitter time. The poor child. The poor, poor child, how she suffered, an agony and a long crucifixion in that nursing home. It was a bitter six weeks which changed the soul of Winifred for ever. As she sat by the bed of her poor, tortured little child, tortured with the agony of the knee, and the still worse agony of these diabolic, but perhaps necessary modern treatments, she felt her heart killed and going cold in her breast. Her little Joyce, her frail, brave, wonderful, little Joyce, frail and small and pale as a white flower! Ah, how had she, Winifred, dared to be so wicked, so wicked, so careless, so sensual.

'Let my heart die! Let my woman's heart of flesh die! Saviour, let my heart die. And save my child. Let my heart die from the world and from the flesh. Oh, destroy my heart that is so wayward. Let my heart of pride die. Let my heart die.'

She prayed beside the bed of her child. And like the mother with the seven swords in her breast, slowly her heart of pride and passion died in her breast, bleeding away. Slowly it died, bleeding away, and she turned to the Church for comfort, to Jesus, to the Mother of God, but most of all, to that great and enduring institution, the Roman Catholic Church. She withdrew into the shadow of the Church. She was a mother with three children. But in her soul she died, her heart of pride and passion and desire bled to death, her soul belonged to her Church, her body belonged to her duty as a mother.

Her duty as a wife did not enter. As a wife she had no sense of duty: only a certain bitterness towards the man with whom she had known such sensuality and distraction. She was purely the *Mater Dolorata*. To the man she was closed as a tomb.

Egbert came to see his child. But Winifred seemed to be always seated there, like the tomb of his manhood and his fatherhood. Poor Winifred: she was still young, still strong and ruddy and beautiful like a ruddy hard flower of the field. Strange—her ruddy, healthy face, so sombre, and her strong, heavy, full-blooded body, so still. She, a nun! Never. And yet the gates of her heart and soul had shut in his face with a slow, resonant clang, shutting him out for ever. There was no need for her to go into a convent. Her will had done it.

And between this young mother and this young father lay the crippled child, like a bit of pale silk floss on the pillow, and a little white pain-quenched face. He could not bear it. He just could not bear it. He turned aside. There was nothing to do but to turn aside. He turned aside, and went hither and thither, desultory. He was still attractive and desirable. But there was a little frown between his brow as if he had been cleft there with a hatchet: cleft right in, for ever, and that was the stigma.

The child's leg was saved: but the knee was locked stiff. The fear now was lest the lower leg should wither, or cease to grow. There must be long-continued massage and treatment, daily treatment, even when the child left the nursing home. And the whole of the expense was borne by the grandfather.

Egbert now had no real home. Winifred with the children and nurse was tied to the little flat in London. He could not live there: he could not contain himself. The cottage was shut up—or lent to friends. He went down sometimes to work in his garden and keep the place in order. Then with the empty house around him at night, all the empty rooms, he felt his heart go wicked. The sense of frustration and futility, like some slow, torpid snake, slowly bit right though his heart. Futility, futility, futility: the horrible marsh-poison went through his veins and killed him.

As he worked in the garden in the silence of day he

would listen for a sound. No sound. No sound of
Winifred from the dark inside of the cottage: no sound
of children's voices from the air, from the common,
from the near distance. No sound, nothing but the old
dark marsh-venomous atmosphere of the place. So he
worked spasmodically through the day, and at night
made a fire and cooked some food alone.

He was alone. He himself cleaned the cottage and
made his bed. But his mending he did not do. His
shirts were slit on the shoulders, when he had been
working, and the white flesh showed through. He would
feel the air and the spots of rain on his exposed flesh.
And he would look again across the common, where the
dark, tufted gorse was dying to seed, and the bits of
cat-heather were coming pink in tufts, like a sprinkling
of sacrificial blood.

His heart went back to the savage old spirit of the
place: the desire for old gods, old, lost passions, the passion of the cold-blooded, darting snakes that hissed and
shot away from him, the mystery of blood-sacrifices, all
the lost, intense sensations of the primeval people of the
place, whose passions seethed in the air still, from those
long days before the Romans came. The seethe of a
lost, dark passion in the air. The presence of unseen
snakes.

A queer, baffled, half-wicked look came on his face.
He could not stay long at the cottage. Suddenly he must
swing on to his bicycle and go—anywhere. Anywhere,
away from the place. He would stay a few days with
his mother in the old home. His mother adored him
and grieved as a mother would. But the little, baffled,
half-wicked smile curled on his face, and he swung
away from his mother's solicitude as from everything else.

Always moving on—from place to place, friend to
friend: and always swinging away from sympathy.
As soon as sympathy, like a soft hand, was reached
out to touch him, away he swerved, instinctively, as a
harmless snake swerves and swerves and swerves away
from an outstretched hand. Away he must go. And
periodically he went back to Winifred.

He was terrible to her now, like a temptation. She had devoted herself to her children and her Church. Joyce was once more on her feet; but, alas! lame, with iron supports to her leg, and a little crutch. It was strange how she had grown into a long, pallid, wild little thing. Strange that the pain had not made her soft and docile, but had brought out a wild, almost maenad temper in the child. She was seven, and long and white and thin, but by no means subdued. Her blonde hair was darkening. She still had long sufferings to face, and, in her own childish consciousness, the stigma of her lameness to bear.

And she bore it. An almost maenad courage seemed to possess her, as if she were a long, thin, young weapon of life. She acknowledged all her mother's care. She would stand by her mother for ever. But some of her father's fine-tempered desperation flashed in her.

When Egbert saw his little girl limping horribly—not only limping but lurching horribly in crippled, childish way, his heart again hardened with chagrin, like steel that is tempered again. There was a tacit understanding between him and his little girl: not what we would call love, but a weapon-like kinship. There was a tiny touch of irony in his manner towards her, contrasting sharply with Winifred's heavy, unleavened solicitude and care. The child flickered back to him with an answering little smile of irony and recklessness: an odd flippancy which made Winifred only the more sombre and earnest.

The Marshalls took endless thought and trouble for the child, searching out every means to save her limb and her active freedom. They spared no effort and no money, they spared no strength of will. With all their slow, heavy power of will they willed that Joyce should save her liberty of movement, should win back her wild, free grace. Even if it took a long time to recover, it should be recovered.

So the situation stood. And Joyce submitted, week after week, month after month, to the tyranny and pain of the treatment. She acknowledged the honourable effort on her behalf. But her flamy reckless spirit was her father's. It was he who had all the glamour for her. He and she were like members of some forbidden secret society who know one another but may not recognize one another. Knowledge they had in common, the same secret of life, the father and the child. But the child stayed in the camp of her mother, honourably, and the father wandered outside like Ishmael, only coming sometimes to sit in the home for an hour or two, an evening or two beside the camp fire, like Ishmael, in a curious silence and tension, with the mocking answer of the desert speaking out of his silence, and annulling the whole convention of the domestic home.

His presence was almost an anguish to Winifred. She prayed against it. That little cleft between his brow, that flickering, wicked little smile that seemed to haunt his face, and above all, the triumphant loneliness, the Ishmael quality. And then the erectness of his supple body, like a symbol. The very way he stood, so quiet, so insidious, like an erect, supple symbol of life, the living body, confronting her downcast soul, was torture to her. He was like a supple living idol moving before her eyes, and she felt if she watched him she was damned.

And he came and made himself at home in her little home. When he was there, moving in his own quiet way, she felt as if the whole great law of sacrifice, by which she had elected to live, were annulled. He annulled by his very presence the laws of her life. And what did he substitute? Ah, against that question she hardened herself in recoil.

It was awful to her to have to have him about— moving about in his shirt-sleeves, speaking in his tenor, throaty voice to the children. Annabel simply adored him, and he teased the little girl. The baby, Barbara, was not sure of him. She had been born a stranger to him. But even the nurse, when she saw his white shoulder of flesh through the slits of his torn shirt, thought it a shame.

Winifred felt it was only another weapon of his against her.

'You have other shirts—why do you wear that old one that is all torn, Egbert?' she said.

'I may as well wear it out,' he said subtly.

He knew she would not offer to mend it for him. She *could* not. And no, she would not. Had she not her own gods to honour? And could she betray them, submitting to his Baal and Ashtaroth? And it was terrible to her, his unsheathed presence, that seemed to annul her and her faith, like another revelation. Like a gleaming idol evoked against her, a vivid life-idol that might triumph.

He came and he went—and she persisted. And then the Great War broke out. He was a man who could not go to the dogs. He could not dissipate himself. He was pure-bred in his Englishness, and even when he would have liked to be vicious, he could not.

So when the war broke out his whole instinct was against it: against war. He had not the faintest desire to overcome any foreigners or to help in their death. He had no conception of Imperial England, and Rule Britannia was just a joke to him. He was a pure-blooded Englishman, perfect in his race, and when he was truly himself he could no more have been aggressive on the score of his Englishness than a rose can be aggressive on the score of its rosiness.

No, he had no desire to defy Germany and to exalt England. The distinction between German and English was not for him the distinction between good and bad. It was the distinction between blue water-flowers and red or white bush-blossoms: just difference. The difference between the wild boar and the wild bear. And a man was good or bad according to his nature, not according to his nationality.

Egbert was well-bred, and this was part of his natural understanding. It was merely unnatural to him to hate a nation *en bloc*. Certain individuals he disliked, and others he liked, and the mass he knew nothing about. Certain deeds he disliked, certain deeds seemed natural to him, and about most deeds he had no particular feeling.

He had, however, the one deepest pure-bred instinct. He recoiled inevitably from having his feelings dictated to him by the mass feeling. His feelings were his own, his understanding was his own, and he would never go back on either, willingly. Shall a man become inferior to his own true knowledge and self, just because the mob expects it of him?

What Egbert felt subtly and without question, his father-in-law felt also in a rough, more combative way. Different as the two men were, they were two real Englishmen, and their instincts were almost the same.

And Godfrey Marshall had the world to reckon with. There was German military aggression, and the English non-military idea of liberty and the 'conquests of peace' —meaning industrialism. Even if the choice between militarism and industrialism were a choice of evils, the elderly man asserted his choice of the latter, perforce. He whose soul was quick with the instinct of power.

Egbert just refused to reckon with the world. He just refused even to decide between German militarism and British industrialism. He chose neither. As for atrocities, he despised the people who committed them, as inferior criminal types. There was nothing national about crime.

And yet, war! War! Just war! Not right or wrong, but just war itself. Should he join? Should he give himself over to war? The question was in his mind for some weeks. Not because he thought England was right and Germany wrong. Probably Germany was wrong, but he refused to make a choice. Not because he felt inspired. No. But just—war.

The deterrent was, the giving himself over into the power of other men, and into the power of the mob-spirit of a democratic army. Should he give himself over? Should he make over his own life and body to the control of something which he *knew* was inferior, in spirit, to his own self? Should he commit himself into the power of an inferior control? Should he? Should he betray himself?

He was going to put himself into the power of his

inferiors, and he knew it. He was going to subjugate himself. He was going to be ordered about by petty *canaille* of non-commissioned officers—and even commissioned officers. He who was born and bred free. Should he do it?

He went to his wife, to speak to her.

'Shall I join up, Winifred?'

She was silent. Her instinct also was dead against it. And yet a certain profound resentment made her answer:

'You have three children dependent on you. I don't know whether you have thought of that.'

It was still only the third month of the war, and the old pre-war ideas were still alive.

'Of course. But it won't make much difference to them. I shall be earning a shilling a day, at least.'

'You'd better speak to father, I think,' she replied heavily. Egbert went to his father-in-law. The elderly man's heart was full of resentment.

'I should say,' he said rather sourly, 'it is the best thing you could do.'

Egbert went and joined up immediately, as a private soldier. He was drafted into the light artillery.

Winifred now had a new duty towards him: the duty of a wife towards a husband who is himself performing his duty towards the world. She loved him still. She would always love him, as far as earthly love went. But it was duty she now lived by. When he came back to her in khaki, a soldier, she submitted to him as a wife. It was her duty. But to his passion she could never again fully submit. Something prevented her, for ever: even her own deepest choice.

He went back again to camp. It did not suit him to be a modern soldier. In the thick, gritty, hideous khaki his subtle physique was extinguished as if he had been killed. In the ugly intimacy of the camp his thoroughbred sensibilities were just degraded. But he had chosen, so he accepted. An ugly little look came on to his face, of a man who has accepted his own degradation.

In the early spring Winifred went down to Crockham

to be there when primroses were out, and the tassels
hanging on the hazel-bushes. She felt something like
a reconciliation towards Egbert, now he was a prisoner
in camp most of his days. Joyce was wild with delight
at seeing the garden and the common again, after the
eight or nine months of London and misery. She was
still lame. She still had the irons up her leg. But she
lurched about with a wild, crippled agility.

Egbert came for a week-end, in his gritty, thick,
sandpaper khaki and puttees and the hideous cap. Nay,
he looked terrible. And on his face a slightly impure
look, a little sore on his lip, as if he had eaten too much
or drunk too much or let his blood become a little unclean. He was almost uglily healthy, with the camp life.
It did not suit him.

Winifred waited for him in a little passion of duty and
sacrifice, willing to serve the soldier, if not the man.
It only made him feel a little more ugly inside. The
week-end was torment to him: the memory of the camp,
the knowledge of the life he led there; even the sight of
his own legs in that abhorrent khaki. He felt as if the
hideous cloth went into his blood and made it gritty
and dirty. Then Winifred so ready to serve the *soldier*,
when she repudiated the man. And this made the grit
worse between his teeth. And the children running
around playing and calling in the rather mincing fashion
of children who have nurses and governesses and literature in the family. And Joyce so lame! It had all
become unreal to him, after the camp. It only set his
soul on edge. He left at dawn on the Monday morning,
glad to get back to the realness and vulgarity of the camp.

Winifred would never meet him again at the cottage
—only in London, where the world was with them.
But sometimes he came alone to Crockham, perhaps
when friends were staying there. And then he would
work awhile in his garden. This summer still it would
flame with blue anchusas and big red poppies, the
mulleins would sway their soft, downy erections in the
air: he loved mulleins: and the honeysuckle would stream
out scent like memory, when the owl was whooing.

Then he sat by the fire with the friends and with Wini-fred's sisters, and they sang the folk-songs. He put on thin civilian clothes and his charm and his beauty and the supple dominancy of his body glowed out again. But Winifred was not there.

At the end of the summer he went to Flanders, into action. He seemed already to have gone out of life, beyond the pale of life. He hardly remembered his life any more, being like a man who is going to take a jump from a height, and is only looking to where he must land.

He was twice slightly wounded, in two months. But not enough to put him off duty for more than a day or two. They were retiring again, holding the enemy back. He was in the rear—three guns. The country was all pleasant, war had not yet trampled it. Only the air seemed shattered, and the land awaiting death. It was a small, unimportant action in which he was engaged.

The guns were stationed on a little bushy hillock just outside a village. But occasionally, it was difficult to say from which direction came the sharp crackle of rifle-fire, and beyond, the far-off thud of cannon. The afternoon was wintry and cold.

A lieutenant stood on a little iron platform at the top of the ladders, taking the sights and giving the aim, calling in a high, tense, mechanical voice. Out of the sky came the sharp cry of the directions, then the warn-ing numbers, then 'Fire!' The shot went, the piston of the gun sprang back, there was a sharp explosion, and a very faint film of smoke in the air. Then the other two guns fired, and there was a lull. The officer was uncertain of the enemy's position. The thick clump of horse-chestnut-trees below was without change. Only in the far distance the sound of heavy firing continued, so far off as to give a sense of peace.

The gorse-bushes on either hand were dark, but a few sparks of flowers showed yellow. He noticed them almost unconsciously as he waited, in the lull. He was in his shirt-sleeves, and the air came chill on his arms.

Again his shirt was slit on the shoulders, and the flesh showed through. He was dirty and unkempt. But his face was quiet. So many things go out of consciousness before we come to the end of consciousness.

Before him, below, was the high road, running between high banks of grass and gorse. He saw the whitish, muddy tracks and deep scores in the road, where the part of the regiment had retired. Now all was still. Sounds that came, came from the outside. The place where he stood was still silent, chill, serene: the white church among the trees beyond seemed like a thought only.

He moved into a lightning-like mechanical response at the sharp cry from the officer overhead. Mechanism, the pure mechanical action of obedience at the guns. Pure mechanical action at the guns. It left the soul unburdened, brooding in dark nakedness. In the end, the soul is alone, brooding on the face of the uncreated flux, as a bird on a dark sea.

Nothing could be seen but the road, and a crucifix knocked slanting and the dark, autumnal fields and woods. There appeared three horsemen on a little eminence, very small, on the crest of a ploughed field. They were our own men. Of the enemy, nothing.

The lull continued. Then suddenly came sharp orders, and a new direction of the guns, and an intense, exciting activity. Yet at the centre the soul remained dark and aloof, alone.

But even so, it was the soul that heard the new sound: the new, deep 'papp!' of a gun that seemed to touch right upon the soul. He kept up the rapid activity at the gun, sweating. But in his soul was the echo of the new, deep sound, deeper than life.

And in confirmation came the awful faint whistling of a shell, advancing almost suddenly into a piercing, tearing shriek that would tear through the membrane of life. He heard it in his ears, but he heard it also in his soul, in tension. There was relief when the thing had swung by and struck, away beyond. He heard the hoarseness of its explosion, and the voice of the soldier calling to the horses. But he did not turn round to look. He only noticed a twig of holly with red berries fall like a gift on to the road below.

Not this time, not this time. Whither thou goest I will go. Did he say it to the shell, or to whom? Whither thou goest I will go. Then, the faint whistling of another shell dawned, and his blood became small and still to receive it. It drew nearer, like some horrible blast of wind; his blood lost consciousness. But in the second of suspension he saw the heavy shell swoop to earth, into the rocky bushes on the right, and earth and stones poured up into the sky. It was as if he heard no sound. The earth and stones and fragments of bush fell to earth again, and there was the same unchanging peace. The Germans had got the aim.

Would they move now? Would they retire? Yes. The officer was giving the last lightning-rapid orders to fire before withdrawing. A shell passed unnoticed in the rapidity of action. And then, into the silence, into the suspense where the soul brooded, finally crashed a noise and a darkness and a moment's flaming agony and horror. Ah, he had seen the dark bird flying towards him, flying home this time. In one instant life and eternity went up in a conflagration of agony, then there was a weight of darkness.

When faintly something began to struggle in the darkness, a consciousness of himself, he was aware of a great load and a clanging sound. To have known the moment of death! And to be forced, before dying, to review it. So, fate, even in death.

There was a resounding of pain. It seemed to sound from the outside of his consciousness: like a loud bell clanging very near. Yet he knew it was himself. He must associate himself with it. After a lapse and a new effort, he identified a pain in his head, a large pain that clanged and resounded. So far he could identify himself with himself. Then there was a lapse.

After a time he seemed to wake up again, and waking, to know that he was at the front, and that he was killed. He did not open his eyes. Light was not yet his. The clanging pain in his head rang out the rest of his consciousness. So he lapsed away from consciousness, in unutterable sick abandon of life.

Bit by bit, like a doom, came the necessity to know. He was hit in the head. It was only a vague surmise at first. But in the swinging of the pendulum of pain, swinging ever nearer and nearer, to touch him into an agony of consciousness and a consciousness of agony, gradually the knowledge emerged—he must be hit in the head—hit on the left brow; if so, there would be blood—was there blood?—could he feel blood in his left eye? Then the clanging seemed to burst the membrane of his brain, like death-madness.

Was there blood on his face? Was hot blood flowing? Or was it dry blood congealing down his cheek? It took him hours even to ask the question: time being no more than an agony in darkness, without measurement.

A long time after he had opened his eyes he realized he was seeing something—something, something, but the effort to recall what was too great. No, no; no recall!

Were they the stars in the dark sky? Was it possible it was stars in the dark sky? Stars? The world? Ah, no, he could not know it! Stars and the world were gone for him, he closed his eyes. No stars, no sky, no world. No, no! The thick darkness of blood alone. It should be one great lapse into the thick darkness of blood in agony.

Death, oh, death! The world all blood, and the blood all writhing with death. The soul like the tiniest little light out on a dark sea, the sea of blood. And the light guttering, beating, pulsing in a windless storm, wishing it could go out, yet unable.

There had been life. There had been Winifred and his children. But the frail death-agony effort to catch at straws of memory, straws of life from the past, brought on too great a nausea. No, no! No Winifred, no children. No world, no people. Better the agony of dissolution ahead than the nausea of the effort back-wards. Better the terrible work should go forward, the dissolving into the black sea of death, in the extremity of dissolution, than that there should be any reaching back towards life. To forget! To forget! Utterly, utterly to forget, in the great forgetting of death. To break the core and the unit of life, and to lapse out on the great darkness. Only that. To break the clue, and mingle and commingle with the one darkness, without afterwards or forwards. Let the black sea of death itself solve the problem of futurity. Let the will of man break and give up.

What was that? A light! A terrible light! Was it figures? Was it legs of a horse colossal—colossal above him: huge, huge?

The Germans heard a slight noise, and started. Then, in the glare of a light-bomb, by the side of the heap of earth thrown up by the shell, they saw the dead face.

THE FOX

THE two girls were usually known by their surnames,
Banford and March. They had taken the farm together,
intending to work it all by themselves: that is, they
were going to rear chickens, make a living by poultry,
and add to this by keeping a cow, and raising one or
two young beasts. Unfortunately, things did not turn
out well.

Banford was a small, thin, delicate thing with spectacles. She, however, was the principal investor, for
March had little or no money. Banford's father, who
was a tradesman in Islington, gave his daughter the
start, for her health's sake, and because he loved her,
and because it did not look as if she would marry.
March was more robust. She had learned carpentry
and joinery at the evening classes in Islington. She
would be the man about the place. They had, moreover, Banford's old grandfather living with them at
the start. He had been a farmer. But unfortunately
the old man died after he had been at Bailey Farm for
a year. Then the two girls were left alone.

They were neither of them young: that is, they were
near thirty. But they certainly were not old. They
set out quite gallantly with their enterprise. They had
numbers of chickens, black Leghorns and white Leghorns, Plymouths, and Wyandottes; also some ducks;
also two heifers in the fields. One heifer, unfortunately,
refused absolutely to stay in the Bailey Farm closes.
No matter how March made up the fences, the heifer
was out, wild in the woods, or trespassing on the neighbouring pasture, and March and Banford were away,
flying after her, with more haste than success. So this
heifer they sold in despair. Then, just before the other
beast was expecting her first calf, the old man died,
and the girls, afraid of the coming event, sold her in a
panic, and limited their attentions to fowls and ducks.

In spite of a little chagrin, it was a relief to have no more cattle on hand. Life was not made merely to be slaved away. Both girls agreed in this. The fowls were quite enough trouble. March had set up her carpenter's bench at the end of the open shed. Here she worked, making coops and doors and other appurtenances. The fowls were housed in the bigger building, which had served as barn and cowshed in old days. They had a beautiful home, and should have been perfectly content. Indeed, they looked well enough. But the girls were disgusted at their tendency to strange illnesses, at their exacting way of life, and at their refusal, obstinate refusal to lay eggs.

March did most of the outdoor work. When she was out and about, in her puttees and breeches, her belted coat and her loose cap, she looked almost like some graceful, loose-balanced young man, for her shoulders were straight, and her movements easy and confident, even tinged with a little indifference, or irony. But her face was not a man's face, ever. The wisps of her crisp dark hair blew about her as she stooped, her eyes were big and wide and dark, when she looked up again, strange, startled, shy, and sardonic at once. Her mouth, too, was almost pinched as if in pain and irony. There was something odd and unexplained about her. She would stand balanced on one hip, looking at the fowls pattering about in the obnoxious fine mud of the sloping yard, and calling to her favourite white hen, which came in answer to her name. But there was an almost satirical flicker in March's big, dark eyes as she looked at her three-toed flock pottering about under her gaze, and the same slight dangerous satire in her voice as she spoke to the favoured Patty, who pecked at March's boot by way of friendly demonstration.

Fowls did not flourish at Bailey Farm, in spite of all that March did for them. When she provided hot food for them in the morning, according to rule, she noticed that it made them heavy and dozy for hours. She expected to see them lean against the pillars of the shed in their languid processes of digestion. And she knew quite well that they ought to be busily scratching and foraging about, if they were to come to any good. So she decided to give them their hot food at night, and let them sleep on it. Which she did. But it made no difference.

War conditions, again, were very unfavourable to poultry keeping. Food was scarce and bad. And when the Daylight Saving Bill was passed, the fowls obstinately refused to go to bed as usual, about nine o'clock in the summer-time. That was late enough, indeed, for there was no peace till they were shut up and asleep. Now they cheerfully walked around, without so much as glancing at the barn, until ten o'clock or later. Both Banford and Marsh disbelieved in living for work alone. They wanted to read or take a cycle ride in the evening, or perhaps March wished to paint curvilinear swans on porcelain, with green background, or else make a marvellous fire-screen by processes of elaborate cabinet work. For she was a creature of odd whims and unsatisfied tendencies. But from all these things she was prevented by the stupid fowls.

One evil there was greater than any other. Bailey Farm was a little homestead, with ancient wooden barn and low-gabled farm-house, lying just one field removed from the edge of the wood. Since the war the fox was a demon. He carried off the hens under the very noses of March and Banford. Banford would start and stare through her big spectacles with all her eyes, as another squawk and flutter took place at her heels. Too late! Another white Leghorn gone. It was disheartening.

They did what they could to remedy it. When it became permitted to shoot foxes, they stood sentinel with their guns, the two of them, at the favoured hours. But it was no good. The fox was too quick for them. So another year passed, and another, and they were living on their losses, as Banford said. They let their farm-house one summer, and retired to live in a railway carriage that was deposited as a sort of outhouse in a corner of the field. This amused them, and helped their finances. None the less, things looked dark.

Although they were usually the best of friends, because Banford, though nervous and delicate, was a warm, generous soul, and March, though so odd and absent in herself, had a strange magnanimity, yet, in the long solitude, they were apt to become a little irritable with one another, tired of one another. March had four-fifths of the work to do, and though she did not mind, there seemed no relief, and it made her eyes flash curiously sometimes. Then Banford, feeling more nerve-worn than ever, would become despondent, and March would speak sharply to her. They seemed to be losing ground, somehow, losing hope as the months went by. There alone in the fields by the wood, with the wide country stretching hollow and dim to the round hills of the White Horse, in the far distance, they seemed to have to live too much off themselves. There was nothing to keep them up—and no hope.

The fox really exasperated them both. As soon as they had let the fowls out, in the early summer mornings, they had to take their guns and keep guard: and then again, as soon as evening began to mellow, they must go once more. And he was so sly. He slid along in the deep grass; he was difficult as a serpent to see. And he seemed to circumvent the girls deliberately. Once or twice March had caught sight of the white tip of his brush, or the ruddy shadow of him in the deep grass, and she had let fire at him. But he made no account of this.

One evening March was standing with her back to the sunset, her gun under her arm, her hair pushed under her cap. She was half watching, half musing. It was her constant state. Her eyes were keen and observant, but her inner mind took no notice of what she saw. She was always lapsing into this odd, rapt state, her mouth rather screwed up. It was a question whether she was there, actually consciously present, or not.

The trees on the wood-edge were a darkish, brownish green in the full light—for it was the end of August. Beyond, the naked, copper-like shafts and limbs of the pine-trees shone in the air. Nearer the rough grass,

with its long brownish stalks all agleam, was full of
light. The fowls were round about—the ducks were
still swimming on the pond under the pine-trees. March
looked at it all, saw it all, and did not see it. She heard
Banford speaking to the fowls in the distance—and she
did not hear. What was she thinking about? Heaven
knows. Her consciousness was, as it were, held back.

She lowered her eyes, and suddenly saw the fox.
He was looking up at her. His chin was pressed down,
and his eyes were looking up. They met her eyes.
And he knew her. She was spellbound—she knew he
knew her. So he looked into her eyes, and her soul
failed her. He knew her, he was not daunted.

She struggled, confusedly she came to herself, and saw
him making off, with slow leaps over some fallen boughs,
slow, impudent jumps. Then he glanced over his
shoulder, and ran smoothly away. She saw his brush
held smooth like a feather, she saw his white buttocks
twinkle. And he was gone, softly, soft as the wind.

She put her gun to her shoulder, but even then
pursed her mouth, knowing it was nonsense to pretend
to fire. So she began to walk slowly after him, in the
direction he had gone, slowly, pertinaciously. She expected to find him. In her heart she was determined
to find him. What she would do when she saw him
again she did not consider. But she was determined to
find him. So she walked abstractedly about on the
edge of the wood, with wide, vivid dark eyes, and a
faint flush in her cheeks. She did not think. In strange
mindlessness she walked hither and thither.

At last she became aware that Banford was calling
her. She made an effort of attention, turned, and gave
some sort of screaming call in answer. Then again she
was striding off towards the homestead. The red sun
was setting, the fowls were retiring towards their roost.
She watched them, white creatures, black creatures,
gathering to the barn. She watched them spellbound
without seeing them. But her automatic intelligence
told her when it was time to shut the door.

She went indoors to supper, which Banford had set

on the table. Banford chatted easily. March seemed to listen, in her distant, manly way. She answered a brief word now and then. But all the time she was as if spellbound. And as soon as supper was over, she rose again to go out, without saying why.

She took her gun again and went to look for the fox. For he had lifted his eyes upon her, and his knowing look seemed to have entered her brain. She did not so much think of him: she was possessed by him. She saw his dark, shrewd, unabashed eye looking into her, knowing her. She felt him invisibly master her spirit. She knew the way he lowered his chin as he looked up, she knew his muzzle, the golden brown, and the greyish white. And again, she saw him glance over his shoulder at her, half inviting, half contemptuous, and cunning. So she went, with her great startled eyes glowing, her gun under her arm, along the wood edge. Meanwhile the night fell, and a great moon rose above the pine-trees. And again Banford was calling.

So she went indoors. She was silent and busy. She examined her gun, and cleaned it, musing abstractedly by the lamplight. Then she went out again, under the great moon, to see if everything was right. When she saw the dark crests of the pine-trees against the blood-red sky, again her heart beat to the fox, the fox. She wanted to follow him, with her gun.

It was some days before she mentioned the affair to Banford. Then suddenly one evening she said:

'The fox was right at my feet on Saturday night.'

'Where?' said Banford, her eyes opening behind her spectacles.

'When I stood just above the pond.'

'Did you fire?' cried Banford.

'No, I didn't.'

'Why not?'

'Why, I was too much surprised, I suppose.'

It was the same old, slow, laconic way of speech March always had. Banford stared at her friend for a few moments.

'You saw him?' she cried.

'Oh, yes! He was looking up at me, cool as any-thing.'

'I tell you,' cried Banford—'the cheek! They 're not afraid of us, Nellie.'

'Oh, no,' said March.

'Pity you didn't get a shot at him,' said Banford.

'Isn't it a pity! I 've been looking for him ever since. But I don't suppose he 'll come so near again.'

'I don't suppose he will,' said Banford.

And she proceeded to forget about it, except that she was more indignant than ever at the impudence of the beggar. March also was not conscious that she thought of the fox. But whenever she fell into her half-musing, when she was half rapt and half intelligently aware of what passed under her vision, then it was the fox which somehow dominated her unconsciousness, possessed the blank half of her musing. And so it was for weeks, and months. No matter whether she had been climbing the trees for the apples, or beating down the last of the damsons, or whether she had been digging out the ditch from the duck-pond, or clearing out the barn, when she had finished, or when she straightened herself, and pushed the wisps of hair away again from her fore-head, and pursed up her mouth again in an odd, screwed fashion, much too old for her years, there was sure to come over her mind the old spell of the fox, as it came when he was looking at her. It was as if she could smell him at these times. And it always recurred, at un-expected moments, just as she was going to sleep at night, or just as she was pouring the water into the teapot to make tea—it was the fox, it came over her like a spell.

So the months passed. She still looked for him un-consciously when she went towards the wood. He had become a settled effect in her spirit, a state permanently established, not continuous, but always recurring. She did not know what she felt or thought: only the state came over her, as when he looked at her.

The months passed, the dark evenings came, heavy, dark November, when March went about in high boots,

ankle deep in mud, when the night began to fall at four
o'clock, and the day never properly dawned. Both
girls dreaded these times. They dreaded the almost
continuous darkness that enveloped them on their
desolate little farm near the wood. Banford was
physically afraid. She was afraid of tramps, afraid lest
someone should come prowling round. March was not
so much afraid as uncomfortable, and disturbed. She
felt discomfort and gloom in all her physique.

Usually the two girls had tea in the sitting-room.
March lighted a fire at dusk, and put on the wood she
had chopped and sawed during the day. Then the long
evening was in front, dark, sodden, black outside, lonely
and rather oppressive inside, a little dismal. March
was content not to talk, but Banford could not keep
still. Merely listening to the wind in the pines outside,
or the drip of water, was too much for her.

One evening the girls had washed up the tea-things
in the kitchen, and March had put on her house shoes,
and taken up a roll of crochet-work, which she worked at
slowly from time to time. So she lapsed into silence.
Banford stared at the red fire, which, being of wood,
needed constant attention. She was afraid to begin to
read too early, because her eyes would not bear any
strain. So she sat staring at the fire, listening to the
distant sounds, sound of cattle lowing, of a dull, heavy,
moist wind, of the rattle of the evening train on the
little railway not far off. She was almost fascinated by
the red glow of the fire.

Suddenly both girls started and lifted their heads.
They heard a footstep—distinctly a footstep. Banford
recoiled in fear. March stood listening. Then rapidly
she approached the door that led into the kitchen.
At the same time they heard the footsteps approach the
back door. They waited a second. The back door
opened softly. Banford gave a loud cry. A man's
voice said softly:

'Hallo!'

March recoiled, and took a gun from a corner.

'What do you want?' she cried, in a sharp voice.

Again the soft, softly vibrating man's voice said:
'Hallo! What's wrong?'

'I shall shoot!' cried March. 'What do you want?'

'Why, what's wrong? What's wrong?' came the soft, wondering, rather scared voice: and a young soldier, with his heavy kit on his back, advanced into the dim light.

'Why,' he said, 'who lives here then?'

'We live here,' said March. 'What do you want?'

'Oh!' came the long, melodious, wonder-note from the young soldier. 'Doesn't William Grenfel live here then?'

'No—you know he doesn't.'

'Do I? Do I? I don't, you see. He *did* live here, because he was my grandfather, and I lived here myself five years ago. What's become of him then?'

The young man—or youth, for he would not be more than twenty—now advanced and stood in the inner doorway. March, already under the influence of his strange, soft, modulated voice, stared at him spellbound. He had a ruddy, roundish face, with fairish hair, rather long, flattened to his forehead with sweat. His eyes were blue, and very bright and sharp. On his cheeks, on the fresh ruddy skin were fine, fair hairs, like a down, but sharper. It gave him a slightly glistening look. Having his heavy sack on his shoulders, he stooped, thrusting his head forward. His hat was loose in one hand. He stared brightly, very keenly from girl to girl, particularly at March, who stood pale, with great dilated eyes, in her belted coat and puttees, her hair knotted in a big crisp knot behind. She still had the gun in her hand. Behind her, Banford, clinging to the sofa-arm, was shrinking away, with half-averted head.

'I thought my grandfather still lived here. I wonder if he's dead.'

'We've been here for three years,' said Banford, who was beginning to recover her wits, seeing something boyish in the round head with its rather long sweaty hair.

'Three years! You don't say so! And you don't know who was here before you?'

'I know it was an old man, who lived by himself.'

'Ay! Yes, that's him! And what became of him then?'

'He died. I know he died.'

'Ay! He's dead then!'

The youth stared at them without changing colour or expression. If he had any expression, besides a slight baffled look of wonder, it was one of sharp curiosity concerning the two girls; sharp, impersonal curiosity, the curiosity of that round young head.

But to March he was the fox. Whether it was the thrusting forward of his head, or the glisten of fine whitish hairs on the ruddy cheek-bones, or the bright, keen eyes, that can never be said: but the boy was to her the fox, and she could not see him otherwise.

'How is it you didn't know if your grandfather was alive or dead?' asked Banford, recovering her natural sharpness.

'Ay, that's it,' replied the softly breathing youth. 'You see, I joined up in Canada, and I hadn't heard for three or four years. I ran away to Canada.'

'And now have you just come from France?'

'Well—from Salonika really.'

There was a pause, nobody knowing quite what to say.

'So you've nowhere to go now?' said Banford rather lamely.

'Oh, I know some people in the village. Anyhow, I can go to the "Swan."'

'You came on the train, I suppose. Would you like to sit down a bit?'

'Well—I don't mind.'

He gave an odd little groan as he swung off his kit. Banford looked at March.

'Put the gun down,' she said. 'We'll make a cup of tea.'

'Ay,' said the youth. 'We've seen enough of rifles.'

He sat down rather tired on the sofa, leaning forward.

March recovered her presence of mind, and went into

the kitchen. There she heard the soft young voice musing:

'Well, to think I should come back and find it like this!' He did not seem sad, not at all—only rather interestedly surprised.

'And what a difference in the place, eh?' he continued, looking round the room.

'You see a difference, do you?' said Banford.

'Yes—don't I!'

His voice was unnaturally clear and bright, though it was the brightness of abundant health.

March was busy in the kitchen preparing another meal. It was about seven o'clock. All the time, while she was active, she was attending to the youth in the sitting-room, not so much listening to what he said as feeling the soft run of his voice. She primmed up her mouth tighter and tighter, puckering it as if it were sewed, in her effort to keep her will uppermost. Yet her large eyes dilated and glowed in spite of her; she lost herself. Rapidly and carelessly she prepared the meal, cutting large chunks of bread and margarine— for there was no butter. She racked her brain to think of something else to put on the tray—she had only bread, margarine, and jam, and the larder was bare. Unable to conjure anything up, she went into the sitting-room with her tray.

She did not want to be noticed. Above all, she did not want him to look at her. But when she came in, and was busy setting the table just behind him, he pulled himself up from his sprawling, and turned and looked over his shoulder. She became pale and wan.

The youth watched her as she bent over the table, looked at her slim, well-shapen legs, at the belted coat dropping around her thighs, at the knot of dark hair, and his curiosity, vivid and widely alert, was again arrested by her.

The lamp was shaded with a dark-green shade, so that the light was thrown downwards and the upper half of the room was dim. His face moved bright under the light, but March loomed shadowy in the distance.

She turned round, but kept her eyes sideways, dropping and lifting her dark lashes. Her mouth unpuckered as she said to Banford:

'Will you pour out?'

Then she went into the kitchen again.

'Have your tea where you are, will you?' said Banford to the youth—'unless you 'd rather come to the table.'

'Well,' said he, 'I 'm nice and comfortable here, aren't I? I will have it here, if you don't mind.'

'There 's nothing but bread and jam,' she said. And she put his plate on a stool by him. She was very happy now, waiting on him. For she loved company. And now she was no more afraid of him than if he were her own younger brother. He was such a boy.

'Nellie,' she called. 'I 've poured you a cup out.'

March appeared in the doorway, took her cup, and sat down in a corner, as far from the light as possible. She was very sensitive in her knees. Having no skirts to cover them, and being forced to sit with them boldly exposed, she suffered. She shrank and shrank, trying not to be seen. And the youth, sprawling low on the couch, glanced up at her, with long, steady, penetrating looks, till she was almost ready to disappear. Yet she held her cup balanced, she drank her tea, screwed up her mouth, and held her head averted. Her desire to be invisible was so strong that it quite baffled the youth. He felt he could not see her distinctly. She seemed like a shadow within the shadow. And ever his eyes came back to her, searching, unremitting, with unconscious fixed attention.

Meanwhile he was talking softly and smoothly to Banford, who loved nothing so much as gossip, and who was full of perky interest, like a bird. Also he ate largely and quickly and voraciously, so that March had to cut more chunks of bread and margarine, for the roughness of which Banford apologized.

'Oh, well,' said March, suddenly speaking, 'if there 's no butter to put on it, it 's no good trying to make dainty pieces.'

Again the youth watched her, and he laughed, with a

sudden, quick laugh, showing his teeth and wrinkling his nose.

'It isn't, is it?' he answered, in his soft, near voice.

It appeared he was Cornish by birth and upbringing. When he was twelve years old he had come to Bailey Farm with his grandfather, with whom he had never agreed very well. So he had run away to Canada, and worked far away in the west. Now he was here—and that was the end of it.

He was very curious about the girls, to find out exactly what they were doing. His questions were those of a farm youth; acute, practical, a little mocking. He was very much amused by their attitude to their losses: for they were amusing on the score of heifers and fowls.

'Oh, well,' broke in March, 'we don't believe in living for nothing but work.'

'Don't you?' he answered. And again the quick young laugh came over his face. He kept his eyes steadily on the obscure woman in the corner.

'But what will you do when you 've used up all your capital?' he said.

'Oh, I don't know,' answered March laconically. 'Hire ourselves out for land-workers, I suppose.'

'Yes, but there won't be any demand for women land-workers now the war 's over,' said the youth.

'Oh, we 'll see. We shall hold on a bit longer yet,' said March, with a plangent, half-sad, half-ironical indifference.

'There wants a man about the place,' said the youth softly.

Banford burst out laughing.

'Take care what you say,' she interrupted. 'We consider ourselves quite efficient.'

'Oh,' came March's slow plangent voice, 'it isn't a case of efficiency, I 'm afraid. If you 're going to do farming you must be at it from morning till night, and you might as well be a beast yourself.'

'Yes, that 's it,' said the youth. 'You aren't willing to put yourselves into it.'

'We aren't,' said March, 'and we know it.'

'We want some of our time for ourselves,' said Banford.

The youth threw himself back on the sofa, his face tight with laughter, and laughed silently but thoroughly. The calm scorn of the girls tickled him tremendously.

'Yes,' he said, 'but why did you begin then?'

'Oh,' said March, 'we had a better opinion of the nature of fowls then than we have now.'

'Of nature altogether, I'm afraid,' said Banford. 'Don't talk to me about nature.'

Again the face of the youth tightened with delighted laughter.

'You haven't a very high opinion of fowls and cattle, haven't you?' he said.

'Oh, no—quite a low one,' said March.

He laughed out.

'Neither fowls nor heifers,' said Banford, 'nor goat, nor the weather.'

The youth broke into a sharp yap of laughter, delighted. The girls began to laugh too, March turning aside her face and wrinkling her mouth in amusement.

'Oh, well,' said Banford, 'we don't mind, do we, Nellie?'

'No,' said March, 'we don't mind.'

The youth was very pleased. He had eaten and drunk his fill. Banford began to question him. His name was Henry Grenfel—no, he was not called Harry, always Henry. He continued to answer with courteous simplicity, grave and charming. March, who was not included, cast long, slow glances at him from her recess, as he sat there on the sofa, his hands clasping his knees, his face under the lamp bright and alert, turned to Banford. She became almost peaceful at last. He was identified with the fox—and he was here in full presence. She need not go after him any more. There in the shadow of her corner she gave herself up to a warm, relaxed peace, almost like sleep, accepting the spell that was on her. But she wished to remain hidden. She was only fully at peace whilst he forgot her, talking to Banford. Hidden in the shadow of the corner, she need not any more be divided in herself, trying to keep up two planes of consciousness. She could at last lapse into the odour of the fox.

For the youth, sitting before the fire in his uniform, sent a faint but distinct odour into the room, indefinable, but something like a wild creature. March no longer tried to reserve herself from it. She was still and soft in her corner like a passive creature in its cave.

At last the talk dwindled. The youth relaxed his clasp of his knees, pulled himself together a little, and looked round. Again he became aware of the silent, half-invisible woman in the corner.

'Well,' he said, unwillingly, 'I suppose I'd better be going, or they'll be in bed at the "Swan."'

'I'm afraid they're in bed anyhow,' said Banford. 'They've all got this influenza.'

'Have they!' he exclaimed. And he pondered. 'Well,' he continued, 'I shall find a place somewhere.'

'I'd say you could stay here, only——' Banford began.

He turned and watched her, holding his head forward.

'What?' he asked.

'Oh, well,' she said, 'propriety, I suppose.' She was rather confused.

'It wouldn't be improper, would it?' he said, gently surprised.

'Not as far as we're concerned,' said Banford.

'And not as far as *I*'m concerned,' he said, with grave *naïveté*. 'After all, it's my own home, in a way.'

Banford smiled at this.

'It's what the village will have to say,' she said.

There was a moment's blank pause.

'What do you say, Nellie?' asked Banford.

'I don't mind,' said March, in her distinct tone. 'The village doesn't matter to me, anyhow.'

'No,' said the youth, quick and soft. 'Why should it? I mean, what should they say?'

'Oh, well,' came March's plangent, laconic voice, 'they'll easily find something to say. But it makes no difference what they say. We can look after ourselves.'

'Of course you can,' said the youth.

'Well, then, stop if you like,' said Banford. 'The spare room is quite ready.'

His face shone with pleasure.

'If you 're quite sure it isn't troubling you too much,' he said, with that soft courtesy which distinguished him.

'Oh, it 's no trouble,' they both said.

He looked, smiled with delight, from one to another.

'It 's awfully nice not to have to turn out again, isn't it?' he said gratefully.

'I suppose it is,' said Banford.

March disappeared to attend to the room. Banford was as pleased and thoughtful as if she had her own young brother home from France. It gave her just the same kind of gratification to attend on him, to get out the bath for him, and everything. Her natural warmth and kindliness had now an outlet. And the youth luxuriated in her sisterly attention. But it puzzled him slightly to know that March was silently working for him too. She was so curiously silent and obliterated. It seemed to him he had not really seen her. He felt he should not know her if he met her in the road.

That night March dreamed vividly. She dreamed she heard a singing outside which she could not understand, a singing that roamed round the house, in the fields, and in the darkness. It moved her so that she felt she must weep. She went out, and suddenly she knew it was the fox singing. He was very yellow and bright, like corn. She went nearer to him, but he ran away and ceased singing. He seemed near, and she wanted to touch him. She stretched out her hand, but suddenly he bit her wrist, and at the same instant, as she drew back, the fox, turning round to bound away, whisked his brush across her face, and it seemed his brush was on fire, for it seared and burned her mouth with a great pain. She awoke with the pain of it, and lay trembling as if she were really seared.

In the morning, however, she only remembered it as a distant memory. She arose and was busy preparing the house and attending to the fowls. Banford flew into the village on her bicycle to try and buy food. She was a hospitable soul. But alas, in the year 1918 there was not much food to buy. The youth came downstairs in his shirt-sleeves. He was young and fresh, but he walked with his head thrust forward, so that his shoulders seemed raised and rounded, as if he had a slight curvature of the spine. It must have been only a manner of bearing himself, for he was young and vigorous. He washed himself and went outside, whilst the women were preparing breakfast.

He saw everything, and examined everything. His curiosity was quick and insatiable. He compared the state of things with that which he remembered before, and cast over in his mind the effect of the changes. He watched the fowls and the ducks, to see their condition; he noticed the flight of wood pigeons overhead: they were very numerous; he saw the few apples high up, which March had not been able to reach; he remarked that they had borrowed a draw-pump, presumably to empty the big soft-water cistern which was on the north side of the house.

'It 's a funny, dilapidated old place,' he said to the girls as he sat at breakfast.

His eyes were wise and childish, with thinking about things. He did not say much, but ate largely. March kept her face averted. She, too, in the early morning could not be aware of him, though something about the glint of his khaki reminded her of the brilliance of her dream-fox.

During the day the girls went about their business. In the morning he attended to the guns, shot a rabbit and a wild duck that was flying high towards the wood. That was a great addition to the empty larder. The girls felt that already he had earned his keep. He said nothing about leaving, however. In the afternoon he went to the village. He came back at tea-time. He had the same alert, forward-reaching look on his roundish face. He hung his hat on a peg with a little swinging gesture. He was thinking about something.

'Well,' he said to the girls, he as sat at table. 'What am I going to do?'

'How do you mean—what are you going to do?' said Banford.

'Where am I going to find a place in the village to stay?' he said.

'I don't know,' said Banford. 'Where do you think of staying?'

'Well'—he hesitated—'at the "Swan" they've got this 'flu, and at the "Plough and Harrow" they've got the soldiers who are collecting the hay for the army: besides, in the private houses, there's ten men and a corporal altogether billeted in the village, they tell me. I'm not sure where I could get a bed.'

He left the matter to them. He was rather calm about it. March sat with her elbows on the table, her two hands supporting her chin, looking at him unconsciously. Suddenly he lifted his clouded blue eyes, and unthinking looked straight into March's eyes. He was startled as well as she. He, too, recoiled a little. March felt the same sly, taunting, knowing spark leap out of his eyes, as he turned his head aside, and fall into her soul, as it had fallen from the dark eyes of the fox. She pursed her mouth as if in pain, as if asleep, too.

'Well, I don't know,' Banford was saying. She seemed reluctant, as if she were afraid of being imposed upon. She looked at March. But, with her weak, troubled sight, she only saw the usual semi-abstraction on her friend's face. 'Why don't you speak, Nellie?' she said.

But March was wide-eyed and silent, and the youth, as if fascinated, was watching her without moving his eyes.

'Go on—answer something,' said Banford. And March turned her head slightly aside, as if coming to consciousness, or trying to come to consciousness.

'What do you expect me to say?' she asked automatically.

'Say what you think,' said Banford.

'It's all the same to me,' said March.

And again there was silence. A pointed light seemed to be on the boy's eyes, penetrating like a needle.

'So it is to me,' said Banford. 'You can stop on here if you like.'

A smile like a cunning little flame came over his face, suddenly and involuntarily. He dropped his head quickly to hide it, and remained with his head dropped, his face hidden.

'You can stop on here if you like. You can please yourself, Henry,' Banford concluded.

Still he did not reply, but remained with his head dropped. Then he lifted his face. It was bright with a curious light, as if exultant, and his eyes were strangely clear as he watched March. She turned her face aside, her mouth suffering as if wounded, and her consciousness dim.

Banford became a little puzzled. She watched the steady, pellucid gaze of the youth's eyes as he looked at March, with the invisible smile gleaming on his face. She did not know how he was smiling, for no feature moved. It seemed only in the gleam, almost the glitter of the fine hairs on his cheeks. Then he looked with quite a changed look at Banford.

'I 'm sure,' he said in his soft, courteous voice, 'you 're awfully good. You 're too good. You don't want to be bothered with me, I 'm sure.'

'Cut a bit of bread, Nellie,' said Banford uneasily, adding: 'It 's no bother, if you like to stay. It 's like having my own brother here for a few days. He 's a boy like you are.'

'That 's awfully kind of you,' the lad repeated. 'I should like to stay ever so much, if you 're sure I 'm not a trouble to you.'

'No, of course you 're no trouble. I tell you, it 's a pleasure to have somebody in the house besides ourselves,' said warm-hearted Banford.

'But Miss March?' he said in his soft voice, looking at her.

'Oh, it 's quite all right as far as I 'm concerned,' said March vaguely.

His face beamed, and he almost rubbed his hands with pleasure.

'Well then,' he said, 'I should love it, if you 'd let me pay my board and help with the work.'

'You 've no need to talk about board,' said Banford.

One or two days went by, and the youth stayed on at the farm. Banford was quite charmed by him. He was so soft and courteous in speech, not wanting to say much himself, preferring to hear what she had to say, and to laugh in his quick, half-mocking way. He helped readily with the work—but not too much. He loved to be out alone with the gun in his hands, to watch, to see. For his sharp-eyed, impersonal curiosity was insatiable, and he was most free when he was quite alone, half-hidden, watching.

Particularly he watched March. She was a strange character to him. Her figure, like a graceful young man's, piqued him. Her dark eyes made something rise in his soul, with a curious elate excitement, when he looked into them, an excitement he was afraid to let be seen, it was so keen and secret. And then her odd, shrewd speech made him laugh outright. He felt he must go further, he was inevitably impelled. But he put away the thought of her and went off towards the wood's edge with the gun.

The dusk was falling as he came home, and with the dusk, a fine, late November rain. He saw the firelight leaping in the window of the sitting-room, a leaping light in the little cluster of the dark buildings. And he thought to himself it would be a good thing to have this place for his own. And then the thought entered him shrewdly: why not marry March? He stood still in the middle of the field for some moments, the dead rabbit hanging still in his hand, arrested by this thought. His mind waited in amazement—it seemed to calculate —and then he smiled curiously to himself in acquiescence. Why not? Why not, indeed? It was a good idea. What if it was rather ridiculous? What did it matter? What if she was older than he? It didn't matter. When he thought of her dark, startled, vulnerable eyes he smiled subtly to himself. He was older than she, really. He was master of her.

He scarcely admitted his intention even to himself. He kept it as a secret even from himself. It was all too uncertain as yet. He would have to see how things went. Yes, he would have to see how things went. If he wasn't careful, she would just simply mock at the idea. He knew, sly and subtle as he was, that if he went to her plainly and said: 'Miss March, I love you and want you to marry me,' her inevitable answer would be: 'Get out. I don't want any of that tomfoolery.' This was her attitude to men and their 'tomfoolery.' If he was not careful, she would turn round on him with her savage, sardonic ridicule, and dismiss him from the farm and from her own mind for ever. He would have to go gently. He would have to catch her as you catch a deer or a woodcock when you go out shooting. It's no good walking out into the forest and saying to the deer: 'Please fall to my gun.' No, it is a slow, subtle battle. When you really go out to get a deer, you gather yourself together, you coil yourself inside yourself, and you advance secretly, before dawn, into the mountains. It is not so much what you do, when you go out hunting, as how you feel. You have to be subtle and cunning and absolutely fatally ready. It becomes like a fate. Your own fate overtakes and determines the fate of the deer you are hunting. First of all, even before you come in sight of your quarry, there is a strange battle, like mesmerism. Your own soul, as a hunter, has gone out to fasten on the soul of the deer, even before you see any deer. And the soul of the deer fights to escape. Even before the deer has any wind of you, it is so. It is a subtle, profound battle of wills which takes place in the invisible. And it is a battle never finished till your bullet goes home. When you are *really* worked up to the true pitch, and you come at last into range, you don't then aim as you do when you are firing at a bottle. It is your own *will* which carries the bullet into the heart of your quarry. The bullet's flight home is a sheer projection of your own fate into the fate of the deer.

It happens like a supreme wish, a supreme act of volition, not as a dodge of cleverness.

He was a huntsman in spirit, not a farmer, and not a soldier stuck in a regiment. And it was as a young hunter that he wanted to bring down March as his quarry, to make her his wife. So he gathered himself subtly together, seemed to withdraw into a kind of invisibility. He was not quite sure how he would go on. And March was suspicious as a hare. So he remained in appearance just the nice, odd stranger-youth, staying for a fortnight on the place.

He had been sawing logs for the fire in the afternoon. Darkness came very early. It was still a cold, raw mist. It was getting almost too dark to see. A pile of short sawed logs lay beside the trestle. March came to carry them indoors, or into the shed, as he was busy sawing the last log. He was working in his shirt-sleeves, and did not notice her approach; she came unwillingly, as if shy. He saw her stooping to the bright-ended logs, and he stopped sawing. A fire like lightning flew down his legs in the nerves.

'March,' he said, in his quiet, young voice.

She looked up from the logs she was piling.

'Yes?' she said.

He looked down on her in the dusk. He could see her not too distinctly.

'I wanted to ask you something,' he said.

'Did you? What was it?' she said. Already the fright was in her voice. But she was too much mistress of herself.

'Why'—his voice seemed to draw out soft and subtle, it penetrated her nerves—'why, what do you think it is?'

She stood up, placed her hands on her hips, and stood looking at him transfixed, without answering. Again he burned with a sudden power.

'Well,' he said, and his voice was so soft it seemed rather like a subtle touch, like the merest touch of a cat's paw, a feeling rather than a sound. 'Well—I wanted to ask you to marry me.'

March felt rather than heard him. She was trying in

vain to turn aside her face. A great relaxation seemed to have come over her. She stood silent, her head slightly on one side. He seemed to be bending towards her, invisibly smiling. It seemed to her fine sparks came out of him.

Then very suddenly she said:

'Don't try any of your tomfoolery on me.'

A quiver went over his nerves. He had missed. He waited a moment to collect himself again. Then he said, putting all the strange softness into his voice, as if he were imperceptibly stroking her:

'Why, it's not tomfoolery. It's not tomfoolery. I mean it. I mean it. What makes you disbelieve me?'

He sounded hurt. And his voice had such a curious power over her; making her feel loose and relaxed. She struggled somewhere for her own power. She felt for a moment that she was lost—lost—lost. The word seemed to rock in her as if she were dying. Suddenly again she spoke.

'You don't know what you are talking about,' she said, in a brief and transient stroke of scorn. 'What nonsense! I'm old enough to be your mother.'

'Yes, I do know what I'm talking about. Yes, I do,' he persisted softly, as if he were producing his voice in her blood. 'I know quite well what I'm talking about. You're not old enough to be my mother. That isn't true. And what does it matter even if it was? You can marry me whatever age we are. What is age to me? And what is age to you? Age is nothing.'

A swoon went over her as he concluded. He spoke rapidly—in the rapid Cornish fashion—and his voice seemed to sound in her somewhere where she was helpless against it. 'Age is nothing!' The soft, heavy insistence of it made her sway dimly out there in the darkness. She could not answer.

A great exultance leaped like fire over his limbs. He felt he had won.

'I want to marry you, you see. Why shouldn't I?' he proceeded, soft and rapid. He waited for her to answer. In the dusk he saw her almost phosphorescent.

Her eyelids were dropped, her face half-averted and
unconscious. She seemed to be in his power. But he
waited, watchful. He dared not yet touch her.

'Say then,' he said, 'say then you 'll marry me.
Say—say!' He was softly insistent.

'What?' she asked, faint, from a distance, like one in
pain. His voice was now unthinkably near and soft.
He drew very near to her.

'Say yes.'

'Oh, I can't,' she wailed helplessly, half-articulate, as
if semi-conscious, and as if in pain, like one who dies.
'How can I?'

'You can,' he said softly, laying his hand gently on
her shoulder as she stood with her head averted and
dropped, dazed. 'You can. Yes, you can. What
makes you say you can't? You can. You can.' And
with awful softness he bent forward and just touched
her neck with his mouth and his chin.

'Don't!' she cried, with a faint mad cry like hysteria,
starting away and facing round on him. 'What do you
mean?' But she had no breath to speak with. It was
as if she was killed.

'I mean what I say,' he persisted softly and cruelly.
'I want you to marry me. I want you to marry me.
You know that, now, don't you? You know that,
now? Don't you? Don't you?'

'What?' she said.

'Know,' he replied.

'Yes,' she said. 'I know you say so.'

'And you know I mean it, don't you?'

'I know you say so.'

'You believe me?' he said.

She was silent for some time. Then she pursed her lips.

'I don't know what I believe,' she said.

'Are you out there?' came Banford's voice, calling
from the house.

'Yes, we 're bringing in the logs,' he answered.

'I thought you 'd gone lost,' said Banford disconso-
lately. 'Hurry up, do, and come and let 's have tea.
The kettle 's boiling.'

He stooped at once, to take an armful of little logs and carry them into the kitchen, where they were piled in a corner. March also helped, filling her arms and carrying the logs on her breast as if they were some heavy child. The night had fallen cold.

When the logs were all in, the two cleaned their boots noisily on the scraper outside, then rubbed them on the mat. March shut the door and took off her old felt hat —her farm-girl hat. Her thick, crisp black hair was loose, her face was pale and strained. She pushed back her hair vaguely, and washed her hands. Banford came hurrying into the dimly lighted kitchen, to take from the oven the scones she was keeping hot.

'Whatever have you been doing all this time?' she asked fretfully. 'I thought you were never coming in. And it's ages since you stopped sawing. What were you doing out there?'

'Well,' said Henry, 'we had to stop that hole in the barn, to keep the rats out.'

'Why, I could see you standing there in the shed. I could see your shirt-sleeves,' challenged Banford.

'Yes, I was just putting the saw away.'

They went in to tea. March was quite mute. Her face was pale and strained and vague. The youth, who always had the same ruddy, self-contained look on his face, as though he were keeping himself to himself, had come to tea in his shirt-sleeves as if he were at home. He bent over his plate as he ate his food.

'Aren't you cold?' said Banford spitefully. 'In your shirt-sleeves.'

He looked up at her, with his chin near his plate, and his eyes very clear, pellucid, and unwavering as he watched her.

'No, I'm not cold,' he said with his usual soft courtesy. 'It's much warmer in here than it is outside, you see.'

'I hope it is,' said Banford, feeling nettled by him. He had a strange suave assurance, and a wide-eyed bright look that got on her nerves this evening.

'But perhaps,' he said softly and courteously, 'you

don't like me coming to tea without my coat. I forgot that.'

'Oh, I don't mind,' said Banford: although she *did*.

'I 'll go and get it, shall I?' he said.

March's dark eyes turned slowly down to him.

'No, don't you bother,' she said in her queer, twanging tone. 'If you feel all right as you are, stop as you are.' She spoke with a crude authority.

'Yes,' said he, 'I *feel* all right, if I 'm not rude.'

'It 's usually considered rude,' said Banford. 'But we don't mind.'

'Go along, "considered rude,"' ejaculated March. 'Who considers it rude?'

'Why you do, Nellie, in anybody else,' said Banford, bridling a little behind her spectacles, and feeling her food stick in her throat.

But March had again gone vague and unheeding, chewing her food as if she did not know she was eating at all. And the youth looked from one to another, with bright, watchful eyes.

Banford was offended. For all his suave courtesy and soft voice, the youth seemed to her impudent. She did not like to look at him. She did not like to meet his clear, watchful eyes, she did not like to see the strange glow in his face, his cheeks with their delicate fine hair, and his ruddy skin that was quite dull and yet which seemed to burn with a curious heat of life. It made her feel a little ill to look at him: the quality of his physical presence was too penetrating, too hot.

After tea the evening was very quiet. The youth rarely went into the village. As a rule he read: he was a great reader, in his own hours. That is, when he did begin, he read absorbedly. But he was not very eager to begin. Often he walked about the fields and along the hedges alone in the dark at night, prowling with a queer instinct for the night, and listening to the wild sounds.

To-night, however, he took a Captain Mayne Reid book from Banford's shelf and sat down with knees wide apart and immersed himself in his story. His brownish fair hair was long, and lay on his head like a

thick cap, combed sideways. He was still in his shirt-
sleeves, and bending forward under the lamplight, with
his knees stuck wide apart and the book in his hand and
his whole figure absorbed in the rather strenuous business
of reading, he gave Banford's sitting-room the look of a
lumber-camp. She resented this. For on her sitting-
room floor she had a red Turkey rug and dark stain
round, the fire-place had fashionable green tiles, the piano
stood open with the latest dance - music — she played
quite well: and on the walls were March's hand-painted
swans and water-lilies. Moreover, with the logs nicely,
tremulously burning in the grate, the thick curtains
drawn, the doors all shut, and the pine-trees hissing
and shuddering in the wind outside, it was cosy, it
was refined and nice. She resented the big, raw, long-
legged youth sticking his khaki knees out and sitting
there with his soldier's shirt-cuffs buttoned on his thick,
red wrists. From time to time he turned a page, and
from time to time he gave a sharp look at the fire, settling
the logs. Then he immersed himself again in the intense
and isolated business of reading.

March, on the far side of the table, was spasmodically
crocheting. Her mouth was pursed in an odd way,
as when she had dreamed the fox's brush burned it, her
beautiful, crisp black hair strayed in wisps. But her
whole figure was absorbed in its bearing, as if she herself
was miles away. In a sort of semi-dream she seemed to
be hearing the fox singing round the house in the wind,
singing wildly and sweetly and like a madness. With
red but well-shaped hands she slowly crocheted the
white cotton, very slowly, awkwardly.

Banford was also trying to read, sitting in her low
chair. But between those two she felt fidgety. She
kept moving and looking round and listening to the
wind, and glancing secretly from one to the other of her
companions. March, seated on a straight chair, with
her knees in their close breeches crossed, and slowly,
laboriously crocheting, was also a trial.

'Oh, dear!' said Banford. 'My eyes are bad to-night.'
And she pressed her fingers on her eyes.

The youth looked up at her with his clear, bright look, but did not speak.

'Are they, Jill?' said March absently.

Then the youth began to read again, and Banford perforce returned to her book. But she could not keep still. After a while she looked up at March, and a queer, almost malignant little smile was on her thin face.

'A penny for them, Nell,' she said suddenly.

March looked round with big, startled black eyes, and went pale as if with terror. She had been listening to the fox singing so tenderly, so tenderly, as he wandered round the house.

'What?' she said vaguely.

'A penny for them,' said Banford sarcastically. 'Or twopence, if they 're as deep as all that.'

The youth was watching with bright, clear eyes from beneath the lamp.

'Why,' came March's vague voice, 'what do you want to waste your money for?'

'I thought it would be well spent,' said Banford.

'I wasn't thinking of anything except the way the wind was blowing,' said March.

'Oh, dear,' replied Banford, 'I could have had as original thoughts as that myself. I 'm afraid I *have* wasted my money this time.'

'Well, you needn't pay,' said March.

The youth suddenly laughed. Both women looked at him: March rather surprised-looking, as if she had hardly known he was there.

'Why, do you ever pay up on these occasions?' he asked.

'Oh, yes,' said Banford. 'We always do. I 've sometimes had to pass a shilling a week to Nellie in the winter time. It costs much less in summer.'

'What, paying for each other's thoughts?' he laughed.

'Yes, when we 've absolutely come to the end of everything else.'

He laughed quickly, wrinkling his nose sharply like a puppy and laughing with quick pleasure, his eyes shining.

'It 's the first time I ever heard of that,' he said.

'I guess you 'd hear of it often enough if you stayed a winter on Bailey Farm,' said Banford lamentably.

'Do you get so tired, then?' he asked.

'So bored,' said Banford.

'Oh!' he said gravely. 'But why should you be bored?'

'Who wouldn't be bored?' said Banford.

'I 'm sorry to hear that,' he said gravely.

'You must be, if you were hoping to have a lively time here,' said Banford.

He looked at her long and gravely.

'Well,' he said, with his odd, young seriousness, 'it 's quite lively enough for me.'

'I 'm glad to hear it,' said Banford.

And she returned to her book. In her thin, frail hair were already many threads of grey, though she was not yet thirty. The boy did not look down, but turned his eyes to March, who was sitting with pursed mouth laboriously crocheting, her eyes wide and absent. She had a warm, pale, fine skin, and a delicate nose. Her pursed mouth looked shrewish. But the shrewish look was contradicted by the curious lifted arch of her dark brows, and the wideness of her eyes; a look of startled wonder and vagueness. She was listening again for the fox, who seemed to have wandered farther off into the night.

From under the edge of the lamplight the boy sat with his face looking up, watching her silently, his eyes round and very clear and intent. Banford, biting her fingers irritably, was glancing at him under her hair. He sat there perfectly still, his ruddy face tilted up from the low level under the light, on the edge of the dimness, and watching with perfect abstract intentness. March suddenly lifted her great, dark eyes from her crocheting, and saw him. She started, giving a little exclamation.

'There he is!' she cried, involuntarily, as if terribly startled.

Banford looked around in amazement, sitting up straight.

'Whatever has got you, Nellie?' she cried.

But March, her face flushed a delicate rose colour, was looking away to the door.

'Nothing! Nothing!' she said crossly. 'Can't one speak?'

'Yes, if you speak sensibly,' said Banford. 'Whatever did you mean?'

'I don't know what I meant,' cried March testily.

'Oh, Nellie, I hope you aren't going jumpy and nervy. I feel I can't stand another *thing*! Whoever did you mean? Did you mean Henry?' cried poor, frightened Banford.

'Yes. I suppose so,' said March laconically. She would never confess to the fox.

'Oh, dear, my nerves are all gone for to-night,' wailed Banford.

At nine o'clock March brought in a tray with bread and cheese and tea—Henry had confessed that he liked a cup of tea. Banford drank a glass of milk, and ate a little bread. And soon she said:

'I'm going to bed, Nellie. I'm all nerves to-night. Are you coming?'

'Yes. I'm coming the minute I've taken the tray away,' said March.

'Don't be long, then,' said Banford fretfully. 'Good night, Henry. You'll see the fire is safe, if you come up last, won't you?'

'Yes, Miss Banford, I'll see it's safe,' he replied in his reassuring way.

March was lighting the candle to go to the kitchen. Banford took her candle and went upstairs. When March came back to the fire, she said to him:

'I suppose we can trust you to put out the fire and everything?' She stood there with her hand on her hip, and one knee loose, her head averted shyly, as if she could not look at him. He had his face lifted, watching her.

'Come and sit down a minute,' he said softly.

'No, I'll be going. Jill will be waiting, and she'll get upset if I don't come.'

'What made you jump like that this evening?' he asked.

'When did I jump?' she retorted, looking at him.

'Why, just now you did,' he said. 'When you cried out.'

'Oh!' she said. 'Then! Why, I thought you were the fox!' And her face screwed into a queer smile, half-ironic.

'The fox! Why the fox?' he asked softly.

'Why, one evening last summer when I was out with the gun I saw the fox in the grass nearly at my feet, looking straight up at me. I don't know—I suppose he made an impression on me.' She turned aside her head again, and let one foot stray loose, self-consciously.

'And did you shoot him?' asked the boy.

'No, he gave me such a start, staring straight at me as he did, and then stopping to look back at me over his shoulder with a laugh on his face.'

'A laugh on his face!' repeated Henry, also laughing. 'He frightened you, did he?'

'No, he didn't frighten me. He made an impression on me, that's all.'

'And you thought I was the fox, did you?' he laughed, with the same queer, quick little laugh, like a puppy wrinkling its nose.

'Yes, I did, for the moment,' she said. 'Perhaps he'd been in my mind without my knowing.'

'Perhaps you think I've come to steal your chickens or something,' he said, with the same young laugh.

But she only looked at him with a wide, dark, vacant eye.

'It's the first time,' he said, 'that I've ever been taken for a fox. Won't you sit down for a minute?' His voice was very soft and cajoling.

'No,' she said. 'Jill will be waiting.' But still she did not go, but stood with one foot loose and her face turned aside, just outside the circle of light.

'But won't you answer my question?' he said, lowering his voice still more.

'I don't know what question you mean.'

'Yes, you do. Of course you do. I mean the question of you marrying me.'

'No, I shan't answer that question,' she said flatly.

'Won't you?' The queer, young laugh came on his nose again. 'Is it because I'm like the fox? Is that why?' And still he laughed.

She turned and looked at him with a long, slow look.

'I wouldn't let that put you against me,' he said. 'Let me turn the lamp low, and come and sit down a minute.'

He put his red hand under the glow of the lamp, and suddenly made the light very dim. March stood there in the dimness quite shadowy, but unmoving. He rose silently to his feet, on his long legs. And now his voice was extraordinarily soft and suggestive, hardly audible.

'You'll stay a moment,' he said. 'Just a moment.' And he put his hand on her shoulder. She turned her face from him. 'I'm sure you don't really think I'm like the fox,' he said, with the same softness and with a suggestion of laughter in his tone, a subtle mockery. 'Do you now?' And he drew her gently towards him and kissed her neck, softly. She winced and trembled and hung away. But his strong, young arm held her, and he kissed her softly again, still on the neck, for her face was averted.

'Won't you answer my question? Won't you now?' came his soft, lingering voice. He was trying to draw her near to kiss her face. And he kissed her cheek softly, near the ear.

At that moment Banford's voice was heard calling fretfully, crossly from upstairs.

'There's Jill!' cried March, starting and drawing erect.

And as she did so, quick as lightning he kissed her on the mouth, with a quick brushing kiss. It seemed to burn through her every fibre. She gave a queer little cry.

'You will, won't you? You will?' he insisted softly.

'Nellie! *Nellie!* Whatever are you so long for?' came Banford's faint cry from the outer darkness.

But he held her fast, and was murmuring with that intolerable softness and insistency:

'You will, won't you? Say yes! Say yes!'

March, who felt as if the fire had gone through her and scathed her, and as if she could do no more, murmured:

'Yes! Yes! Anything you like! Anything you like! Only let me go! Only let me go! Jill's calling.'

'You know you've promised,' he said insidiously.

'Yes! Yes! I do!' Her voice suddenly rose into a shrill cry. 'All right, Jill, I'm coming.'

Startled, he let her go, and she went straight upstairs.

In the morning at breakfast, after he had looked round the place and attended to the stock and thought to himself that one could live easily enough here, he said to Banford:

'Do you know what, Miss Banford?'

'Well, what?' said the good-natured, nervy Banford.

He looked at March, who was spreading jam on her bread.

'Shall I tell?' he said to her.

She looked up at him, and a deep pink colour flushed over her face.

'Yes, if you mean Jill,' she said. 'I hope you won't go talking all over the village, that's all.' And she swallowed her dry bread with difficulty.

'Whatever's coming?' said Banford, looking up with wide, tired, slightly reddened eyes. She was a thin, frail little thing, and her hair, which was delicate and thin, was bobbed, so it hung softly by her worn face in its faded brown and grey.

'Why, what do you think?' he said, smiling like one who has a secret.

'How do I know?' said Banford.

'Can't you guess?' he said, making bright eyes, and smiling, pleased with himself.

'I'm sure I can't. What's more, I'm not going to to try.'

'Nellie and I are going to be married.'

Banford put down her knife out of her thin, delicate

fingers, as if she would never take it up to eat any more. She stared with blank, reddened eyes.

'You what?' she exclaimed.

'We 're going to get married. Aren't we, Nellie?' and he turned to March.

'You say so, anyway,' said March laconically. But again she flushed with an agonized flush. She, too, could swallow no more.

Banford looked at her like a bird that has been shot: a poor, little sick bird. She gazed at her with all her wounded soul in her face, at the deep-flushed March.

'Never!' she exclaimed, helpless.

'It 's quite right,' said the bright and gloating youth.

Banford turned aside her face, as if the sight of the food on the table made her sick. She sat like this for some moments, as if she were sick. Then, with one hand on the edge of the table, she rose to her feet.

'I 'll *never* believe it, Nellie,' she cried. 'It 's absolutely impossible!'

Her plaintive, fretful voice had a thread of hot anger and despair.

'Why? Why shouldn't you believe it?' asked the youth, with all his soft, velvety impertinence in his voice.

Banford looked at him from her wide, vague eyes, as if he were some creature in a museum.

'Oh,' she said languidly, 'because she can never be such a fool. She can't lose her self-respect to such an extent.' Her voice was cold and plaintive, drifting.

'In what way will she lose her self-respect?' asked the boy.

Banford looked at him with vague fixity from behind her spectacles.

'If she hasn't lost it already,' she said.

He became very red, vermilion, under the slow vague stare from behind the spectacles.

'I don't see it at all,' he said.

'Probably you don't. I shouldn't expect you would,' said Banford, with that straying mild tone of remoteness which made her words even more insulting.

He sat stiff in his chair, staring with hot, blue eyes from his scarlet face. An ugly look had come on his brow.

'My word, she doesn't know what she's letting herself in for,' said Banford, in her plaintive, drifting, insulting voice.

'What has it got to do with you, anyway?' said the youth, in a temper.

'More than it has to do with you, probably,' she replied, plaintive and venomous.

'Oh, has it! I don't see that at all,' he jerked out.

'No, you wouldn't,' she answered, drifting.

'Anyhow,' said March, pushing back her chair and rising uncouthly, 'it's no good arguing about it.' And she seized the bread and the teapot, and strode away to the kitchen.

Banford let her fingers stray across her brow and along her hair, like one bemused. Then she turned and went away upstairs.

Henry sat stiff and sulky in his chair, with his face and his eyes on fire. March came and went, clearing the table. But Henry sat on, stiff with temper. He took no notice of her. She had regained her composure and her soft, even, creamy complexion. But her mouth was pursed up. She glanced at him each time as she came to take things from the table, glanced from her large, curious eyes, more in curiosity than anything. Such a long, red-faced, sulky boy! That was all he was. He seemed as remote from her as if his red face were a red chimney-pot on a cottage across the fields, and she looked at him just as objectively, as remotely.

At length he got up and stalked out into the fields with the gun. He came in only at dinner-time, with the devil still in his face, but his manners quite polite. Nobody said anything particular; they sat each one at the sharp corner of a triangle, in obstinate remoteness. In the afternoon he went out again at once with the gun. He came in at nightfall with a rabbit and a pigeon. He stayed in all the evening, but hardly opened his mouth. He was in the devil of a temper, feeling he had been insulted.

Banford's eyes were red, she had evidently been crying. But her manner was more remote and super-
cilious than ever; the way she turned her head if he
spoke at all, as if he were some tramp or inferior intruder
of that sort, made his blue eyes go almost black with
rage. His face looked sulkier. But he never forgot
his polite intonation, if he opened his mouth to speak.

March seemed to flourish in this atmosphere. She
seemed to sit between the two antagonists with a little
wicked smile on her face, enjoying herself. There was
even a sort of complacency in the way she laboriously
crocheted this evening.

When he was in bed, the youth could hear the two
women talking and arguing in their room. He sat up
in bed and strained his ears to hear what they said.
But he could hear nothing, it was too far off. Yet he
could hear the soft, plaintive drip of Banford's voice,
and March's deeper note.

The night was quite, frosty. Big stars were snapping
outside, beyond the ridge-tops of the pine-trees. He
listened and listened. In the distance he heard a fox
yelping: and the dogs from the farms barking in answer.
But it was not that he wanted to hear. It was what
the two women were saying.

He got stealthily out of bed, and stood by his door.
He could hear no more than before. Very, very carefully he began to lift the door latch. After quite a time
he had his door open. Then he stepped stealthily out
into the passage. The old oak planks were cold under
his feet, and they creaked preposterously. He crept
very, very gently up the one step, and along by the wall,
till he stood outside their door. And there he held his
breath and listened. Banford's voice:

'No, I simply couldn't stand it. I should be dead in
a month. Which is just what he would be aiming at,
of course. That would just be his game, to see me in
the churchyard. No, Nellie, if you were to do such a
thing as to marry him, you could never stop here. I
couldn't, I couldn't live in the same house with him.
Oh——h! I feel quite sick with the smell of his clothes.

And his red face simply turns me over. I can't eat my food when he's at the table. What a fool I was ever to let him stop. One ought *never* to try to do a kind action. It always flies back in your face like a boomerang.'

'Well, he's only got two more days,' said March.

'Yes, thank heaven. And when he's gone he'll never come in this house again. I feel so bad while he's here. And I know, I know he's only counting what he can get out of you. I *know* that's all it is. He's just a good-for-nothing, who doesn't want to work, and who thinks he'll live on us. But he won't live on me. If you're such a fool, then it's your own look out. Mrs Burgess knew him all the time he was here. And the old man could never get him to do any steady work. He was off with the gun on every occasion, just as he is now. Nothing but the gun! Oh, I do hate it. You don't know what you're doing, Nellie, you don't. If you marry him he'll just make a fool of you. He'll go off and leave you stranded. I know he will, if he can't get Bailey Farm out of us—and he's not going to, while I live. While I live he's never going to set foot here. I know what it would be. He'd soon think he was master of both of us, as he thinks he's master of you already.'

'But he isn't,' said Nellie.

'He thinks he is, anyway. And that's what he wants: to come and be master here. Yes, imagine it! That's what we've got the place together for, is it, to be bossed and bullied by a hateful red-faced boy, a beastly labourer? Oh, we *did* make a mistake when we let him stop. We ought never to have lowered ourselves. And I've had such a fight with all the people here, not to be pulled down to their level. No, he's not coming here. And then you see—if he can't have the place, he'll run off to Canada or somewhere again, as if he'd never known you. And here you'll be, absolutely ruined and made a fool of. I know I shall never have any peace of mind again.'

'We'll tell him he can't come here. We'll tell him that,' said March.

'Oh, don't you bother; I'm going to tell him that, and other things as well, before he goes. He's not going to have all his own way while I've got the strength left to speak. Oh, Nellie, he'll despise you, he'll despise you, like the awful little beast he is, if you give way to him. I'd no more trust him than I'd trust a cat not to steal. He's deep, he's deep, and he's bossy, and he's selfish through and through, as cold as ice. All he wants is to make use of you. And when you're no more use to him, then I pity you.'

'I don't think he's as bad as all that,' said March.

'No, because he's been playing up to you. But you'll find out, if you see much more of him. Oh, Nellie, I can't bear to think of it.'

'Well, it won't hurt you, Jill darling.'

'Won't it! Won't it! I shall never know a moment's peace again while I live, nor a moment's happiness. No, Nellie——' And Banford began to weep bitterly.

The boy outside could hear the stifled sound of the woman's sobbing, and could hear March's soft, deep, tender voice comforting, with wonderful gentleness and tenderness, the weeping woman.

His eyes were so round and wide that he seemed to see the whole night, and his ears were almost jumping off his head. He was frozen stiff. He crept back to bed, but felt as if the top of his head were coming off. He could not sleep. He could not keep still. He rose, quietly dressed himself, and crept out on to the landing once more. The women were silent. He went softly downstairs and out to the kitchen.

Then he put on his boots and his overcoat, and took the gun. He did not think to go away from the farm. No, he only took the gun. As softly as possible he unfastened the door and went out into the frosty December night. The air was still, the stars bright, the pine-trees seemed to bristle audibly in the sky. He went stealthily away down a fence-side, looking for something to shoot. At the same time he remembered that he ought not to shoot and frighten the women.

So he prowled round the edge of the gorse cover, and

through the grove of tall old hollies, to the woodside. There he skirted the fence, peering through the darkness with dilated eyes that seemed to be able to grow black and full of sight in the dark, like a cat's. An owl was slowly and mournfully whooing round a great oak-tree. He stepped stealthily with his gun, listening, listening, watching.

As he stood under the oaks of the wood-edge he heard the dogs from the neighbouring cottage up the hill yelling suddenly and startlingly, and the wakened dogs from the farms around barking answer. And suddenly, it seemed to him England was little and tight, he felt the landscape was constricted even in the dark, and that there were too many dogs in the night, making a noise like a fence of sound, like the network of English hedges netting the view. He felt the fox didn't have a chance. For it must be the fox that had started all this hullabaloo.

Why not watch for him, anyhow! He would, no doubt, be coming sniffing round. The lad walked downhill to where the farmstead with its few pine-trees crouched blackly. In the angle of the long shed, in the black dark, he crouched down. He knew the fox would be coming. It seemed to him it would be the last of the foxes in this loudly barking, thick-voiced England, tight with innumerable little houses.

He sat a long time with his eyes fixed unchanging upon the open gateway, where a little light seemed to fall from the stars or from the horizon, who knows. He was sitting on a log in a dark corner with the gun across his knees. The pine-trees snapped. Once a chicken fell off its perch in the barn with a loud crawk and cackle and commotion that startled him, and he stood up, watching with all his eyes, thinking it might be a rat. But he *felt* it was nothing. So he sat down again with the gun on his knees and his hands tucked in to keep them warm, and his eyes fixed unblinking on the pale reach of the open gateway. He felt he could smell the hot, sickly, rich smell of live chickens on the cold air.

And then—a shadow. A sliding shadow in the gateway. He gathered all his vision into a concentrated spark, and saw the shadow of the fox, the fox creeping on his belly through the gate. There he went, on his belly, like a snake. The boy smiled to himself and brought the gun to his shoulder. He knew quite well what would happen. He knew the fox would go to where the fowl-door was boarded up, and sniff there. He knew he would lie there for a minute, sniffing the fowls within. And then he would start again prowling under the edge of the old barn, waiting to get in.

The fowl-door was at the top of a slight incline. Soft, soft as a shadow the fox slid up this incline, and crouched with his nose to the boards. And at the same moment there was the awful crash of a gun reverberating between the old buildings, as if all the night had gone smash. But the boy watched keenly. He saw even the white belly of the fox as the beast beat his paws in death. So he went forward.

There was a commotion everywhere. The fowls were scuffling and crawking, the ducks were quark-quarking, the pony had stamped wildly to his feet. But the fox was on his side, struggling in his last tremors. The boy bent over him and smelt his foxy smell.

There was a sound of a window opening upstairs, then March's voice calling:

'Who is it?'

'It's me,' said Henry; 'I've shot the fox.'

'Oh, goodness! You nearly frightened us to death.'

'Did I? I'm awfully sorry.'

'Whatever made you get up?'

'I heard him about.'

'And have you shot him?'

'Yes, he's here,' and the boy stood in the yard holding up the warm, dead brute. 'You can't see, can you? Wait a minute.' And he took his flashlight from his pocket, and flashed it on to the dead animal. He was holding it by the brush. March saw, in the middle of the darkness, just the reddish fleece and the white belly and the white underneath of the pointed chin, and the queer, dangling paws. She did not know what to say.

'He's a beauty,' he said. 'He will make you a lovely fur.'

'You don't catch me wearing a fox fur,' she replied.

'Oh!' he said. And he switched off the light.

'Well, I should think you'll come in and go to bed again now,' she said.

'Probably I shall. What time is it?'

'What time is it, Jill?' called March's voice. It was a quarter to one.

That night March had another dream. She dreamed that Banford was dead, and that she, March, was sobbing her heart out. Then she had to put Banford into her coffin. And the coffin was the rough wood-box in which the bits of chopped wood were kept in the kitchen, by the fire. This was the coffin, and there was no other, and March was in agony and dazed bewilderment, looking for something to line the box with, something to make it soft with, something to cover up the poor, dead darling. Because she couldn't lay her in there just in her white, thin night-dress, in the horrible wood-box. So she hunted and hunted, and picked up thing after thing, and threw it aside in the agony of dream-frustration. And in her dream-despair all she could find that would do was a fox-skin. She knew that it wasn't right, that this was not what she should have. But it was all she could find. And so she folded the brush of the fox, and laid her darling Jill's head on this, and she brought round the skin of the fox and laid it on the top of the body, so that it seemed to make a whole ruddy, fiery coverlet, and she cried and cried, and woke to find the tears streaming down her face.

The first thing that both she and Banford did in the morning was to go out to see the fox. Henry had hung it up by the heels in the shed, with its poor brush falling backwards. It was a lovely dog-fox in its prime, with a handsome, thick, winter coat: a lovely golden-red colour, with grey as it passed to the belly, and the belly all white, and a great full brush with a delicate black and grey and pure white tip.

'Poor brute!' said Banford. 'If it wasn't such a thieving wretch, you'd feel sorry for it.'

March said nothing, but stood with her foot trailing aside, one hip out; her face was pale and her eyes big and black, watching the dead animal that was suspended upside down. White and soft as snow his belly: white and soft as snow. She passed her hand softly down it. And his wonderful black-glinted brush was full and frictional, wonderful. She passed her hand down this also, and quivered. Time after time she took the full fur of that thick tail between her fingers, and passed her hand slowly downwards. Wonderful, sharp, thick, splendour of a tail. And he was dead! She pursed her lips, and her eyes went black and vacant. Then she took the head in her hand.

Henry was sauntering up, so Banford walked rather pointedly away. March stood there bemused, with the head of the fox in her hand. She was wondering, wondering, wondering over his long fine muzzle. For some reason it reminded her of a spoon or a spatula. She felt she could not understand it. The beast was a strange beast to her, incomprehensible, out of her range. Wonderful silver whiskers he had, like ice-threads. And pricked ears with hair inside. But that long, long, slender spoon of a nose!—and the marvellous white teeth beneath! It was to thrust forward and bite with, deep, deep into the living prey, to bite and bite the blood.

'He's a beauty, isn't he?' said Henry, standing by.

'Oh, yes, he's a fine big fox. I wonder how many chickens he's responsible for,' she replied.

'A good many. Do you think he's the same one you saw in the summer?'

'I should think very likely he is,' she replied.

He watched her, but he could make nothing of her. Partly she was so shy and virgin, and partly she was so grim, matter-of-fact, shrewish. What she said seemed to him so different from the look of her big, queer, dark eyes.

'Are you going to skin him?' she asked.

'Yes, when I 've had breakfast, and got a board to peg him on.'

'My word, what a strong smell he 's got! Pooo! It 'll take some washing off one's hands. I don't know why I was so silly as to handle him.' And she looked at her right hand, that had passed down his belly and along his tail, and had even got a tiny streak of blood from one dark place in his fur.

'Have you seen the chickens when they smell him, how frightened they are?' he said.

'Yes, aren't they!'

'You must mind you don't get some of his fleas.'

'Oh, fleas!' she replied, nonchalant.

Later in the day she saw the fox's skin nailed flat on a board, as if crucified. It gave her an uneasy feeling.

The boy was angry. He went about with his mouth shut, as if he had swallowed part of his chin. But in behaviour he was polite and affable. He did not say anything about his intention. And he left March alone.

That evening they sat in the dining-room. Banford wouldn't have him in her sitting-room any more. There was a very big log on the fire. And everybody was busy. Banford had letters to write, March was sewing a dress, and he was mending some little contrivance.

Banford stopped her letter-writing from time to time to look round and rest her eyes. The boy had his head down, his face hidden over his job.

'Let 's see,' said Banford. 'What train do you go by, Henry?'

He looked up straight at her.

'The morning train. In the morning,' he said.

'What, the eight-ten or the eleven-twenty?'

'The eleven-twenty, I suppose,' he said.

'That is the day after to-morrow?' said Banford.

'Yes, the day after to-morrow.'

'Mm!' murmured Banford, and she returned to her writing. But as she was licking her envelope, she asked:

'And what plans have you made for the future, if I may ask?'

'Plans?' he said, his face very bright and angry.

'I mean about you and Nellie, if you are going on with this business. When do you expect the wedding to come off?' She spoke in a jeering tone.

'Oh, the wedding!' he replied. 'I don't know.'

'Don't you know anything?' said Banford. 'Are you going to clear out on Friday and leave things no more settled than they are?'

'Well, why shouldn't I? We can always write letters.'

'Yes, of course you can. But I wanted to know because of this place. If Nellie is going to get married all of a sudden, I shall have to be looking round for a new partner.'

'Couldn't she stay on here if she were married?' he said. He knew quite well what was coming.

'Oh,' said Banford, 'this is no place for a married couple. There's not enough work to keep a man going, for one thing. And there's no money to be made. It's quite useless your thinking of staying on here if you marry. Absolutely!'

'Yes, but I wasn't thinking of staying on here,' he said.

'Well, that's what I want to know. And what about Nellie, then? How long is *she* going to be here with me, in that case.'

The two antagonists looked at one another.

'That I can't say,' he answered.

'Oh, go along,' she cried petulantly. 'You must have some idea what you are going to do, if you ask a woman to marry you. Unless it's all a hoax.'

'Why should it be a hoax? I am going back to Canada.'

'And taking her with you?'

'Yes, certainly.'

'You hear that, Nellie?' said Banford.

March, who had had her head bent over her sewing, now looked up with a sharp, pink blush on her face, and a queer, sardonic laugh in her eyes and on her twisted mouth.

'That's the first time I've heard that I was going to Canada,' she said.

'Well, you have to hear it for the first time, haven't you?' said the boy.

'Yes, I suppose I have,' she said nonchalantly. And she went back to her sewing.

'You 're quite ready, are you, to go to Canada? Are you, Nellie?' asked Banford.

March looked up again. She let her shoulders go slack, and let her hand that held the needle lie loose in her lap.

'It depends on *how* I 'm going,' she said. 'I don't think I want to go jammed up in the steerage, as a soldier's wife. I 'm afraid I 'm not used to that way.'

The boy watched her with bright eyes.

'Would you rather stay over here while I go first?' he asked.

'I would, if that 's the only alternative,' she replied.

'That 's much the wisest. Don't make it any fixed engagement,' said Banford. 'Leave yourself free to go or not after he 's got back and found you a place, Nellie. Anything else is madness, madness.'

'Don't you think,' said the youth, 'we ought to get married before I go—and then go together, or separate, according to how it happens?'

'I think it 's a terrible idea,' cried Banford.

But the boy was watching March.

'What do you think?' he asked her.

She let her eyes stray vaguely into space.

'Well, I don't know,' she said. 'I shall have to think about it.'

'Why?' he asked pertinently.

'Why?' She repeated his question in a mocking way, and looked at him laughing, though her face was pink again. 'I should think there 's plenty of reasons why.'

He watched her in silence. She seemed to have escaped him. She had got into league with Banford against him. There was again the queer sardonic look about her; she would mock stoically at everything he said or which life offered.

'Of course,' he said, 'I don't want to press you to do anything you don't wish to do.'

'I should think not, indeed,' cried Banford indignantly.

At bedtime Banford said plaintively to March:

'You take my hot bottle up for me, Nellie, will you.'

'Yes, I'll do it,' said March, with the kind of willing unwillingness she so often showed towards her beloved but uncertain Jill.

The two women went upstairs. After a time March called from the top of the stairs: 'Good night, Henry. I shan't be coming down. You'll see to the lamp and the fire, won't you?'

The next day Henry went about with the cloud on his brow and his young cub's face shut up tight. He was cogitating all the time. He had wanted March to marry him and go back to Canada with him. And he had been sure she would do it. Why he wanted her he didn't know. But he did want her. He had set his mind on her. And he was convulsed with a youth's fury at being thwarted. To be thwarted, to be thwarted! It made him so furious inside that he did not know what to do with himself. But he kept himself in hand. Because even now things might turn out differently. She might come over to him. Of course she might. It was her business to do so.

Things drew to a tension again towards evening. He and Banford had avoided each other all day. In fact, Banford went in to the little town by the 11.20 train. It was market day. She arrived back on the 4.25. Just as the night was falling Henry saw her little figure in a dark blue coat and a dark blue tam-o'-shanter hat crossing the first meadow from the station. He stood under one of the wild pear-trees, with the old dead leaves round his feet. And he watched the little blue figure advancing persistently over the rough winter-ragged meadow. She had her arms full of parcels, and advanced slowly, frail thing she was, but with that devilish little certainty which he so detested in her. He stood invisible under the pear-tree, watching her every step. And if looks could have affected her, she would have felt a log of iron on each of her ankles as she made her way forward. 'You're a nasty little thing, you are,' he was saying softly, across the distance. 'You're a nasty little thing. I hope you'll be paid back for all the harm you've done me for nothing. I hope you will—you nasty little thing. I hope you'll have to pay for it. You will, if wishes are anything. You nasty little creature that you are.'

She was toiling slowly up the slope. But if she had been slipping back at every step towards the Bottomless Pit, he would not have gone to help her with her parcels. Aha, there went March, striding with her long, land stride in her breeches and her short tunic! Striding downhill at a great pace, and even running a few steps now and then, in her great solicitude and desire to come to the rescue of the little Banford. The boy watched her with rage in his heart. See her leap a ditch, and run, run as if a house was on fire, just to get to that creeping, dark little object down there! So, the Banford just stood still and waited. And March strode up and took *all* the parcels except a bunch of yellow chrysanthemums. These the Banford still carried — yellow chrysanthemums!

'Yes, you look well, don't you,' he said softly into the dusk air. 'You look well, pottering up there with a bunch of flowers, you do. I'd make you eat them for your tea, if you hug them so tight. And I'd give them you for breakfast again, I would. I'd give you flowers. Nothing but flowers.'

He watched the progress of the two women. He could hear their voices: March always outspoken and rather scolding in her tenderness, Banford murmuring rather vaguely. They were evidently good friends. He could not hear what they said till they came to the fence of the home meadow, which they must climb. Then he saw March manfully climbing over the bars with all her packages in her arms, and on the still air he heard Banford's fretful:

'Why don't you let me help you with the parcels?' She had a queer, plaintive hitch in her voice. Then came March's robust and reckless:

'Oh, I can manage. Don't you bother about me. You've all you can do to get yourself over.'

'Yes, that's all very well,' said Banford fretfully. 'You say, "Don't you bother about me," and then all the while you feel injured because nobody thinks of you.'

'When do I feel injured?' said March.

'Always. You always feel injured. Now you're feeling injured because I won't have that boy to come and live on the farm.'

'I'm not feeling injured at all,' said March.

'I know you are. When he's gone you'll sulk over it. I know you will.'

'Shall I?' said March. 'We'll see.'

'Yes, we *shall* see, unfortunately. I can't think how you can make yourself so cheap. I can't *imagine* how you can lower yourself like it.'

'I haven't lowered myself,' said March.

'I don't know what you call it, then. Letting a boy like that come so cheeky and impudent and make a mug of you. I don't know what you think of yourself. How much respect do you think he's going to have for you afterwards? My word, I wouldn't be in your shoes, if you married him.'

'Of course you wouldn't. My boots are a good bit too big for you, and not half dainty enough,' said March, with rather a miss-fire sarcasm.

'I thought you had too much pride, really I did. A woman's got to hold herself high, especially with a youth like that. Why, he's impudent. Even the way he forced himself on us at the start.'

'We asked him to stay,' said March.

'Not till he'd almost forced us to. And then he's so cocky and self-assured. My word, he puts my back up. I simply can't imagine how you can let him treat you so cheaply.'

'I don't let him treat me cheaply,' said March. 'Don't you worry yourself, nobody's going to treat me cheaply. And even you aren't, either.' She had a tender defiance, and a certain fire in her voice.

'Yes, it's sure to come back to me,' said Banford

bitterly. 'That's always the end of it. I believe you only do it to spite me.'

They went now in silence up the steep, grassy slope and over the brow, through the gorse-bushes. On the other side of the hedge the boy followed in the dusk, at some little distance. Now and then, through the huge ancient hedge of hawthorn, risen into trees, he saw the two dark figures creeping up the hill. As he came to the top of the slope he saw the homestead dark in the twilight, with a huge old pear-tree leaning from the near gable, and a little yellow light twinkling in the small side windows of the kitchen. He heard the clink of the latch and saw the kitchen door open into light as the two women went indoors. So, they were at home.

And so!—this was what they thought of him. It was rather in his nature to be a listener, so he was not at all surprised whatever he heard. The things people said about him always missed him personally. He was only rather surprised at the women's way with one another. And he disliked the Banford with an acid dislike. And he felt drawn to the March again. He felt again irresistibly drawn to her. He felt there was a secret bond, a secret thread between him and her, something very exclusive, which shut out everybody else and made him and her possess each other in secret.

He hoped again that she would have him. He hoped with his blood suddenly firing up that she would agree to marry him quite quickly: at Christmas, very likely. Christmas was not far off. He wanted, whatever else happened, to snatch her into a hasty marriage and a consummation with him. Then for the future, they could arrange later. But he hoped it would happen as he wanted it. He hoped that to-night she would stay a little while with him, after Banford had gone upstairs. He hoped he could touch her soft, creamy cheek, her strange, frightened face. He hoped he could look into her dilated, frightened dark eyes, quite near. He hoped he might even put his hand on her bosom and feel her soft breasts under her tunic. His heart beat deep and powerful as he thought of that. He wanted very much to do so. He wanted to make sure of her soft woman's breasts under her tunic. She always kept the brown linen coat buttoned so close up to her throat. It seemed to him like some perilous secret, that her soft woman's breasts must be buttoned up in that uniform. It seemed to him, moreover, that they were so much softer, tenderer, more lovely and lovable, shut up in that tunic, than were the Banford's breasts, under her soft blouses and chiffon dresses. The Banford would have little iron breasts, he said to himself. For all her frailty and fretfulness and delicacy, she would have tiny iron breasts. But March, under her crude, fast, workman's tunic, would have soft, white breasts, white and unseen. So he told himself, and his blood burned.

When he went in to tea, he had a surprise. He appeared at the inner door, his face very ruddy and vivid and his blue eyes shining, dropping his head forward as he came in, in his usual way, and hesitating in the doorway to watch the inside of the room, keenly and cautiously, before he entered. He was wearing a long-sleeved waistcoat. His face seemed extraordinarily like a piece of the out-of-doors come indoors: as holly berries do. In his second of pause in the doorway he took in the two women sitting at table, at opposite ends, saw them sharply. And to his amazement March was dressed in a dress of dull, green silk crape. His mouth came open in surprise. If she had suddenly grown a moustache he could not have been more surprised.

'Why,' he said, 'do you wear a dress, then?'

She looked up, flushing a deep rose colour, and twisting her mouth with a smile, said:

'Of course I do. What else do you expect me to wear, but a dress?'

'A land-girl's uniform, of course,' said he.

'Oh,' she cried, nonchalant, 'that's only for this dirty, mucky work about here.'

'Isn't it your proper dress, then?' he said.

'No, not indoors it isn't,' she said. But she was blushing all the time as she poured out his tea. He sat down in his chair at table, unable to take his eyes off her. Her dress was a perfectly simple slip of bluey-green crape, with a line of gold stitching round the top and round the sleeves, which came to the elbow. It was cut just plain and round at the top, and showed her white, soft throat. Her arms he knew, strong and firm muscled, for he had often seen her with her sleeves rolled up. But he looked her up and down, up and down.

Banford, at the other end of the table, said not a word, but piggled with the sardine on her plate. He had forgotten her existence. He just simply stared at March, while he ate his bread and margarine in huge mouthfuls, forgetting even his tea.

'Well, I never knew anything make such a difference!' he murmured, across his mouthfuls.

'Oh, goodness!' cried March, blushing still more. 'I might be a pink monkey!'

And she rose quickly to her feet and took the teapot to the fire, to the kettle. And as she crouched on the hearth with her green slip about her, the boy stared more wide-eyed than ever. Through the crape her woman's form seemed soft and womanly. And when she stood up and walked he saw her legs move soft within her modernly short skirt. She had on black silk stockings, and small patent shoes with little gold buckles.

No, she was another being. She was something quite different. Seeing her always in the hard-cloth breeches, wide on the hips, buttoned on the knee, strong as armour, and in the brown puttees and thick boots, it had never occurred to him that she had a woman's legs and feet. Now it came upon him. She had a woman's soft, skirted legs, and she was accessible. He blushed to the roots of his hair, shoved his nose in his tea-cup, and drank his tea with a little noise that made Banford simply squirm: and strangely, suddenly he felt a man, no longer a youth. He felt a man, with all a man's grave weight of responsibility. A curious quietness and gravity came over his soul. He felt a man, quiet, with a little of the heaviness of male destiny upon him.

She was soft and accessible in her dress. The thought went home in him like an everlasting responsibility.

'Oh, for goodness' sake, say something, somebody,' cried Banford fretfully. 'It might be a funeral.' The boy looked at her, and she could not bear his face.

'A funeral!' said March, with a twisted smile. 'Why, that breaks my dream.'

Suddenly she had thought of Banford in the wood-box for a coffin.

'What, have you been dreaming of a wedding?' said Banford sarcastically.

'Must have been,' said March.

'Whose wedding?' asked the boy.

'I can't remember,' said March.

She was shy and rather awkward that evening, in spite of the fact that, wearing a dress, her bearing was much more subdued than in her uniform. She felt unpeeled and rather exposed. She felt almost improper.

They talked desultorily about Henry's departure next morning, and made the trivial arrangement. But of the matter on their minds, none of them spoke. They were rather quiet and friendly this evening; Banford had practically nothing to say. But inside herself she seemed still, perhaps kindly.

At nine o'clock March brought in the tray with the everlasting tea and a little cold meat which Banford had managed to procure. It was the last supper, so Banford did not want to be disagreeable. She felt a bit sorry for the boy, and felt she must be as nice as she could.

He wanted her to go to bed. She was usually the first. But she sat on in her chair under the lamp, glancing at her book now and then, and staring into the fire. A deep silence had come into the room. It was broken by March asking, in a rather small tone:

'What time is it, Jill?'

'Five past ten,' said Banford, looking at her wrist.

And then not a sound. The boy had looked up from the book he was holding between his knees. His rather wide, cat-shaped face had its obstinate look, his eyes were watchful.

'What about bed?' said March at last.

'I'm ready when you are,' said Banford.

'Oh, very well,' said March. 'I'll fill your bottle.'

She was as good as her word. When the hot-water bottle was ready, she lit a candle and went upstairs with it. Banford remained in her chair, listening acutely. March came downstairs again.

'There you are, then,' she said. 'Are you going up?'

'Yes, in a minute,' said Banford. But the minute passed, and she sat on in her chair under the lamp.

Henry, whose eyes were shining like a cat's as he watched from under his brows, and whose face seemed wider, more chubbed and cat-like with unalterable obstinacy, now rose to his feet to try his throw.

'I think I'll go and look if I can see the she-fox,' he said. 'She may be creeping round. Won't you come as well for a minute, Nellie, and see if we can see anything?'

'Me!' cried March, looking up with her startled, wondering face.

'Yes. Come on,' he said. It was wonderful how soft and warm and coaxing his voice could be, how near. The very sound of it made Banford's blood boil. 'Come on for a minute,' he said, looking down into her uplifted, unsure face.

And she rose to her feet as if drawn up by his young, ruddy face that was looking down on her.

'I should think you're never going out at this time of night, Nellie!' cried Banford.

'Yes, just for a minute,' said the boy, looking round on her, and speaking with an odd, sharp yelp in his voice.

March looked from one to the other, as if confused, vague. Banford rose to her feet for battle.

'Why, it's ridiculous. It's bitter cold. You'll catch your death in that thin frock. And in those slippers. You're not going to do any such thing.'

There was a moment's pause. Banford turtled up like a little fighting cock, facing March and the boy.

'Oh, I don't think you need worry yourself,' he replied. 'A moment under the stars won't do anybody any damage. I'll get the rug off the sofa in the dining-room. You're coming, Nellie.'

His voice had so much anger and contempt and fury in it as he spoke to Banford: and as much tenderness and proud authority as he spoke to March, that the latter answered:

'Yes, I'm coming.'

And she turned with him to the door.

Banford, standing there in the middle of the room, suddenly burst into a long wail and a spasm of sobs. She covered her face with her poor, thin hands, and her thin shoulders shook in an agony of weeping. March looked back from the door.

'Jill!' she cried in a frantic tone, like someone just coming awake. And she seemed to start towards her darling.

But the boy had March's arm in his grip, and she could not move. She did not know why she could not move. It was as in a dream when the heart strains and the body cannot stir.

'Never mind,' said the boy softly. 'Let her cry. Let her cry. She will have to cry sooner or later. And the tears will relieve her feelings. They will do her good.'

So he drew March slowly through the doorway. But her last look was back to the poor little figure which stood in the middle of the room with covered face and thin shoulders shaken with bitter weeping.

In the dining-room he picked up the rug and said:

'Wrap yourself up in this.'

She obeyed—and they reached the kitchen door, he holding her soft and firm by the arm, though she did not know it. When she saw the night outside she started back.

'I must go back to Jill,' she said. 'I *must*! Oh, yes, I must.'

Her tone sounded final. The boy let go of her and she turned indoors. But he seized her again and arrested her.

'Wait a minute,' he said. 'Wait a minute. Even if you go, you're not going yet.'

'Leave go! Leave go!' she cried. 'My place is at Jill's side. Poor little thing, she's sobbing her heart out.'

'Yes,' said the boy bitterly. 'And your heart too, and mine as well.'

'Your heart?' said March. He still gripped her and detained her.

'Isn't it as good as her heart?' he said. 'Or do you think it's not?'

'Your heart?' she said again, incredulous.

'Yes, mine! Mine! Do you think I haven't *got* a heart?' And with his hot grasp he took her hand and pressed it under his left breast. 'There's my heart,' he said, 'if you don't believe in it.'

It was wonder which made her attend. And then she felt the deep, heavy, powerful stroke of his heart, terrible, like something from beyond. It was like something from beyond, something awful from outside, signalling to her. And the signal paralysed her. It beat upon her very soul, and made her helpless. She forgot Jill. She could not think of Jill any more. She could not think of her. That terrible signalling from outside!

The boy put his arm round her waist.

'Come with me,' he said gently. 'Come and let us say what we've got to say.'

And he drew her outside, closed the door. And she went with him darkly down the garden path. That he should have a beating heart! And that he should have his arm round her, outside the blanket! She was too confused to think who he was or what he was.

He took her to a dark corner of the shed, where there was a tool-box with a lid, long and low.

'We'll sit here a minute,' he said.

And obediently she sat down by his side.

'Give me your hand,' he said.

She gave him both her hands, and he held them between his own. He was young, and it made him tremble.

'You'll marry me. You'll marry me before I go back, won't you?' he pleaded.

'Why, aren't we both a pair of fools?' she said.

He had put her in the corner, so that she should not look out and see the lighted window of the house, across the dark yard and garden. He tried to keep her all there inside the shed with him.

'In what way a pair of fools?' he said. 'If you go back to Canada with me, I've got a job and a good wage waiting for me, and it's a nice place, near the mountains. Why shouldn't you marry me? Why shouldn't we marry? I should like to have you there with me. I should like to feel I'd got somebody there, at the back of me, all my life.'

'You'd easily find somebody else who'd suit you better,' she said.

'Yes, I might easily find another girl. I know I could. But not one I really wanted. I've never met one I really wanted, for good. You see, I'm thinking of all my life. If I marry, I want to feel it's for all my life. Other girls: well, they're just girls, nice enough to go a walk with now and then. Nice enough for a bit of play. But when I think of my life, then I should be very sorry to have to marry one of them, I should indeed.'

'You mean they wouldn't make you a good wife.'

'Yes, I mean that. But I don't mean they wouldn't do their duty by me. I mean—I don't know what I mean. Only when I think of my life, and of you, then the two things go together.'

'And what if they didn't?' she said, with her odd, sardonic touch.

'Well, I think they would.'

They sat for some time silent. He held her hands in his, but he did not make love to her. Since he had realized that she was a woman, and vulnerable, accessible, a certain heaviness had possessed his soul. He did not want to make love to her. He shrank from any such performance, almost with fear. She was a woman, and vulnerable, accessible to him finally, and he held back from that which was ahead, almost with dread. It was a kind of darkness he knew he would enter finally, but of which he did not want as yet even to think. She was the woman, and he was responsible for the strange vulnerability he had suddenly realized in her.

'No,' she said at last, 'I 'm a fool. I know I 'm a fool.'

'What for?' he asked.

'To go on with this business.'

'Do you mean me?' he asked.

'No, I mean myself. I 'm making a fool of myself, and a big one.'

'Why, because you don't want to marry me, really?'

'Oh, I don't know whether I 'm against it, as a matter of fact. That 's just it. I don't know.'

He looked at her in the darkness, puzzled. He did not in the least know what she meant.

'And don't you know whether you like to sit here with me this minute, or not?' he asked.

'No, I don't really. I don't know whether I wish I was somewhere else, or whether I like being here. I don't know, really.'

'Do you wish you were with Miss Banford? Do you wish you 'd gone to bed with her?' he asked, as a challenge.

She waited a long time before she answered:

'No,' she said at last. 'I don't wish that.'

'And do you think you would spend all your life with her—when your hair goes white, and you are old?' he said.

'No,' she said, without much hesitation. 'I don't see Jill and me two old women together.'

'And don't you think, when I 'm an old man and you 're an old woman, we might be together still, as we are now?' he said.

'Well, not as we are now,' she replied. 'But I could imagine—no, I can't. I can't imagine you an old man. Besides, it 's dreadful!'

'What, to be an old man?'

'Yes, of course.'

'Not when the time comes,' he said. 'But it hasn't come. Only it will. And when it does, I should like to think you 'd be there as well.'

'Sort of old age pensions,' she said dryly.

Her kind of witless humour always startled him. He never knew what she meant. Probably she didn't quite know herself.

'No,' he said, hurt.

'I don't know why you harp on old age,' she said. 'I'm not ninety.'

'Did anybody ever say you were?' he asked, offended.

They were silent for some time, pulling different ways in the silence.

'I don't want you to make fun of me,' he said.

'Don't you?' she replied, enigmatic.

'No, because just this minute I'm serious. And when I'm serious, I believe in not making fun of it.'

'You mean nobody else must make fun of you,' she replied.

'Yes, I mean that. And I mean I don't believe in making fun of it myself. When it comes over me so that I'm serious, then—there it is, I don't want it to be laughed at.'

She was silent for some time. Then she said, in a vague, almost pained voice:

'No, I'm not laughing at you.'

A hot wave rose in his heart.

'You believe me, do you?' he asked.

'Yes, I believe you,' she replied, with a twang of her old tired nonchalance, as if she gave in because she was tired. But he didn't care. His heart was hot and clamorous.

'So you agree to marry me before I go?—perhaps at Christmas?'

'Yes, I agree.'

'There!' he exclaimed. 'That's settled it.'

And he sat silent, unconscious, with all the blood burning in all his veins, like fire in all the branches and twigs of him. He only pressed her two hands to his chest, without knowing. When the curious passion began to die down, he seemed to come awake to the world.

'We'll go in, shall we?' he said: as if he realized it was cold.

She rose without answering.

'Kiss me before we go, now you 've said it,' he said.

And he kissed her gently on the mouth, with a young, frightened kiss. It made her feel so young, too, and frightened, and wondering: and tired, tired, as if she were going to sleep.

They went indoors. And in the sitting-room, there, crouched by the fire like a queer little witch, was Banford. She looked round with reddened eyes as they entered, but did not rise. He thought she looked frightening, unnatural, crouching there and looking round at them. Evil he thought her look was, and he crossed his fingers.

Banford saw the ruddy, elate face of the youth: he seemed strangely tall and bright and looming. And March had a delicate look on her face; she wanted to hide her face, to screen it, to let it not be seen.

'You 've come at last,' said Banford uglily.

'Yes, we 've come,' said he.

'You 've been long enough for anything,' she said.

'Yes, we have. We 've settled it. We shall marry as soon as possible,' he replied.

'Oh, you 've settled it, have you! Well, I hope you won't live to repent it,' said Banford.

'I hope so too,' he replied.

'Are you going to bed *now*, Nellie?' said Banford.

'Yes, I 'm going now.'

'Then for goodness' sake come along.'

March looked at the boy. He was glancing with his very bright eyes at her and at Banford. March looked at him wistfully. She wished she could stay with him. She wished she had married him already, and it was all over. For oh, she felt suddenly so safe with him. She felt so strangely safe and peaceful in his presence. If only she could sleep in his shelter, and not with Jill. She felt afraid of Jill. In her dim, tender state, it was agony to have to go with Jill and sleep with her. She wanted the boy to save her. She looked again at him.

And he, watching with bright eyes, divined something of what she felt. It puzzled and distressed him that she must go with Jill.

'I shan't forget what you've promised,' he said, looking clear into her eyes, right into her eyes, so that he seemed to occupy all her self with his queer, bright look.

She smiled to him, faintly, gently. She felt safe again—safe with him.

But in spite of all the boy's precautions, he had a set-back. The morning he was leaving the farm he got March to accompany him to the market-town, about six miles away, where they went to the registrar and had their names stuck up as two people who were going to marry. He was to come at Christmas, and the wedding was to take place then. He hoped in the spring to be able to take March back to Canada with him, now the war was really over. Though he was so young, he had saved some money.

'You never have to be without *some* money at the back of you, if you can help it,' he said.

So she saw him off in the train that was going west: his camp was on Salisbury Plain. And with big, dark eyes she watched him go, and it seemed as if everything real in life was retreating as the train retreated with his queer, chubby, ruddy face, that seemed so broad across the cheeks, and which never seemed to change its expression, save when a cloud of sulky anger hung on the brow, or the bright eyes fixed themselves in their stare. This was what happened now. He leaned there out of the carriage window as the train drew off, saying good-bye and staring back at her, but his face quite unchanged. There was no emotion on his face. Only his eyes tightened and became fixed and intent in their watching like a cat's when suddenly she sees something and stares. So the boy's eyes stared fixedly as the train drew away, and she was left feeling intensely forlorn. Failing his physical presence, she seemed to have nothing of him. And she had nothing of anything. Only his face was fixed in her mind: the full, ruddy, unchanging cheeks, and the straight snout of a nose, and the two eyes staring above. All she could remember was how he suddenly wrinkled his nose when he laughed, as a puppy does when he is playfully growling. But him, himself, and what he was—she knew nothing, she had nothing of him when he left her.

On the ninth day after he had left her he received this letter:

Dear Henry,

I have been over it all again in my mind, this business of me and you, and it seems to me impossible. When you aren't there I see what a fool I am. When you are there you seem to blind me to things as they actually are. You make me see things all unreal, and I don't know what. Then when I am alone again with Jill I seem to come to my own senses and realize what a fool I am making of myself, and how I am treating you unfairly. Because it must be unfair to you for me to go on with this affair when I can't feel in my heart that I really love you. I know people talk a lot of stuff and nonsense about love, and I don't want to do that. I want to keep to plain facts and act in a sensible way. And that seems to me what I 'm not doing. I don't see on what grounds I am going to marry you. I know I am not head over heels in love with you, as I have fancied myself to be with fellows when I was a young fool of a girl. You are an absolute stranger to me, and it seems to me you will always be one. So on what grounds am I going to marry you? When I think of Jill, she is ten times more real to me. I know her and I 'm awfully fond of her, and I hate myself for a beast if I ever hurt her little finger. We have a life together. And even if it can't last for ever, it is a life while it does last. And it might last as long as either of us lives. Who knows how long we 've got to live? She is a delicate little thing, perhaps nobody but me knows how delicate. And as for me, I feel I might fall down the well any day. What I don't seem to see at all is you. When I think of what I 've been and what I 've done with you, I 'm afraid I am a few screws loose. I should be sorry to think that softening of the brain is setting in so soon, but that is what it seems like. You are such an absolute stranger, and so different from what I 'm used to, and we don't seem to have a thing in common. As for love, the very word seems impossible. I know what love means even in Jill's case, and I know that in this affair with you it 's an absolute impossibility. And then going to Canada. I 'm sure I must have been clean off my chump when I promised such a thing. It makes me feel fairly frightened of myself. I feel I might do something really silly, that I wasn't responsible for—and end my days in a lunatic asylum. You may think that 's all I 'm fit for after the way I 've gone on, but it isn't a very nice thought for me. Thank goodness Jill is here, and her being here makes me feel sane again, else I don't know what I might do; I might have an accident with the gun one evening. I love Jill, and she makes me feel safe and sane, with her loving anger against me for being such a fool. Well, what I want to say is, won't you let us cry the whole thing off? I can't marry you, and really, I won't do such a thing if it seems to me wrong. It is all a great mistake. I 've made a complete fool of myself, and all I can do is to apologize to you and ask you please to forget it, and please to take no further notice of me. Your fox skin is nearly ready, and seems all right. I will post it to you if you will let me know if this address is still right, and if you will accept my apology for the awful and lunatic way I have behaved with you, and then let the matter rest.

Jill sends her kindest regards. Her mother and father are staying with us over Christmas.

Yours very sincerely,
Ellen March.

The boy read this letter in camp as he was cleaning his kit. He set his teeth, and for a moment went almost pale, yellow round the eyes with fury. He said nothing and saw nothing and felt nothing but a livid rage that was quite unreasoning. Balked! Balked again! Balked! He wanted the woman, he had fixed like doom upon having her. He felt that was his doom, his destiny,

and his reward, to have this woman. She was his
heaven and hell on earth, and he would have none
elsewhere. Sightless with rage and thwarted madness
he got through the morning. Save that in his mind
he was lurking and scheming towards an issue, he would
have committed some insane act. Deep in himself he
felt like roaring and howling and gnashing his teeth
and breaking things. But he was too intelligent. He
knew society was on top of him, and he must scheme.
So with his teeth bitten together, and his nose curiously
slightly lifted, like some creature that is vicious, and
his eyes fixed and staring, he went through the morning's
affairs drunk with anger and suppression. In his mind
was one thing—Banford. He took no heed of all
March's outpouring: none. One thorn rankled, stuck
in his mind. Banford. In his mind, in his soul, in his
whole being, one thorn rankling to insanity. And he
would have to get it out. He would have to get the
thorn of Banford out of his life, if he died for it.

With this one fixed idea in his mind, he went to ask
for twenty-four hours' leave of absence. He knew it
was not due to him. His consciousness was super-
naturally keen. He knew where he must go—he must
go to the captain. But how could he get at the captain?
In that great camp of wooden huts and tents he had
no idea where his captain was.

But he went to the officers' canteen. There was his
captain standing talking with three other officers.
Henry stood in the doorway at attention.

'May I speak to Captain Berryman?' The captain
was Cornish like himself.

'What do you want?' called the captain.

'May I speak to you, captain?'

'What do you want?' replied the captain, not stirring
from among his group of fellow-officers.

Henry watched his superior for a minute without
speaking.

'You won't refuse me, sir, will you?' he asked gravely.

'It depends what it is.'

'Can I have twenty-four hours' leave?'

'No, you 've no business to ask.'

'I know I haven't. But I must ask you.'

'You 've had your answer.'

'Don't send me away, captain.'

There was something strange about the boy as he stood there so everlasting in the doorway. The Cornish captain felt the strangeness at once, and eyed him shrewdly.

'Why, what 's afoot?' he said, curious.

'I 'm in trouble about something. I must go to Blewbury,' said the boy.

'Blewbury, eh? After the girls?'

'Yes, it is a woman, captain.' And the boy, as he stood there with his head reaching forward a little, went suddenly terribly pale, or yellow, and his lips seemed to give off pain. The captain saw and paled a little also. He turned aside.

'Go on, then,' he said. 'But for God's sake don't cause any trouble of any sort.'

'I won't, captain, thank you.'

He was gone. The captain, upset, took a gin and bitters. Henry managed to hire a bicycle. It was twelve o'clock when he left the camp. He had sixty miles of wet and muddy cross-roads to ride. But he was in the saddle and down the road without a thought of food.

At the farm, March was busy with a work she had had some time in hand. A bunch of Scotch fir-trees stood at the end of the open shed, on a little bank where ran the fence between two of the gorse-shaggy meadows. The furthest of these trees was dead—it had died in the summer, and stood with all its needles brown and sere in the air. It was not a very big tree. And it was absolutely dead. So March determined to have it, although they were not allowed to cut any of the timber. But it would make such splendid firing, in these days of scarce fuel.

She had been giving a few stealthy chops at the trunk for a week or more, every now and then hacking away for five minutes, low down, near the ground, so no one should notice. She had not tried the saw, it was such hard work, alone. Now the tree stood with a great yawning gap in his base, perched as it were on one sinew, and ready to fall. But he did not fall.

It was late in the damp December afternoon, with cold mists creeping out of the woods and up the hollows, and darkness waiting to sink in from above. There was a bit of yellowness where the sun was fading away beyond the low woods of the distance. March took her axe and went to the tree. The small thud-thud of her blows resounded rather ineffectual about the wintry homestead. Banford came out wearing her thick coat, but with no hat on her head, so that her thin, bobbed hair blew on the uneasy wind that sounded in the pines and in the wood.

'What I'm afraid of,' said Banford, 'is that it will fall on the shed and we sh'll have another job repairing that.'

'Oh, I don't think so,' said March, straightening herself, and wiping her arm over her hot brow. She was flushed red, her eyes were very wide open and queer, her upper lip lifted away from her two white, front teeth with a curious, almost rabbit-look.

A little stout man in a black overcoat and a bowler hat came pottering across the yard. He had a pink face and a white beard and smallish, pale-blue eyes. He was not very old, but nervy, and he walked with little short steps.

'What do you think, father?' said Banford. 'Don't you think it might hit the shed in falling?'

'Shed, no!' said the old man. 'Can't hit the shed. Might as well say the fence.'

'The fence doesn't matter,' said March, in her high voice.

'Wrong as usual, am I!' said Banford, wiping her straying hair from her eyes.

The tree stood as it were on one spelch of itself, leaning, and creaking in the wind. It grew on the bank of a little dry ditch between the two meadows. On the top of the bank straggled one fence, running to the bushes uphill. Several trees clustered there in the corner of the field near the shed and near the gate which led into the yard. Towards this gate, horizontal across the weary meadows, came the grassy, rutted approach from the high road. There trailed another rickety fence, long split poles joining the short, thick, wide-apart uprights. The three people stood at the back of the tree, in the corner of the shed meadow, just above the yard gate. The house, with its two gables and its porch, stood tidy in a little grassed garden across the yard. A little, stout, rosy-faced woman in a little red woollen shoulder shawl had come and taken her stand in the porch.

'Isn't it down yet?' she cried, in a high little voice.

'Just thinking about it,' called her husband. His tone towards the two girls was always rather mocking and satirical. March did not want to go on with her hitting while he was there. As for him, he wouldn't lift a stick from the ground if he could help it, complaining, like his daughter, of rheumatics in his shoulder. So the three stood there a moment silent in the cold afternoon, in the bottom corner near the yard.

They heard the far-off taps of a gate, and craned to look. Away across, on the green horizontal approach, a figure was just swinging on to a bicycle again, and lurching up and down over the grass, approaching.

'Why, it's one of our boys—it's Jack,' said the old man.

'Can't be,' said Banford.

March craned her head to look. She alone recognized the khaki figure. She flushed, but said nothing.

'No, it isn't Jack, I don't think,' said the old man, staring with little round blue eyes under his white lashes.

In another moment the bicycle lurched into sight, and the rider dropped off at the gate. It was Henry, his face wet and red and spotted with mud. He was altogether a muddy sight.

'Oh!' cried Banford, as if afraid. 'Why, it's Henry!'

'What!' muttered the old man. He had a thick,

rapid, muttering way of speaking, and was slightly deaf. 'What? What? Who is it? Who is it, do you say? That young fellow? That young fellow of Nellie's? Oh! Oh!' and the satiric smile came on his pink face and white eyelashes.

Henry, pushing the wet hair off his steaming brow, had caught sight of them and heard what the old man said. His hot, young face seemed to flame in the cold light.

'Oh, are you all there!' he said, giving his sudden, puppy's little laugh. He was so hot and dazed with cycling he hardly knew where he was. He leaned the bicycle against the fence and climbed over into the corner on to the bank, without going into the yard.

'Well, I must say, we weren't expecting *you*,' said Banford laconically.

'No, I suppose not,' said he, looking at March.

She stood aside, slack, with one knee drooped and the axe resting its head loosely on the ground. Her eyes were wide and vacant, and her upper lip lifted from her teeth in that helpless, fascinated rabbit-look. The moment she saw his glowing, red face it was all over with her. She was as helpless as if she had been bound. The moment she saw the way his head seemed to reach forward.

'Well, who is it? Who is it, anyway?' asked the smiling, satiric old man in his muttering voice.

'Why, Mr Grenfel, whom you 've heard us tell about, father,' said Banford coldly.

'Heard you tell about, I should think so. Heard of nothing else practically,' muttered the elderly man, with his queer little jeering smile on his face. 'How do you do?' he added, suddenly reaching out his hand to Henry.

The boy shook hands just as startled. Then the two men fell apart.

'Cycled over from Salisbury Plain, have you?' asked the old man.

'Yes.'

'Hm! Longish ride. How long d' it take you, eh? Some time, eh? Several hours, I suppose.'

'About four.'

'Eh? Four! Yes, I should have thought so. When are you going back, then?'

'I 've got till to-morrow evening.'

'Till to-morrow evening, eh? Yes. Hm! Girls weren't expecting you, were they?'

And the old man turned his pale-blue, round little eyes under their white lashes mockingly towards the girls. Henry also looked round. He had become a little awkward. He looked at March, who was still staring away into the distance as if to see where the cattle were. Her hand was on the pommel of the axe, whose head rested loosely on the ground.

'What were you doing there?' he asked in his soft, courteous voice. 'Cutting a tree down?'

March seemed not to hear, as if in a trance.

'Yes,' said Banford. 'We 've been at it for over a week.'

'Oh! And have you done it all by yourselves then?'

'Nellie 's done it all, I 've done nothing,' said Banford.

'Really! You must have worked quite hard,' he said, addressing himself in a curious gentle tone direct to March. She did not answer, but remained, half averted, staring away towards the woods above as if in a trance.

'Nellie!' cried Banford sharply. 'Can't you answer?'

'What—me?' cried March, starting round, and looking from one to the other. 'Did any one speak to me?'

'Dreaming!' muttered the old man, turning aside to smile. 'Must be in love, eh, dreaming in the day-time!'

'Did you say anything to me?' said March, looking at the boy as from a strange distance, her eyes wide and doubtful, her face delicately flushed.

'I said you must have worked hard at the tree,' he replied courteously.

'Oh that! Bit by bit. I thought it would have come down by now.'

'I 'm thankful it hasn't come down in the night, to frighten us to death,' said Banford.

'Let me just finish it for you, shall I?' said the boy.
March slanted the axe-shaft in his direction.

'Would you like to?' she said.

'Yes, if you wish it,' he said.

'Oh, I'm thankful when the thing's down, that's all,' she replied, nonchalant.

'Which way is it going to fall?' said Banford. 'Will it hit the shed?'

'No, it won't hit the shed,' he said. 'I should think it will fall there—quite clear. Though it might give a twist and catch the fence.'

'Catch the fence!' cried the old man. 'What, catch the fence! When it's leaning at that angle? Why, it's further off than the shed. It won't catch the fence.'

'No,' said Henry, 'I don't suppose it will. It has plenty of room to fall quite clear, and I suppose it will fall clear.'

'Won't tumble backwards on top of *us*, will it?' asked the old man, sarcastic.

'No, it won't do that,' said Henry, taking off his short overcoat and his tunic. 'Ducks! Ducks! Go back!'

A line of four brown-speckled ducks led by a brown-and-green drake were stemming away downhill from the upper meadow, coming like boats running on a ruffled sea, cockling their way top speed downwards towards the fence and towards the little group of people, and cackling as excitedly as if they brought news of the Spanish Armada.

'Silly things! Silly things!' cried Banford, going forward to turn them off. But they came eagerly towards her, opening their yellow-green beaks and quacking as if they were so excited to say something.

'There's no food. There's nothing here. You must wait a bit,' said Banford to them. 'Go away. Go away. Go round to the yard.'

They didn't go, so she climbed the fence to swerve them round under the gate and into the yard. So off they waggled in an excited string once more, wagging their rumps like the stems of little gondolas, ducking under the bar of the gate. Banford stood on the top of the bank, just over the fence, looking down on the other three.

Henry looked up at her, and met her queer, round-pupilled, weak eyes staring behind her spectacles. He was perfectly still. He looked away, up at the weak, leaning tree. And as he looked into the sky, like a huntsman who is watching a flying bird, he thought to himself: 'If the tree falls in just such a way, and spins just so much as it falls, then the branch there will strike her exactly as she stands on top of that bank.'

He looked at her again. She was wiping the hair from her brow again, with that perpetual gesture. In his heart he had decided her death. A terrible still force seemed in him, and a power that was just his. If he turned even a hairbreadth in the wrong direction, he would lose the power.

'Mind yourself, Miss Banford,' he said. And his heart held perfectly still, in the terrible pure will that she should not move.

'Who, me, mind myself?' she cried, her father's jeering tone in her voice. 'Why, do you think you might hit me with the axe?'

'No, it's just possible the tree might, though,' he answered soberly. But the tone of his voice seemed to her to imply that he was only being falsely solicitous, and trying to make her move because it was his will to move her.

'Absolutely impossible,' she said.

He heard her. But he held himself icy still, lest he should lose his power.

'No, it's just possible. You'd better come down this way.'

'Oh, all right. Let us see some crack Canadian tree-felling,' she retorted.

'Ready, then,' he said, taking the axe, looking round to see he was clear.

There was a moment of pure, motionless suspense, when the world seemed to stand still. Then suddenly his form seemed to flash up enormously tall and fearful, he gave two swift, flashing blows, in immediate succession, the tree was severed, turning slowly, spinning strangely in the air and coming down like a sudden darkness on the earth. No one saw what was happening except himself. No one heard the strange little cry which the Banford gave as the dark end of the bough swooped down, down on her. No one saw her crouch a little and receive the blow on the back of the neck. No one saw her flung outwards and laid, a little twitching heap, at the foot of the fence. No one except the boy. And he watched with intense bright eyes, as he would watch a wild goose he had shot. Was it winged, or dead? Dead!

Immediately he gave a loud cry. Immediately March gave a wild shriek that went far, far down the afternoon. And the father started a strange bellowing sound.

The boy leaped the fence and ran to the figure. The back of the neck and head was a mass of blood, of horror. He turned it over. The body was quivering with little convulsions. But she was dead really. He knew it, that it was so. He knew it in his soul and his blood. The inner necessity of his life was fulfilling itself, it was he who was to live. The thorn was drawn out of his bowels. So he put her down gently. She was dead.

He stood up. March was standing there petrified and absolutely motionless. Her face was dead white, her eyes big black pools. The old man was scrambling horribly over the fence.

'I'm afraid it's killed her,' said the boy.

The old man was making curious, blubbering noises as he huddled over the fence. 'What!' cried March, starting electric.

'Yes, I'm afraid,' repeated the boy.

March was coming forward. The boy was over the fence before she reached it.

'What do you say, killed her?' she asked in a sharp voice.

'I'm afraid so,' he answered softly.

She went still whiter, fearful. The two stood facing one another. Her black eyes gazed on him with the last look of resistance. And then in a last agonized failure she began to grizzle, to cry in a shivery little fashion of a child that doesn't want to cry, but which is beaten from within, and gives that little first shudder of sobbing which is not yet weeping, dry and fearful.

He had won. She stood there absolutely helpless, shuddering her dry sobs and her mouth trembling rapidly. And then, as in a child, with a little crash came the tears and the blind agony of sightless weeping. She sank down on the grass, and sat there with her hands on her breast and her face lifted in sightless, convulsed weeping. He stood above her, looking down on her, mute, pale, and everlasting seeming. He never moved, but looked down on her. And among all the torture of the scene, the torture of his own heart and bowels, he was glad, he had won.

After a long time he stooped to her and took her hands.

'Don't cry,' he said softly. 'Don't cry.'

She looked up at him with tears running from her eyes, a senseless look of helplessness and submission. So she gazed on him as if sightless, yet looking up to him. She would never leave him again. He had won her. And he knew it and was glad, because he wanted her for his life. His life must have her. And now he had won her. It was what his life must have.

But if he had won her, he had not yet got her. They were married at Christmas as he had planned, and he got again ten days' leave. They went to Cornwall, to his own village, on the sea. He realized that it was awful for her to be at the farm any more.

But though she belonged to him, though she lived in his shadow, as if she could not be away from him, she was not happy. She did not want to leave him: and yet she did not feel free with him. Everything around her seemed to watch her, seemed to press on her. He had won her, he had her with him, she was his wife. And she—she belonged to him, she knew it. But she was not glad. And he was still foiled. He realized that though he was married to her and possessed her in every possible way, apparently, and though she *wanted* him to possess her, she wanted it, she wanted nothing else, now, still he did not quite succeed.

Something was missing. Instead of her soul swaying with new life, it seemed to droop, to bleed, as if it were wounded. She would sit for a long time with her hand in his, looking away at the sea. And in her dark, vacant eyes was a sort of wound, and her face looked a little peaked. If he spoke to her, she would turn to him with a faint new smile, the strange, quivering little smile of a woman who has died in the old way of love, and can't quite rise to the new way. She still felt she ought to *do* something, to strain herself in some direction. And there was nothing to do, and no direction in which to strain herself. And she could not quite accept the submergence which his new love put upon her. If she was in love, she ought to *exert* herself, in some way, loving. She felt the weary need of our day to *exert* herself in love. But she knew that in fact she must no more exert herself in love. He would not have the love which exerted itself towards him. It made his brow go black. No, he wouldn't let her exert her love towards him. No, she had to be passive, to acquiesce, and to be submerged under the surface of love. She had to be like the seaweeds she saw as she peered down from the boat, swaying for ever delicately under water, with all their delicate fibrils put tenderly out upon the flood, sensitive, utterly sensitive and receptive within the shadowy sea, and never, never rising and looking forth above water while they lived. Never. Never looking forth from the water until they died, only then washing, corpses, upon the surface. But while they lived, always submerged, always beneath the wave. Beneath the wave they might have powerful roots, stronger than iron; they might be tenacious and danger-ous in their soft waving within the flood. Beneath the water they might be stronger, more indestructible than resistant oak-trees are on land. But it was always under water, always under water. And she, being a woman, must be like that.

And she had been so used to the very opposite. She had had to take all the thought for love and for life, and all the responsibility. Day after day she had been responsible for the coming day, for the coming year: for her dear Jill's health and happiness and well-being. Verily, in her own small way, she had felt herself responsible for the well-being of the world. And this had been her great stimulant, this grand feeling that, in her own small sphere, she was responsible for the well-being of the world.

And she had failed. She knew that, even in her small way, she had failed. She had failed to satisfy her own feeling of responsibility. It was so difficult. It seemed so grand and easy at first. And the more you tried, the more difficult it became. It had seemed so easy to make one beloved creature happy. And the more you tried, the worse the failure. It was terrible. She had been all her life reaching, reaching, and what she reached for seemed so near, until she had stretched to her utmost limit. And then it was always beyond her.

Always beyond her, vaguely, unrealizably beyond her, and she was left with nothingness at last. The life she reached for, the happiness she reached for, the well-being she reached for all slipped back, became unreal, the further she stretched her hand. She wanted some goal, some finality—and there was none. Always this ghastly reaching, reaching, striving for something that might be just beyond. Even to make Jill happy. She was glad Jill was dead. For she had realized that she could never make her happy. Jill would always be fretting herself thinner and thinner, weaker and weaker. Her pains grew worse instead of less. It would be so for ever. She was glad she was dead.

And if Jill had married a man it would have been just the same. The woman striving, striving to make the man happy, striving within her own limits for the well-being of her world. And always achieving failure. Little, foolish successes in money or in ambition. But at the very point where she most wanted success, in the anguished effort to make some one beloved human being happy and perfect, there the failure was almost cata-strophic. You wanted to make your beloved happy, and his happiness seemed always achievable. If only you did just this, that, and the other. And you did this, that, and the other, in all good faith, and every time the failure became a little more ghastly. You could love yourself to ribbons, and strive and strain yourself to the bone, and things would go from bad to worse, bad to worse, as far as happiness went. The awful mistake of happiness.

Poor March, in her goodwill and her responsibility, she had strained herself till it seemed to her that the whole of life and everything was only a horrible abyss of nothingness. The more you reach after the fatal flower of happiness, which trembles so blue and lovely in a crevice just beyond your grasp, the more fearfully you become aware of the ghastly and awful gulf of the precipice below you, into which you will inevitably plunge, as into the bottomless pit, if you reach any further. You pluck flower after flower—it is never *the* flower. The flower itself—its calyx is a horrible gulf, it is the bottomless pit.

That is the whole history of the search for happiness, whether it be your own or somebody else's that you want to win. It ends, and it always ends, in the ghastly sense of the bottomless nothingness into which you will inevitably fall if you strain any further.

And women? What goal can any woman conceive, except happiness? Just happiness, for herself and the whole world. That, and nothing else. And so, she assumes the responsibility, and sets off towards her goal. She can see it there, at the foot of the rainbow. Or she can see it a little way beyond, in the blue distance. Not far, not far.

But the end of the rainbow is a bottomless gulf down which you can fall for ever without arriving, and the blue distance is a void pit which can swallow you and all your efforts into its emptiness, and still be no emptier.

You and all your efforts. So, the illusion of attainable happiness!

Poor March, she had set off so wonderfully towards the blue goal. And the farther and farther she had gone, the more fearful had become the realization of emptiness. An agony, an insanity at last.

She was glad it was over. She was glad to sit on the shore and look westwards over the sea, and know the great strain had ended. She would never strain for love and happiness any more. And Jill was safely dead. Poor Jill, poor Jill. It must be sweet to be dead.

For her own part, death was not her destiny. She would have to leave her destiny to the boy. But then, the boy. He wanted more than that. He wanted her to give herself without defences, to sink and become submerged in him. And she—she wanted to sit still, like a woman on the last milestone, and watch. She wanted to see, to know, to understand. She wanted to be alone: with him at her side.

And he! He did not want her to watch any more, to see any more, to understand any more. He wanted to veil her woman's spirit, as Orientals veil the woman's face. He wanted her to commit herself to him, and to put her independent spirit to sleep. He wanted to take away from her all her effort, all that seemed her very *raison d'être*. He wanted to make her submit, yield, blindly pass away out of all her strenuous consciousness. He wanted to take away her consciousness, and make her just his woman. Just his woman.

And she was so tired, so tired, like a child that wants to go to sleep, but which fights against sleep, as if sleep were death. She seemed to stretch her eyes wider in the obstinate effort and tension of keeping awake. She *would* keep awake. She *would* know. She *would* consider and judge and decide. She *would* have the reins of her own life between her own hands. She *would* be an independent woman, to the last. But she was so tired, so tired of everything. And sleep seemed near. And there was such rest in the boy.

Yet there, sitting in a niche of the high, wild cliffs of west Cornwall, looking over the westward sea, she stretched her eyes wider and wider. Away to the west, Canada, America. She *would* know and she *would* see what was ahead. And the boy, sitting beside her, staring down at the gulls, had a cloud between his brows and the strain of discontent in his eyes. He wanted her asleep, at peace in him. He wanted her at peace, asleep in him. And *there* she was, dying with the strain of her own wakefulness. Yet she would not sleep: no, never. Sometimes he thought bitterly that he ought to have left her. He ought never to have killed Banford. He should have left Banford and March to kill one another.

But that was only impatience: and he knew it. He was waiting, waiting to go west. He was aching almost in torment to leave England, to go west, to take March away. To leave this shore! He believed that as they crossed the seas, as they left this England which he so hated, because in some way it seemed to have stung him with poison, she would go to sleep. She would close her eyes at last, and give in to him.

And then he would have her, and he would have his own life at last. He chafed, feeling he hadn't got his own life. He would never have it till she yielded and slept in him. Then he would have all his own life as a young man and a male, and she would have all her own life as a woman and a female. There would be no more of this awful straining. She would not be a man any more, an independent woman with a man's responsibility. Nay, even the responsibility for her own soul she would have to commit to him. He knew it was so, and obstinately held out against her, waiting for the surrender.

'You 'll feel better when once we get over the seas to Canada over there,' he said to her as they sat among the rocks on the cliff.

She looked away to the sea's horizon, as if it were not real. Then she looked round at him, with the strained, strange look of a child that is struggling against sleep.

'Shall I?' she said.

'Yes,' he answered quietly.

And her eyelids dropped with the slow motion, sleep weighing them unconscious. But she pulled them open again to say:

'Yes, I may. I can't tell. I can't tell what it will be like over there.'

'If only we could go soon!' he said, with pain in his voice.

THE WOMAN WHO RODE AWAY

I

SHE had thought that this marriage, of all marriages, would be an adventure. Not that the man himself was exactly magical to her. A little, wiry, twisted fellow, twenty years older than herself, with brown eyes and greying hair, who had come to America a scrap of a wastrel, from Holland, years ago, as a tiny boy, and from the gold-mines of the west had been kicked south into Mexico, and now was more or less rich, owning silver-mines in the wilds of the Sierra Madre: it was obvious that the adventure lay in his circumstances, rather than his person. But he was still a little dynamo of energy, in spite of accidents survived, and what he had accomplished he had accomplished alone. One of those human oddments there is no accounting for.

When she actually *saw* what he had accomplished, her heart quailed. Great green-covered, unbroken mountain-hills, and in the midst of the lifeless isolation, the sharp pinkish mounds of the dried mud from the silver-works. Under the nakedness of the works, the walled-in, one-story adobe house, with its garden inside, and its deep inner veranda with tropical climbers on the sides. And when you looked up from this shut-in flowered patio, you saw the huge pink cone of the silver-mud refuse, and the machinery of the extracting plant against heaven above. No more.

To be sure, the great wooden doors were often open. And then she could stand outside, in the vast open world. And see great, void, tree-clad hills piling behind one another, from nowhere into nowhere. They were green in autumn time. For the rest, pinkish, stark dry and abstract.

And in his battered Ford car her husband would take her into the dead, thrice-dead little Spanish town forgotten among the mountains. The great, sun-dried dead church, the dead *portales*, the hopeless covered market-place, where, the first time she went, she saw a dead dog lying between the meat stalls and the vegetable array, stretched out as if for ever, nobody troubling to throw it away. Deadness within deadness.

Everybody feebly talking silver, and showing bits of ore. But silver was at a standstill. The Great War came and went. Silver was a dead market. Her husband's mines were closed down. But she and he lived on in the adobe house under the works, among the flowers that were never very flowery to her.

She had two children, a boy and a girl. And her eldest, the boy, was nearly ten years old before she aroused from her stupor of subjected amazement. She was now thirty-three, a large, blue-eyed, dazed woman, beginning to grow stout. Her little, wiry, tough, twisted, brown-eyed husband was fifty-three, a man as tough as wire, tenacious as wire, still full of energy, but dimmed by the lapse of silver from the market, and by some curious inaccessibility on his wife's part.

He was a man of principles, and a good husband. In a way, he doted on her. He never quite got over his dazzled admiration of her. But essentially, he was still a bachelor. He had been thrown out on the world, a little bachelor, at the age of ten. When he married he was over forty, and had enough money to marry on. But his capital was all a bachelor's. He was boss of his own works, and marriage was the last and most intimate bit of his own works.

He admired his wife to extinction, he admired her body, all her points. And she was to him always the rather dazzling Californian girl from Berkeley, whom he had first known. Like any sheik, he kept her guarded among those mountains of Chihuahua. He was jealous of her as he was of his silver-mine: and that is saying a lot.

At thirty-three she really was still the girl from Berkeley, in all but physique. Her conscious development had stopped mysteriously with her marriage, completely arrested. Her husband had never become real to her, neither mentally nor physically. In spite of his late sort of passion for her, he never meant anything to her, physically. Only morally he swayed her, downed her, kept her in an invincible slavery.

So the years went by, in the adobe house strung round the sunny patio, with the silver-works overhead. Her husband was never still. When the silver went dead, he ran a ranch lower down, some twenty miles away, and raised pure-bred hogs, splendid creatures. At the same time, he hated pigs. He was a squeamish waif of an idealist, and really hated the physical side of life. He loved work, work, work, and making things. His marriage, his children, were something he was making, part of his business, but with a sentimental income this time.

Gradually her nerves began to go wrong; she must get out. She must get out. So he took her to El Paso for three months. And at least it was the United States.

But he kept his spell over her. The three months ended: back she was, just the same, in her adobe house among those eternal green or pinky-brown hills, void as only the undiscovered is void. She taught her children, she supervised the Mexican boys who were her servants. And sometimes her husband brought visitors, Spaniards or Mexicans or occasionally white men.

He really loved to have white men staying on the place. Yet he had not a moment's peace when they were there. It was as if his wife were some peculiar secret vein of ore in his mines, which no one must be aware of except himself. And she was fascinated by the young gentlemen, mining engineers, who were his guests at times. He, too, was fascinated by a real gentleman. But he was an old-timer miner with a wife, and if a gentleman looked at his wife, he felt as if his mine were being looted, the secrets of it pried out.

It was one of these young gentlemen who put the idea

into her mind. They were all standing outside the great wooden doors of the patio, looking at the outer world. The eternal, motionless hills were all green, it was September, after the rains. There was no sign of anything, save the deserted mine, the deserted works, and a bunch of half-deserted miners' dwellings.

'I wonder,' said the young man, 'what there is behind those great blank hills.'

'More hills,' said Lederman. 'If you go that way, Sonora and the coast. This way is the desert—you came from there—and the other way, hills and mountains.'

'Yes, but what *lives* in the hills and the mountains? *Surely* there is something wonderful? It looks *so* like nowhere on earth; like being on the moon.'

'There's plenty of game, if you want to shoot. And Indians, if you call *them* wonderful.'

'Wild ones?'

'Wild enough.'

'But friendly?'

'It depends. Some of them are quite wild, and they don't let anybody near. They kill a missionary at sight. And where a missionary can't get, nobody can.'

'But what does the Government say?'

'They're so far from everywhere, the Government leaves 'em alone. And they're wily; if they think there'll be trouble, they send a delegation to Chihuahua and make a formal submission. The Government is glad to leave it at that.'

'And do they live quite wild, with their own savage customs and religion?'

'Oh, yes. They use nothing but bows and arrows. I've seen them in town, in the plaza, with funny sort of hats with flowers round them, and a bow in one hand, quite naked except for a sort of shirt, even in cold weather—striding round with their savages' bare legs.'

'But don't you suppose it's wonderful, up there in their secret villages?'

'No. What would there be wonderful about it?

Savages are savages, and all savages behave more or less alike: rather low-down and dirty, insanitary, with a few cunning tricks, and struggling to get enough to eat.'

'But surely they have old, old religions and mysteries —it *must* be wonderful, surely it must.'

'I don't know about mysteries—howling and heathen practices, more or less indecent. No, I see nothing wonderful in that kind of stuff. And I wonder that you should, when you have lived in London or Paris or New York——'

'Ah, *everybody* lives in London or Paris or New York,' said the young man, as if this were an argument.

And this peculiar vague enthusiasm for unknown Indians found a full echo in the woman's heart. She was overcome by a foolish romanticism more unreal than a girl's. She felt it was her destiny to wander into the secret haunts of these timeless, mysterious, marvellous Indians of the mountains.

She kept her secret. The young man was departing, her husband was going with him down to Torreon, on business; would be away for some days. But before the departure, she made her husband talk about the Indians; about the wandering tribes, resembling the Navajo, who were still wandering free; and the Yaquis of Sonora; and the different groups in the different valleys of Chihuahua State.

There was supposed to be one tribe, the Chilchuis, living in a high valley to the south, who were the sacred tribe of all the Indians. The descendants of Montezuma and the old Aztec or Totonac kings still lived among them, and the old priests still kept up the ancient religion, and offered human sacrifices—so it was said. Some scientists had been to the Chilchui country, and had come back gaunt and exhausted with hunger and bitter privation, bringing various curious, barbaric objects of worship, but having seen nothing extraordinary in the hungry, stark villages of savages.

Though Lederman talked in this off-hand way, it was obvious he felt some of the vulgar excitement at the idea of ancient and mysterious savages.

'How far away are they?' she asked.

'Oh—three days on horseback—past Cuchitee and a little lake there is up there.'

Her husband and the young man departed. The woman made her crazy plans. Of late, to break the monotony of her life, she had harassed her husband into letting her go riding with him, occasionally, on horseback. She was never allowed to go out alone. The country truly was not safe, lawless and crude.

But she had her own horse, and she dreamed of being free as she had been as a girl, among the hills of California.

Her daughter, nine years old, was now in a tiny convent in the little half-deserted Spanish mining-town five miles away.

'Manuel,' said the woman to her house-servant, 'I'm going to ride to the convent to see Margarita, and take her a few things. Perhaps I shall stay the night in the convent. You look after Freddy and see everything is all right till I come back.'

'Shall I ride with you on the master's horse, or shall Juan?' asked the servant.

'Neither of you. I shall go alone.'

The young man looked her in the eyes, in protest. Absolutely impossible that the woman should ride alone!

'I shall go alone,' repeated the large, placid-seeming, fair-complexioned woman, with peculiar overbearing emphasis. And the man silently, unhappily yielded.

'Why are you going alone, mother?' asked her son, as she made up parcels of food.

'Am I *never* to be let alone? Not one moment of my life?' she cried, with sudden explosion of energy. And the child, like the servant, shrank into silence.

She set off without a qualm, riding astride on her strong roan horse, and wearing a riding suit of coarse linen, a riding skirt over her linen breeches, a scarlet neck-tie over her white blouse, and a black felt hat on her head. She had food in her saddle-bags, an army canteen with water, and a large, native blanket tied on behind the saddle. Peering into the distance, she set off from her home. Manuel and the little boy stood in the gateway to watch her go. She did not even turn to wave them farewell.

But when she had ridden about a mile, she left the wild road and took a small trail to the right, that led into another valley, over steep places and past great trees, and through another deserted mining-settlement. It was September, the water was running freely in the little stream that had fed the now-abandoned mine. She got down to drink, and let the horse drink too.

She saw natives coming through the trees, away up the slope. They had seen her, and were watching her closely. She watched in turn. The three people, two women and a youth, were making a wide detour, so as not to come too close to her. She did not care. Mounting, she trotted ahead up the silent valley, beyond the silver-works, beyond any trace of mining. There was still a rough trail that led over rocks and loose stones into the valley beyond. This trail she had already ridden with her husband. Beyond that she knew she must go south.

Curiously she was not afraid, although it was a frightening country, the silent, fatal-seeming mountain-slopes, the occasional distant, suspicious, elusive natives among the trees, the great carrion birds occasionally hovering, like great flies, in the distance, over some carrion or some ranch house or some group of huts.

As she climbed, the trees shrank and the trail ran through a thorny scrub, that was trailed over with blue convolvulus and an occasional pink creeper. Then these flowers lapsed. She was nearing the pine-trees.

She was over the crest, and before her another silent, void, green-clad valley. It was past midday. Her horse turned to a little runlet of water, so she got down to eat her midday meal. She sat in silence looking at the motionless unliving valley, and at the sharp-peaked hills, rising higher to rock and pine-trees, southwards. She rested two hours in the heat of the day, while the horse cropped around her.

Curious that she was neither afraid nor lonely. Indeed,

the loneliness was like a drink of cold water to one who is very thirsty. And a strange elation sustained her from within.

She travelled on, and camped at night in a valley beside a stream, deep among the bushes. She had seen cattle and had crossed several trails. There must be a ranch not far off. She heard the strange wailing shriek of a mountain lion, and the answer of dogs. But she sat by her small camp fire in a secret hollow place and was not really afraid. She was buoyed up always by the curious, bubbling elation within her.

It was very cold before dawn. She lay wrapped in her blanket looking at the stars, listening to her horse shivering, and feeling like a woman who has died and passed beyond. She was not sure that she had not heard, during the night, a great crash at the centre of herself, which was the crash of her own death. Or else it was a crash at the centre of the earth, and meant something big and mysterious.

With the first peep of light she got up, numb with cold, and made a fire. She ate hastily, gave her horse some pieces of oil-seed cake, and set off again. She avoided any meeting—and since she met nobody, it was evident that she in turn was avoided. She came at last in sight of the village of Cuchitee, with its black houses with their reddish roofs, a sombre, dreary little cluster below another silent, long-abandoned mine. And beyond, a long, great mountain-side, rising up green and light to the darker, shaggier green of pine-trees. And beyond the pine-trees stretches of naked rock against the sky, rock slashed already and brindled with white stripes of snow. High up, the new snow had already begun to fall.

And now, as she neared, more or less, her destination, she began to go vague and disheartened. She had passed the little lake among yellowing aspen-trees whose white trunks were round and suave like the white round arms of some woman. What a lovely place! In California she would have raved about it. But here she looked and saw that it was lovely, but she didn't care. She was weary and spent with her two nights in the open, and was afraid of the coming night. She didn't know where she was going, or what she was going for. Her horse plodded dejectedly on, towards that immense and forbidding mountain-slope, following a stony little trail. And if she had had any will of her own left, she would have turned back, to the village, to be protected and sent home to her husband.

But she had no will of her own. Her horse splashed through a brook, and turned up a valley, under immense yellowing cottonwood-trees. She must have been near nine thousand feet above sea-level, and her head was light with the altitude and with weariness. Beyond the cottonwood-trees she could see, on each side, the steep sides of mountain-slopes hemming her in, sharp-plumaged with overlapping aspen, and, higher up, with sprouting, pointed spruce and pine-tree. Her horse went on automatically. In this tight valley, on this slight trail, there was nowhere to go but ahead, climbing.

Suddenly her horse jumped, and three men in dark blankets were on the trail before her.

'Adios!' came the greeting, in the full, restrained Indian voice.

'Adios!' she replied, in her assured, American woman's voice.

'Where are you going?' came the quiet question, in Spanish.

The men in the dark *serapes* had come closer, and were looking up at her.

'On ahead,' she replied coolly, in her hard, Saxon Spanish.

These were just natives to her; dark-faced, strongly built men in dark *serapes* and straw hats. They would have been the same as the men who worked for her husband, except, strangely, for the long black hair that fell over their shoulders. She noted this long black hair with a certain distaste. These must be the wild Indians she had come to see.

'Where do you come from?' the same man asked. It was always the one man who spoke. He was young, with quick, large, bright black eyes that glanced sideways at her. He had a soft black moustache on his dark face, and a sparse tuft of beard, loose hairs on his chin. His long black hair, full of life, hung unrestrained on his shoulders. Dark as he was, he did not look as if he had washed lately.

His two companions were the same, but older men, powerful and silent. One had a thin black line of moustache, but was beardless. The other had the smooth cheeks and the sparse dark hairs marking the lines of his chin with the beard characteristic of the Indians.

'I come from far away,' she replied, with half-jocular evasion.

This was received in silence.

'But where do you live?' asked the young man, with that same quiet insistence.

'In the north,' she replied airily.

Again there was a moment's silence. The young man conversed quietly, in Indian, with his two companions.

'Where do you want to go, up this way?' he asked suddenly, with challenge and authority, pointing briefly up the trail.

'To the Chilchui Indians,' answered the woman laconically.

The young man looked at her. His eyes were quick and black, and inhuman. He saw, in the full evening light, the faint sub-smile of assurance on her rather large, calm, fresh-complexioned face; the weary, bluish lines under her large blue eyes; and in her eyes, as she looked down at him, a half-childish, half-arrogant confidence in her own female power. But in her eyes also, a curious look of trance.

'*Usted es señora?* You are a lady?' the Indian asked her.

'Yes, I am a lady,' she replied complacently.

'With a family?'

'With a husband and two children, boy and girl,' she said.

The Indian turned to his companions and translated, in the low, gurgling speech, like hidden water running. They were evidently at a loss.

'Where is your husband?' asked the young man.

'Who knows?' she replied airily. 'He has gone away on business for a week.'

The black eyes watched her shrewdly. She, for all her weariness, smiled faintly in the pride of her own adventure and the assurance of her own womanhood, and the spell of the madness that was on her.

'And what do *you* want to do?' the Indian asked her.

'I want to visit the Chilchui Indians—to see their houses and to know their gods,' she replied.

The young man turned and translated quickly, and there was a silence almost of consternation. The grave elder men were glancing at her sideways, with strange looks, from under their decorated hats. And they said something to the young man, in deep chest-voices.

The latter still hesitated. Then he turned to the woman.

'Good!' he said. 'Let us go. But we cannot arrive until to-morrow. We shall have to make a camp to-night.'

'Good!' she said. 'I can make a camp.'

Without more ado, they set off at a good speed up the stony trail. The young Indian ran alongside her horse's head, the other two ran behind. One of them had taken a thick stick, and occasionally he struck her horse a resounding blow on the haunch, to urge him forward. This made the horse jump, and threw her back in the saddle, which, tired as she was, made her angry.

'Don't do that!' she cried, looking round angrily at the fellow. She met his black, large, bright eyes, and for the first time her spirit really quailed. The man's eyes were not human to her, and they did not see her as a beautiful white woman. He looked at her with a black, bright inhuman look, and saw no woman in her at all. As if she were some strange, unaccountable *thing*, incomprehensible to him, but inimical. She sat in her saddle in wonder, feeling once more as if she had died. And again he struck her horse, and jerked her badly in the saddle.

All the passionate anger of the spoilt white woman rose in her. She pulled her horse to a standstill, and turned with blazing eyes to the man at her bridle.

'Tell that fellow not to touch my horse again,' she cried.

She met the eyes of the young man, and in their bright black inscrutability she saw a fine spark, as in a snake's eye, of derision. He spoke to his companion in the rear, in the low tones of the Indian. The man with the stick listened without looking. Then, giving a strange low cry to the horse, he struck it again on the rear, so that it leaped forward spasmodically up the stony trail, scattering the stones, pitching the weary woman in her seat.

The anger flew like a madness into her eyes, she went white at the gills. Fiercely she reined in her horse. But before she could turn, the young Indian had caught the reins under the horse's throat, jerked them forward, and was trotting ahead rapidly, leading the horse.

The woman was powerless. And along with her supreme anger there came a slight thrill of exultation. She knew she was dead.

The sun was setting, a great yellow light flooded the last of the aspens, flared on the trunks of the pine-trees, the pine-needles bristled and stood out with dark lustre, the rocks glowed with unearthly glamour. And through this effulgence the Indian at her horse's head trotted unweariedly on, his dark blanket swinging, his bare legs glowing with a strange transfigured ruddiness in the powerful light, and his straw hat with its half-absurd decorations of flowers and feathers shining showily above his river of long black hair. At times he would utter a low call to the horse, and then the other Indian, behind, would fetch the beast a whack with the stick.

The wonder-light faded off the mountains, the world began to grow dark, a cold air breathed down. In the sky, half a moon was struggling against the glow in the west. Huge shadows came down from steep rocky slopes. Water was rushing. The woman was conscious only of her fatigue, her unspeakable fatigue, and the cold wind from the heights. She was not aware how moonlight replaced daylight. It happened while she travelled unconscious with weariness.

For some hours they travelled by moonlight. Then suddenly they came to a standstill. The men conversed in low tones for a moment.

'We camp here,' said the young man.

She waited for him to help her down. He merely stood holding the horse's bridle. She almost fell from the saddle, so fatigued.

They had chosen a place at the foot of rocks that still gave off a little warmth of the sun. One man cut pine-boughs, another erected little screens of pine-boughs against the rock for shelter, and put boughs of balsam pine for beds. The third made a small fire, to heat tortillas. They worked in silence.

The woman drank water. She did not want to eat—only to lie down.

'Where do I sleep?' she asked.

The young man pointed to one of the shelters. She crept in and lay inert. She did not care what happened to her, she was so weary, and so beyond everything. Through the twigs of spruce she could see the three men squatting round the fire on their hams, chewing the tortillas they picked from the ashes with their dark fingers, and drinking water from a gourd. They talked in low, muttering tones, with long intervals of silence. Her saddle and saddle-bags lay not far from the fire, unopened, untouched. The men were not interested in her nor her belongings. There they squatted with their hats on their heads, eating, eating mechanically, like animals, the dark *serape* with its fringe falling to the ground before and behind, the powerful dark legs naked and squatting like an animal's, showing the dirty white shirt and the sort of loin-cloth which was the only other garment, underneath. And they showed no more sign of interest in her than if she had been a piece of venison they were bringing home from the hunt, and had hung inside a shelter.

After a while they carefully extinguished the fire, and went inside their own shelter. Watching through the screen of boughs, she had a moment's thrill of fear and anxiety, seeing the dark forms cross and pass silently in the moonlight. Would they attack her now?

But no! They were as if oblivious of her. Her horse was hobbled; she could hear it hopping wearily. All was silent, mountain-silent, cold, deathly. She slept and woke and slept in a semi-conscious numbness of cold and fatigue. A long, long night, icy and eternal, and she was aware that she had died.

II

Yet when there was a stirring, and a clink of flint and steel, and the form of a man crouching like a dog over a bone, at a red splutter of fire, and she knew it was morning coming, it seemed to her the night had passed too soon.

When the fire was going, she came out of her shelter with one real desire left: for coffee. The men were warming more *tortillas*.

'Can we make coffee?' she asked.

The young man looked at her, and she imagined the same faint spark of derision in his eyes. He shook his head.

'We don't take it,' he said. 'There is no time.'

And the elder men, squatting on their haunches, looked up at her in the terrible paling dawn, and there was not even derision in their eyes. Only that intense, yet remote, inhuman glitter which was terrible to her. They were inaccessible. They could not see her as a woman at all. As if she *were* not a woman. As if, perhaps, her whiteness took away all her womanhood, and left her as some giant, female white ant. That was all they could see in her.

Before the sun was up, she was in the saddle again, and they were climbing steeply, in the icy air. The sun came, and soon she was very hot, exposed to the glare in the bare places. It seemed to her they were climbing to the roof of the world. Beyond against heaven were slashes of snow.

During the course of the morning, they came to a place where the horse could not go farther. They rested for a time with a great slant of living rock in front of them, like the glossy breast of some earth-beast. Across this rock, along a wavering crack, they had to go. It seemed to her that for hours she went in torment, on her hands and knees, from crack to crevice, along the slanting face of this pure rock-mountain. An Indian in front and an Indian behind walked slowly erect, shod with sandals of braided leather. But she in her riding-boots dared not stand erect.

Yet what she wondered, all the time, was why she persisted in clinging and crawling along these mile-long sheets of rock. Why she did not hurl herself down, and have done! The world was below her.

When they emerged at last on a stony slope, she looked back, and saw the third Indian coming carrying her saddle and saddle-bags on his back, the whole hung from a band across his forehead. And he had his hat in his hand, as he stepped slowly, with the slow, soft, heavy tread of the Indian, unwavering in the chinks of rock, as if along a scratch in the mountain's iron shield.

The stony slope led downwards. The Indians seemed to grow excited. One ran ahead at a slow trot, disappearing round the curve of stones. And the track curved round and down, till at last, in the full blaze of the mid-morning sun, they could see a valley below them, between walls of rock, as in a great wide chasm let in the mountains. A green valley, with a river, and trees, and clusters of low flat sparkling houses. It was all tiny and perfect, three thousand feet below. Even the flat bridge over the stream, and the square with the houses around it, the bigger buildings piled up at opposite ends of the square, the tall cottonwood-trees, the pastures and stretches of yellow-sere maize, the patches of brown sheep or goats in the distance, on the slopes, the railed enclosures by the stream-side. There it was, all small and perfect, looking magical, as any place will look magical, seen from the mountains above. The unusual thing was that the low houses glittered white, whitewashed, looking like crystals of salt, or silver. This frightened her.

They began the long, winding descent at the head of the *barranca*, following the stream that rushed and fell. At first it was all rocks; then the pine-trees began, and soon, the silver-limbed aspens. The flowers of autumn, big pink daisy-like flowers, and white ones, and many yellow flowers, were in profusion. But she had to sit down and rest, she was so weary. And she saw the bright flowers shadowily, as pale shadows hovering, as one who is dead must see them.

At length came grass and pasture-slopes between mingled aspen and pine-trees. A shepherd, naked in the sun save for his hat and his cotton loin-cloth, was driving his brown sheep away. In a grove of trees they sat and waited, she and the young Indian. The one with the saddle had also gone forward.

They heard the sound of someone coming. It was three men, in fine *serapes* of red and orange and yellow and black, and with brilliant feather head-dresses. The oldest had his grey hair braided with fur, and his red and orange-yellow *serape* was covered with curious black markings, like a leopard-skin. The other two were not grey-haired, but they were elders too. Their blankets were in stripes, and their head-dresses not so elaborate.

The young Indian addressed the elders in a few quiet words. They listened without answering or looking at him or at the woman, keeping their faces averted and their eyes turned to the ground, only listening. And at length they turned and looked at the woman.

The old chief, or medicine-man, whatever he was, had a deeply wrinkled and lined face of dark bronze, with a few sparse grey hairs round the mouth. Two long braids of grey hair, braided with fur and coloured feathers, hung on his shoulders. And yet, it was only his eyes that mattered. They were black and of extraordinary piercing strength, without a qualm of misgiving in their demonish, dauntless power. He looked into the eyes of the white woman with a long, piercing look, seeking she knew not what. She summoned all her strength to meet his eyes and keep up her guard. But it was no good. He was not looking at her as one human being looks at another. He never even perceived her resistance or her challenge, but looked past them both, into she knew not what.

She could see it was hopeless to expect any human communication with this old being.

He turned and said a few words to the young Indian.

'He asks what do you seek here?' said the young man in Spanish.

'I? Nothing! I only came to see what it was like.'

This was again translated, and the old man turned his eyes on her once more. Then he spoke again, in his low muttering tone, to the young Indian.

'He says, why does she leave her house with the white men? Does she want to bring the white man's God to the Chilchui?'

'No,' she replied, foolhardy. 'I came away from the white man's God myself. I came to look for the God of the Chilchui.'

Profound silence followed, when this was translated. Then the old man spoke again, in a small voice almost of weariness.

'Does the white woman seek the gods of the Chilchui because she is weary of her own God?' came the question.

'Yes, she does. She is tired of the white man's God,' she replied, thinking that was what they wanted her to say. She would like to serve the gods of the Chilchui.

She was aware of an extraordinary thrill of triumph and exultance passing through the Indians, in the tense silence that followed when this was translated. Then they all looked at her with piercing black eyes, in which a steely covetous intent glittered incomprehensible. She was the more puzzled, as there was nothing sensual or sexual in the look. It had a terrible purity that was beyond her. She was afraid, she would have been paralysed with fear, had not something died within her, leaving her with a cold, watchful wonder only.

The elders talked a little while, then the two went away, leaving her with the young man and the oldest chief. The old man now looked at her with a certain solicitude.

'He says, are you tired?' asked the young man.

'Very tired,' she said.

'The men will bring you a carriage,' said the young Indian.

The carriage, when it came, proved to be a litter consisting of a sort of hammock of dark woollen frieze, slung on to a pole which was borne on the shoulders of two long-haired Indians. The woollen hammock was spread on the ground, she sat down on it, and the two men raised the pole to their shoulders. Swinging rather as if she were in a sack, she was carried out of the grove of trees, following the old chief, whose leopard-spotted blanket moved curiously in the sunlight.

They had emerged in the valley-head. Just in front were the maize-fields, with ripe ears of maize. The corn was not very tall, in this high altitude. The well-worn path went between it, and all she could see was the erect form of the old chief, in the flame and black *serape*, stepping soft and heavy and swift, his head forward, looking neither to right nor left. Her bearers followed, stepping rhythmically, the long blue-black hair glistening like a river down the naked shoulders of the man in front.

They passed the maize, and came to a big wall or earthwork made of earth and adobe bricks. The wooden doors were open. Passing on, they were in a network of small gardens, full of flowers and herbs and fruit-trees, each garden watered by a tiny ditch of running water. Among each cluster of trees and flowers was a small, glittering white house, windowless, and

with closed door. The place was a network of little
paths, small streams, and little bridges among square,
flowering gardens.

Following the broadest path—a soft narrow track
between leaves and grass, a path worn smooth by
centuries of human feet, no hoof of horse nor any wheel
to disfigure it—they came to the little river of swift
bright water, and crossed on a log bridge. Everything
was silent—there was not a human being anywhere.
The road went on under magnificent cottonwood-trees.
It emerged suddenly outside the central *plaza* or square
of the village.

This was a long oblong of low white houses with flat
roofs, and two bigger buildings, having as it were little
square huts piled on top of bigger long huts, stood at
either end of the oblong, facing each other rather
askew. Every little house was a dazzling white, save
for the great round beam-ends which projected under
the flat eaves, and for the flat roofs. Round each of
the bigger buildings, on the outside of the square, was a
stockyard fence, inside which was a garden with trees
and flowers, and various small houses.

Not a soul was in sight. They passed silently between
the houses into the central square. This was quite
bare and arid, the earth trodden smooth by endless
generations of passing feet, passing across from door
to door. All the doors of the windowless houses gave
on to this blank square, but all the doors were closed.
The firewood lay near the threshold, a clay oven was
still smoking, but there was no sign of moving life.

The old man walked straight across the square to the
big house at the end, where the two upper stories, as
in a house of toy bricks, stood each one smaller than
the lower one. A stone staircase, outside, led up to the
roof of the first story.

At the foot of this staircase the litter-bearers stood
still, and lowered the woman to the ground.

'You will come up,' said the young Indian who spoke
Spanish.

She mounted the stone stairs to the earthen roof of

the first house, which formed a platform round the wall of the second story. She followed around this plat-form to the back of the big house. There they descended again, into the garden at the rear.

So far they had seen no one. But now two men appeared, bareheaded, with long braided hair, and wear-ing a sort of white shirt gathered into a loin-cloth. These went along with the three newcomers, across the garden where red flowers and yellow flowers were bloom-ing, to a long, low white house. There they entered without knocking.

It was dark inside. There was a low murmur of men's voices. Several men were present, their white shirts showing in the gloom, their dark faces invisible. They were sitting on a great log of smooth old wood, that lay along the far wall. And save for this log, the room seemed empty. But no, in the dark at one end was a couch, a sort of bed, and someone lying there, covered with furs.

The old Indian in the spotted *serape*, who had accom-panied the woman, now took off his hat and his blanket and his sandals. Laying them aside, he approached the couch, and spoke in a low voice. For some moments there was no answer. Then an old man with the snow-white hair hanging round his darkly-visible face, roused himself like a vision, and leaned on one elbow, looking vaguely at the company, in tense silence.

The grey-haired Indian spoke again, and then the young Indian, taking the woman's hand, led her for-ward. In her linen riding-habit, and black boots and hat, and her pathetic bit of a red tie, she stood there beside the fur-covered bed of the old, old man, who sat reared up, leaning on one elbow, remote as a ghost, his white hair streaming in disorder, his face almost black, yet with a far-off intentness, not of this world, leaning forward to look at her.

His face was so old, it was like dark glass, and the few curling hairs that sprang white from his lips and chin were quite incredible. The long white locks fell un-braided and disorderly on either side of the glassy dark face. And under a faint powder of white eyebrows, the black eyes of the old chief looked at her as if from the far, far dead, seeing something that was never to be seen.

At last he spoke a few deep, hollow words, as if to the dark air.

'He says, do you bring your heart to the god of the Chilchui?' translated the young Indian.

'Tell him yes,' she said, automatically.

There was a pause. The old Indian spoke again, as if to the air. One of the men present went out. There was a silence as if of eternity in the dim room that was lighted only through the open door.

The woman looked round. Four old men with grey hair sat on the log by the wall facing the door. Two other men, powerful and impassive, stood near the door. They all had long hair, and wore white shirts gathered into a loin-cloth. Their powerful legs were naked and dark. There was a silence like eternity.

At length the man returned, with white and dark clothing on his arm. The young Indian took them, and holding them in front of the woman, said:

'You must take off your clothes, and put these on.'

'If all you men will go out,' she said.

'No one will hurt you,' he said quietly.

'Not while you men are here,' she said.

He looked at the two men by the door. They came quickly forward, and suddenly gripped her arms as she stood, without hurting her, but with great power. Then two of the old men came, and with curious skill slit her boots down with keen knives, and drew them off, and slit her clothing so that it came away from her. In a few moments she stood there white and uncovered. The old man on the bed spoke, and they turned her round for him to see. He spoke again, and the young Indian deftly took the pins and comb from her fair hair so that it fell over her shoulders in a bunchy tangle.

Then the old man spoke again. The Indian led her to the bedside. The white-haired, glassy-dark old man moistened his finger-tips at his mouth, and most delicately touched her on the breasts and on the body, then on the back. And she winced strangely each time, as the finger-tips drew along her skin, as if Death itself were touching her.

And she wondered, almost sadly, why she did not feel ashamed in her nakedness. She only felt sad and lost. Because nobody felt ashamed. The elder men were all dark and tense with some other deep, gloomy, incomprehensible emotion, which suspended all her agitation, while the young Indian had a strange look of ecstasy on his face. And she, she was only utterly strange and beyond herself, as if her body were not her own.

They gave her the new clothing: a long white cotton shift, that came to her knees; then a tunic of thick blue woollen stuff, embroidered with scarlet and green flowers. It was fastened over one shoulder only, and belted with a braid sash of scarlet and black wool.

When she was thus dressed, they took her away, barefoot, to a little house in the stockaded garden. The young Indian told her she might have what she wanted. She asked for water to wash herself. He brought it in a jar, together with a long wooden bowl. Then he fastened the gate-door of her house, and left her a prisoner. She could see through the bars of the gate-door of her house, the red flowers of the garden, and a humming-bird. Then from the roof of the big house she heard the long, heavy sound of a drum, unearthly to her in its summons, and an uplifted voice calling from the house-top in a strange language, with a far-away emotionless intonation, delivering some speech or message. And she listened as if from the dead.

But she was very tired. She lay down on a couch of skins, pulling over her the blanket of dark wool, and she slept, giving up everything.

When she woke it was late afternoon, and the young Indian was entering with a basket-tray containing food, *tortillas*, and corn-mush with bits of meat, probably mutton, and a drink made of honey, and some fresh plums. He brought her also a long garland of red and

yellow flowers with knots of blue buds at the end. He
sprinkled the garland with water from a jar, then offered
it to her, with a smile. He seemed very gentle and
thoughtful, and on his face and in his dark eyes was a
curious look of triumph and ecstasy, that frightened
her a little. The glitter had gone from the black eyes,
with their curving dark lashes, and he would look at her
with this strange soft glow of ecstasy that was not quite
human, and terribly impersonal, and which made her
uneasy.

'Is there anything you want?' he said, in his low,
slow, melodious voice, that always seemed withheld,
as if he were speaking aside to someone else, or as if
he did not want to let the sound come out to her.

'Am I going to be kept a prisoner here?' she asked.

'No, you can walk in the garden to-morrow,' he said
softly. Always this curious solicitude.

'Do you like that drink?' he said, offering her a little
earthenware cup. 'It is very refreshing.'

She sipped the liquor curiously. It was made with
herbs and sweetened with honey, and had a strange,
lingering flavour. The young man watched her with
gratification.

'It has a peculiar taste,' she said.

'It is very refreshing,' he replied, his black eyes
resting on her always with that look of gratified ecstasy.
Then he went away. And presently she began to be
sick, and to vomit violently, as if she had no control
over herself.

Afterwards she felt a great soothing languor steal
over her, her limbs felt strong and loose and full of
languor, and she lay on her couch listening to the
sounds of the village, watching the yellowing sky,
smelling the scent of burning cedar-wood, or pine-
wood. So distinctly she heard the yapping of tiny
dogs, the shuffle of far-off feet, the murmur of voices, so
keenly she detected the smell of smoke, and flowers,
and evening falling, so vividly she saw the one bright
star infinitely remote, stirring above the sunset, that
she felt as if all her senses were diffused on the air, that

she could distinguish the sound of evening flowers unfolding, and the actual crystal sound of the heavens, as the vast belts of the world-atmosphere slid past one another, and as if the moisture ascending and the moisture descending in the air resounded like some harp in the cosmos.

She was a prisoner in her house, and in the stockaded garden, but she scarcely minded. And it was days before she realized that she never saw another woman. Only the men, the elderly men of the big house, that she imagined must be some sort of temple, and the men priests of some sort. For they always had the same colours, red, orange, yellow, and black, and the same grave, abstracted demeanour.

Sometimes an old man would come and sit in her room with her, in absolute silence. None spoke any language but Indian, save the one younger man. The older men would smile at her, and sit with her for an hour at a time, sometimes smiling at her when she spoke in Spanish, but never answering save with this slow, benevolent-seeming smile. And they gave off a feeling of almost fatherly solicitude. Yet their dark eyes, brooding over her, had something away in their depths that was awesomely ferocious and relentless. They would cover it with a smile, at once, if they felt her looking. But she had seen it.

Always they treated her with this curious impersonal solicitude, this utterly impersonal gentleness, as an old man treats a child. But underneath it she felt there was something else, something terrible. When her old visitor had gone away, in his silent, insidious, fatherly fashion, a shock of fear would come over her; though of what she knew not.

The young Indian would sit and talk with her freely, as if with great candour. But with him, too, she felt that everything real was unsaid. Perhaps it was un-speakable. His big dark eyes would rest on her almost cherishingly, touched with ecstasy, and his beautiful, slow, languorous voice would trail out its simple, un-grammatical Spanish. He told her he was the grandson

of the old, old man, son of the man in the spotted *serape*;
and they were caciques, kings from the old, old days,
before even the Spaniards came. But he himself had
been in Mexico City, and also in the United States.
He had worked as a labourer, building the roads in Los
Angeles. He had travelled as far as Chicago.

'Don't you speak English, then?' she asked.

His eyes rested on her with a curious look of duplicity
and conflict, and he mutely shook his head.

'What did you do with your long hair, when you were
in the United States?' she asked. 'Did you cut it off?'

Again, with the look of torment in his eyes, he shook
his head.

'No,' he said, in a low, subdued voice, 'I wore a hat,
and a handkerchief tied round my head.'

And he relapsed into silence, as if of tormented
memories.

'Are you the only man of your people who has been
to the United States?' she asked him.

'Yes. I am the only one who has been away from
here for a long time. The others came back soon, in one
week. They don't stay away. The old men don't
let them.'

'And why did you go?'

'The old men want me to go—because I shall be the
cacique——'

He talked always with the same *naïveté*, an almost
childish candour. But she felt that this was perhaps
just the effect of his Spanish. Or perhaps speech
altogether was unreal to him. Anyhow, she felt that
all the real things were kept back.

He came and sat with her a good deal—sometimes
more than she wished—as if he wanted to be near her.
She asked him if he was married. He said he was—
with two children.

'I should like to see your children,' she said.

But he answered only with that smile, a sweet, almost
ecstatic smile, above which the dark eyes hardly
changed from their enigmatic abstraction.

It was curious, he would sit with her by the hour,

without ever making her self-conscious, or sex-conscious. He seemed to have no sex, as he sat there so still and gentle and apparently submissive, with his head bent a little forward, and the river of glistening black hair streaming maidenly over his shoulders.

Yet when she looked again, she saw his shoulders broad and powerful, his eyebrows black and level, the short, curved, obstinate black lashes over his lowered eyes, the small, fur-like line of moustache above his blackish, heavy lips, and the strong chin, and she knew that in some other mysterious way he was darkly and powerfully male. And he, feeling her watching him, would glance up at her swiftly with a dark, lurking look in his eyes, which immediately he veiled with that half-sad smile.

The days and the weeks went by, in a vague kind of contentment. She was uneasy sometimes, feeling she had lost the power over herself. She was not in her own power, she was under the spell of some other control. And at times she had moments of terror and horror. But then these Indians would come and sit with her, casting their insidious spell over her by their very silent presence, their silent, sexless, powerful physical presence. As they sat they seemed to take her will away, leaving her will-less and victim to her own indifference. And the young man would bring her sweetened drink, often the same emetic drink, but sometimes other kinds. And after drinking, the languor filled her heavy limbs, her senses seemed to float in the air, listening, hearing. They had brought her a little female dog, which she called Flora. And once, in the trance of her senses, she felt she *heard* the little dog conceive, in her tiny womb, and begin to be complex, with young. And another day she could hear the vast sound of the earth going round, like some immense arrow-string booming.

But as the days grew shorter and colder, when she was cold, she would get a sudden revival of her will, and a desire to go out, to go away. And she insisted to the young man, she wanted to go out.

So one day, they let her climb to the topmost roof of the big house where she was, and look down the square. It was the day of the big dance, but not everybody was dancing. Women with babies in their arms stood in their doorways, watching. Opposite, at the other end of the square, there was a throng before the other big house, and a small, brilliant group on the terrace-roof of the first story, in front of wide open doors of the upper story. Through these wide open doors she could see fire glinting in darkness and priests in head-dresses of black and yellow and scarlet feathers, wearing robe-like blankets of black and red and yellow, with long green fringes, were moving about. A big drum was beating slowly and regularly, in the dense, Indian silence. The crowd below waited.

Then a drum started on a high beat, and there came the deep, powerful burst of men singing a heavy, savage music, like a wind roaring in some timeless forest, many mature men singing in one breath, like the wind; and long lines of dancers walked out from under the big house. Men with naked, golden-bronze bodies and streaming black hair, tufts of red and yellow feathers on their arms, and kilts of white frieze with a bar of heavy red and black and green embroidery round their waists, bending slightly forward and stamping the earth in their absorbed, monotonous stamp of the dance, a fox-fur, hung by the nose from their belt behind, swaying with the sumptuous swaying of a beautiful fox-fur, the tip of the tail writhing above the dancer's heels. And after each man, a woman with a strange elaborate head-dress of feathers and sea-shells, and wearing a short black tunic, moving erect, holding up tufts of feathers in each hand, swaying her wrists rhythmically and subtly beating the earth with her bare feet.

So, the long line of the dance unfurling from the big house opposite. And from the big house beneath her, strange scent of incense, strange tense silence, then the answering burst of inhuman male singing, and the long line of the dance unfurling.

It went on all day, the insistence of the drum, the

cavernous, roaring, storm-like sound of male singing, the incessant swinging of the fox-skins behind the powerful, gold-bronze, stamping legs of the men, the autumn sun from a perfect blue heaven pouring on the rivers of black hair, men's and women's, the valley all still, the walls of rock beyond, the awful huge bulking of the mountain against the pure sky, its snow seething with sheer whiteness.

For hours and hours she watched, spell-bound, and as if drugged. And in all the terrible persistence of the drumming and the primeval, rushing deep singing, and the endless stamping of the dance of fox-tailed men, the tread of heavy, bird-erect women in their black tunics, she seemed at last to feel her own death; her own obliteration. As if she were to be obliterated from the field of life again. In the strange towering symbols on the heads of the changeless, absorbed women she seemed to read once more the *Mene Mene Tekel Upharsin*. Her kind of womanhood, intensely personal and individual, was to be obliterated again, and the great primeval symbols were to tower once more over the fallen individual independence of woman. The sharpness and the quivering nervous consciousness of the highly-bred white woman was to be destroyed again, womanhood was to be cast once more into the great stream of impersonal sex and impersonal passion. Strangely, as if clairvoyant, she saw the immense sacrifice prepared. And she went back to her little house in a trance of agony.

After this, there was always a certain agony when she heard the drums at evening, and the strange uplifted savage sound of men singing round the drum, like wild creatures howling to the invisible gods of the moon and the vanished sun. Something of the chuckling, sobbing cry of the coyote, something of the exultant bark of the fox, the far-off wild melancholy exultance of the howling wolf, the torment of the puma's scream, and the insistence of the ancient fierce human male, with his lapses of tenderness and his abiding ferocity.

Sometimes she would climb the high roof after nightfall, and listen to the dim cluster of young men round the drum on the bridge just beyond the square, singing by the hour. Sometimes there would be a fire, and in the fire-glow, men in their white shirts or naked save for a loin-cloth, would be dancing and stamping like spectres, hour after hour in the dark cold air, within the fire-glow, for ever dancing and stamping like turkeys, or dropping squatting by the fire to rest, throwing their blankets round them.

'Why do you all have the same colours?' she asked the young Indian. 'Why do you all have red and yellow and black, over your white shirts? And the women have black tunics?'

He looked into her eyes, curiously, and the faint, evasive smile came on to his face. Behind the smile lay a soft, strange malignancy.

'Because our men are the fire and the daytime, and our women are the spaces between the stars at night,' he said.

'Aren't the women even stars?' she said.

'No. We say they are the spaces between the stars, that keep the stars apart.'

He looked at her oddly, and again the touch of derision came into his eyes.

'White people,' he said, 'they know nothing. They are like children, always with toys. We know the sun, and we know the moon. And we say, when a white woman sacrifice herself to our gods, then our gods will begin to make the world again, and the white man's gods will fall to pieces.'

'How sacrifice herself?' she asked quickly.

And he as quickly covered, covered himself with a subtle smile.

'She sacrifice her own gods and come to our gods, I mean that,' he said, soothingly.

But she was not reassured. An icy pang of fear and certainty was at her heart.

'The sun he is alive at one end of the sky,' he continued, 'and the moon lives at the other end. And the man all the time have to keep the sun happy in his side of the sky, and the woman have to keep the moon quiet at her side of the sky. All the time she have to work at this. And the sun can't ever go into the house of the moon, and the moon can't ever go into the house of the sun, in the sky. So the woman, she asks the moon to come into her cave, inside her. And the man, he draws the sun down till he has the power of the sun. All the time he do this. Then when the man gets a woman, the sun goes into the cave of the moon, and that is how everything in the world starts.'

She listened, watching him closely, as one enemy watches another who is speaking with double meaning.

'Then,' she said, 'why aren't you Indians masters of the white men?'

'Because,' he said, 'the Indian got weak, and lost his power with the sun, so the white men stole the sun. But they can't keep him—they don't know how. They got him, but they don't know what to do with him, like a boy who catch a big grizzly bear, and can't kill him, and can't run away from him. The grizzly bear eats the boy that catch him, when he wants to run away from him. White men don't know what they are doing with the sun, and white women don't know what they do with the moon. The moon she got angry with white women, like a puma when someone kills her little ones. The moon, she bites white women—here inside,' and he pressed his side. 'The moon, she is angry in a white woman's cave. The Indian can see it. And soon,' he added, 'the Indian women get the moon back and keep her quiet in their house. And the Indian men get the sun, and the power over all the world. White men don't know what the sun is. They never know.'

He subsided into a curious exultant silence.

'But,' she faltered, 'why do you hate us so? Why do you hate me?'

He looked up suddenly with a light on his face, and a startling flame of a smile.

'No, we don't hate,' he said softly, looking with a curious glitter into her face.

'You do,' she said, forlorn and hopeless.

And after a moment's silence, he rose and went away.

III

Winter had now come, in the high valley, with snow that melted in the day's sun, and nights that were bitter cold. She lived on, in a kind of daze, feeling her power ebbing more and more away from her, as if her will were leaving her. She felt always in the same relaxed, confused, victimized state, unless the sweetened herb drink would numb her mind altogether, and release her senses into a sort of heightened, mystic acuteness and a feeling as if she were diffusing out deliciously into the harmony of things. This at length became the only state of consciousness she really recognized: this exquisite sense of bleeding out into the higher beauty and harmony of things. Then she could actually hear the great stars in heaven, which she saw through her door, speaking from their motion and brightness, saying things perfectly to the cosmos, as they trod in perfect ripples, like bells on the floor of heaven, passing one another and grouping in the timeless dance, with the spaces of dark between. And she could hear the snow on a cold, cloudy day twittering and faintly whistling in the sky, like birds that flock and fly away in autumn, suddenly calling farewell to the invisible moon, and slipping out of the plains of the air, releasing peaceful warmth. She herself would call to the arrested snow to fall from the upper air. She would call to the unseen moon to cease to be angry, to make peace again with the unseen sun like a woman who ceases to be angry in her house. And she would smell the sweetness of the moon relaxing to the sun in the wintry heaven, when the snow fell in a faint, cold-perfumed relaxation, as the peace of the sun mingled again in a sort of unison with the peace of the moon.

She was aware too of the sort of shadow that was on the Indians of the valley, a deep stoical disconsolation, almost religious in its depth.

'We have lost our power over the sun, and we are trying to get him back. But he is wild with us, and shy

like a horse that has got away. We have to go through
a lot.' So the young Indian said to her, looking into her
eyes with a strained meaning. And she, as if bewitched,
replied:

'I hope you will get him back.'

The smile of triumph flew over his face.

'Do you hope it?' he said.

'I do,' she answered fatally.

'Then all right,' he said. 'We shall get him.'

And he went away in exultance.

She felt she was drifting on some consummation,
which she had no will to avoid, yet which seemed heavy
and finally terrible to her.

It must have been almost December, for the days were
short when she was taken again before the aged man,
and stripped of her clothing, and touched with the old
finger-tips.

The aged cacique looked her in the eyes, with his
eyes of lonely, far-off, black intentness, and murmured
something to her.

'He wants you to make a sign of peace,' the young
man translated, showing her the gesture. 'Peace and
farewell to him.'

She was fascinated by the black, glass-like, intent
eyes of the old cacique, that watched her without
blinking, like a basilisk's, overpowering her. In their
depths also she saw a certain fatherly compassion, and
pleading. She put her hand before her face, in the
required manner, making the sign of peace and farewell.
He made the sign of peace back again to her, then sank
among his furs. She thought he was going to die, and
that he knew it.

There followed a day of ceremonial, when she was
brought out before all the people, in a blue blanket
with white fringe, and holding blue feathers in her hands.
Before an altar of one house she was perfumed with
incense and sprinkled with ash. Before the altar of
the opposite house she was fumigated again with incense
by the gorgeous, terrifying priests in yellow and scarlet
and black, their faces painted with scarlet paint. And

then they threw water on her. Meanwhile she was faintly aware of the fire on the altar, the heavy, heavy sound of a drum, the heavy sound of men beginning powerfully, deeply, savagely to sing, the swaying of the crowd of faces in the *plaza* below, and the formation for a sacred dance.

But at this time her commonplace consciousness was numb, she was aware of her immediate surroundings as shadows, almost immaterial. With refined and heightened senses she could hear the sound of the earth winging on its journey, like a shot arrow, the ripple-rustling of the air, and the boom of the great arrow-string. And it seemed to her that there were two great influences in the upper air, one golden towards the sun, and one invisible silver; the first travelling like rain ascending to the gold presence sunwards, the second like rain silverily descending the ladders of space towards the hovering, lurking clouds over the snowy mountain-top. Then between them, another presence, waiting to shake himself free of moisture, of heavy white snow that had mysteriously collected about him. And in summer, like a scorched eagle, he would wait to shake himself clear of the weight of heavy sunbeams. And he was coloured like fire. And he was always shaking himself clear, of snow or of heavy heat, like an eagle rustling.

Then there was a still stranger presence, standing watching from the blue distance, always watching. Sometimes running in upon the wind, or shimmering in the heat-waves. The blue wind itself, rushing as it were out of the holes into the sky, rushing out of the sky down upon the earth. The blue wind, the go-between, the invisible ghost that belonged to two worlds, that played upon the ascending and the descending chords of the rains.

More and more her ordinary personal consciousness had left her, she had gone into that other state of passional cosmic consciousness, like one who is drugged. The Indians, with their heavily religious natures, had made her succumb to their vision.

Only one personal question she asked the young Indian:

'Why am I the only one that wears blue?'

'It is the colour of the wind. It is the colour of what goes away and is never coming back, but which is always here, waiting like death among us. It is the colour of the dead. And it is the colour that stands away off, looking at us from the distance, that cannot come near to us. When we go near, it goes farther. It can't be near. We are all brown and yellow and black hair, and white teeth and red blood. We are the ones that are here. You with blue eyes, you are the messengers from the far-away, you cannot stay, and now it is time for you to go back.'

'Where to?' she asked.

'To the way-off things like the sun and the blue mother of rain, and tell them that we are the people on the world again, and we can bring the sun to the moon again, like a red horse to a blue mare; we are the people. The white women have driven back the moon in the sky, won't let her come to the sun. So the sun is angry. And the Indian must give the moon to the sun.'

'How?' she said.

'The white woman got to die and go like a wind to the sun, tell him the Indians will open the gate to him. And the Indian women will open the gate to the moon. The white women don't let the moon come down out of the blue corral. The moon used to come down among the Indian women, like a white goat among the flowers. And the sun want to come down to the Indian men, like an eagle to the pine-trees. The sun, he is shut out behind the white man, and the moon she is shut out behind the white woman, and they can't get away. They are angry, everything in the world gets angrier. The Indian says, he will give the white woman to the sun, so the sun will leap over the white man and come to the Indian again. And the moon will be surprised, she will see the gate open, and she not know which way to go. But the Indian woman will call to the moon, *Come! Come! Come back into my grasslands. The*

wicked white woman can't harm you any more. Then
the sun will look over the heads of the white men, and
see the moon in the pastures of our women, with the
Red Men standing around like pine-trees. Then he will
leap over the heads of the white men, and come running
past to the Indians through the spruce-trees. And we,
who are red and black and yellow, we who stay, we shall
have the sun on our right hand and the moon on our
left. So we can bring the rain down out of the blue
meadows, and up out of the black; and we can call
the wind that tells the corn to grow, when we ask him,
and we shall make the clouds to break, and the sheep
to have twin lambs. And we shall be full of power, like
a spring day. But the white people will be a hard
winter, without snow——'

'But,' said the white woman, 'I don't shut out the
moon—how can I?'

'Yes,' he said, 'you shut the gate, and then laugh,
think you have it all your own way.'

She could never quite understand the way he looked
at her. He was always so curiously gentle, and his
smile was so soft. Yet there was such a glitter in his
eyes, and an unrelenting sort of hate came out of his
words, a strange, profound, impersonal hate. Personally
he liked her, she was sure. He was gentle with her,
attracted by her in some strange, soft, passionless way.
But impersonally he hated her with a mystic hatred.
He would smile at her, winningly. Yet if, the next
moment, she glanced round at him unawares, she would
catch that gleam of pure after-hate in his eyes.

'Have I got to die and be given to the sun?' she
asked.

'Some time,' he said, laughing evasively. 'Some time
we all die.'

They were gentle with her, and very considerate with
her. Strange men, the old priests and the young
cacique alike, they watched over her and cared for her
like women. In their soft, insidious understanding,
there was something womanly. Yet their eyes, with
that strange glitter, and their dark, shut mouths that

would open to the broad jaw, the small, strong, white teeth, had something very primitively male and cruel.

One wintry day, when the snow was falling, they took her to a great dark chamber in the big house. The fire was burning in a corner on a high raised dais under a sort of hood or canopy of adobe-work. She saw in the fire-glow the glowing bodies of the almost naked priests, and strange symbols on the roof and walls of the chamber. There was no door or window in the chamber, they had descended by a ladder from the roof. And the fire of pinewood danced continually, showing walls painted with strange devices, which she could not understand, and a ceiling of poles making a curious pattern of black and red and yellow, and alcoves or niches in which were curious objects she could not discern.

The older priests were going through some ceremony near the fire, in silence, intense Indian silence. She was seated on a low projection of the wall, opposite the fire, two men seated beside her. Presently they gave her a drink from a cup, which she took gladly, because of the semi-trance it would induce.

In the darkness and in the silence she was accurately aware of everything that happened to her; how they took off her clothes, and, standing her before a great, weird device on the wall, coloured blue and white and black, washed her all over with water and the *amole* infusion; washed even her hair, softly, carefully, and dried it on white cloths, till it was soft and glistening. Then they laid her on a couch under another great indecipherable image of red and black and yellow, and now rubbed all her body with sweet-scented oil, and massaged all her limbs, and her back, and her sides, with a long, strange, hypnotic massage. Their dark hands were incredibly powerful, yet soft with a watery softness she could not understand. And the dark faces, leaning near her white body, she saw were darkened with red pigment, with lines of yellow round the cheeks. And the dark eyes glittered absorbed, as the hands worked upon the soft white body of the woman.

They were so impersonal, absorbed in something that

was beyond her. They never saw her as a personal woman; she could tell that. She was some mystic object to them, some vehicle of passions too remote for her to grasp. Herself in a state of trance, she watched their faces bending over her, dark, strangely glistening with the transparent red paint, and lined with bars of yellow. And in this weird, luminous-dark mask of living face, the eyes were fixed with an unchanging steadfast gleam, and the purplish-pigmented lips were closed in a full, sinister, sad grimness. The immense fundamental sadness, the grimness of ultimate decision, the fixity of revenge, and the nascent exultance of those that are going to triumph—these things she could read in their faces, as she lay and was rubbed into a misty glow by their uncanny dark hands. Her limbs, her flesh, her very bones at last seemed to be diffusing into a roseate sort of mist, in which her consciousness hovered like some sun-gleam in a flushed cloud.

She knew the gleam would fade, the cloud would go grey. But at present she did not believe it. She knew she was a victim; that all this elaborate work upon her was the work of victimizing her. But she did not mind. She wanted it.

Later, they put a short blue tunic on her and took her to the upper terrace, and presented her to the people. She saw the *plaza* below her full of dark faces and of glittering eyes. There was no pity; only the curious hard exultance. The people gave a subdued cry when they saw her, and she shuddered. But she hardly cared.

Next day was the last. She slept in a chamber of the big house. At dawn they put on her a big blue blanket with a fringe, and led her out into the *plaza*, among the throng of silent, dark-blanketed people. There was pure white snow on the ground, and the dark people in their dark-brown blankets looked like inhabitants of another world.

A large drum was slowly pounding, and an old priest was declaiming from a housetop. But it was not till noon that a litter came forth, and the people gave that low, animal cry which was so moving. In the sack-like litter sat the old, old cacique, his white hair braided with black braid and large turquoise stones. His face was like a piece of obsidian. He lifted his hand in token, and the litter stopped in front of her. Fixing her with his old eyes, he spoke to her for a few moments, in his hollow voice. No one translated.

Another litter came, and she was placed in it. Four priests moved ahead, in their scarlet and yellow and black, with plumed head-dresses. Then came the litter of the old cacique. Then the light drums began, and two groups of singers burst simultaneously into song, male and wild. And the golden-red, almost naked men, adorned with ceremonial feathers and kilts, the rivers of black hair down their backs, formed into two files and began to tread the dance. So they threaded out of the snowy *plaza*, in two long, sumptuous lines of dark red-gold and black and fur, swaying with a faint tinkle of bits of shell and flint, winding over the snow between the two bee-clusters of men who sang around the drum.

Slowly they moved out, and her litter, with its attendance of feathered, lurid, dancing priests, moved after. Everybody danced the tread of the dance-step, even, subtly, the litter-bearers. And out of the *plaza* they went, past smoking ovens, on the trail to the great cottonwood-trees, that stood like grey-silver lace against the blue sky, bare and exquisite above the snow. The river, diminished, rushed among fangs of ice. The chequer-squares of gardens within fences were all snowy, and the white houses now looked yellowish.

The whole valley glittered intolerably with pure snow, away to the walls of the standing rock. And across the flat cradle of snow-bed wound the long thread of the dance, shaking slowly and sumptuously in its orange and black motion. The high drums thudded quickly, and on the crystalline frozen air the swell and roar of the chant of savages was like an obsession.

She sat looking out of her litter with big, transfixed blue eyes, under which were the wan markings of her drugged weariness. She knew she was going to die, among the glisten of this snow, at the hands of this savage, sumptuous people. And as she stared at the blaze of the blue sky above the slashed and ponderous mountain, she thought: 'I am dead already. What difference does it make, the transition from the dead I am to the dead I shall be, very soon!' Yet her soul sickened and felt wan.

The strange procession trailed on, in perpetual dance, slowly across the plain of snow, and then entered the slopes between the pine-trees. She saw the copper-dark men dancing the dance-tread, onwards, between the copper-pale tree trunks. And at last she, too, in her swaying litter, entered the pine-trees.

They were travelling on and on, upwards, across the snow under the trees, past the superb shafts of pale, flaked copper, the rustle and shake and tread of the threading dance, penetrating into the forest, into the mountain. They were following a stream - bed; but the stream was dry, like summer, dried up by the frozen-ness of the head-waters. There were dark, red-bronze willow-bushes with wattles like wild hair, and pallid aspen-trees looking cold flesh against the snow. Then jutting dark rocks.

At last she could tell that the dancers were moving forward no more. Nearer and nearer she came upon the drums, as to a lair of mysterious animals. Then through the bushes she emerged into a strange amphi-theatre. Facing was a great wall of hollow rock, down the front of which hung a great, dripping, fang-like spoke of ice. The ice came pouring over the rock from the precipice above, and then stood arrested, dripping out of high heaven, almost down to the hollow stones where the stream-pool should be below. But the pool was dry.

On either side the dry pool the lines of dancers had formed, and the dance was continuing without inter-mission, against a background of bushes.

But what she felt was that fanged inverted pinnacle of ice, hanging from the lip of the dark precipice above. And behind the great rope of ice she saw the leopard-like figures of priests climbing the hollow cliff face, to the cave that like a dark socket bored a cavity, an orifice, half-way up the crag.

Before she could realize, her litter-bearers were staggering in the footholds, climbing the rock. She, too, was behind the ice. There it hung, like a curtain that is not spread, but hangs like a great fang. And near above her was the orifice of the cave sinking dark into the rock. She watched it as she swayed upwards.

On the platform of the cave stood the priests, waiting in all their gorgeousness of feathers and fringed robes, watching her ascent. Two of them stooped to help her litter-bearer. And at length she was on the platform of the cave, far in behind the shaft of ice, above the hollow amphitheatre among the bushes below, where men were dancing, and the whole populace of the village was clustered in silence.

The sun was sloping down the afternoon sky, on the left. She knew that this was the shortest day of the year, and the last day of her life. They stood her facing the iridescent column of ice, which fell down marvellously arrested, away in front of her.

Some signal was given, and the dance below stopped. There was now absolute silence. She was given a little to drink, then two priests took off her mantle and her tunic, and in her strange pallor she stood there, between the lurid robes of the priests, beyond the pillar of ice, beyond and above the dark-faced people. The throng below gave the low, wild cry. Then the priest turned her round, so she stood with her back to the open world, her long blonde hair to the people below. And they cried again.

She was facing the cave, inwards. A fire was burning and flickering in the depths. Four priests had taken off their robes, and were almost as naked as she was. They were powerful men in the prime of life, and they kept their dark, painted faces lowered.

From the fire came the old, old priest, with an incense-pan. He was naked and in a state of barbaric ecstasy. He fumigated his victim, reciting at the same time in a hollow voice. Behind him came another robeless priest, with two flint knives.

When she was fumigated, they laid her on a large flat stone, the four powerful men holding her by the outstretched arms and legs. Behind stood the aged man, like a skeleton covered with dark glass, holding a knife and transfixedly watching the sun; and behind him again was another naked priest, with a knife.

She felt little sensation, though she knew all that was happening. Turning to the sky, she looked at the yellow sun. It was sinking. The shaft of ice was like a shadow between her and it. And she realized that the yellow rays were filling half the cave, though they had not reached the altar where the fire was, at the far end of the funnel-shaped cavity.

Yes, the rays were creeping round slowly. As they grew ruddier, they penetrated farther. When the red sun was about to sink, he would shine full through the shaft of ice deep into the hollow of the cave, to the innermost.

She understood now that this was what the men were waiting for. Even those that held her down were bent and twisted round, their black eyes watching the sun with a glittering eagerness, and awe, and craving. The black eyes of the aged cacique were fixed like black mirrors on the sun, as if sightless, yet containing some terrible answer to the reddening winter planet. And all the eyes of the priests were fixed and glittering on the sinking orb, in the reddening, icy silence of the winter afternoon.

They were anxious, terribly anxious, and fierce. Their ferocity wanted something, and they were waiting the moment. And their ferocity was ready to leap out into a mystic exultance, of triumph. But still they were anxious.

Only the eyes of that oldest man were not anxious. Black, and fixed, and as if sightless, they watched the sun, seeing beyond the sun. And in their black, empty concentration there was power, power intensely abstract and remote, but deep, deep to the heart of the earth, and the heart of the sun. In absolute motionlessness he watched till the red sun should send his ray through the column of ice. Then the old man would strike, and strike home, accomplish the sacrifice and achieve the power.

The mastery that man must hold, and that passes from race to race.

THINGS

THEY were true idealists, from New England. But that is some time ago: before the War. Several years before the War, they met and married; he a tall, keen-eyed young man from Connecticut, she a smallish, demure, Puritan-looking young woman from Massachusetts. They both had a little money. Not much, however. Even added together, it didn't make three thousand dollars a year. Still—they were free. Free!

Ah! Freedom! To be free to live one's own life! To be twenty-five and twenty-seven, a pair of true idealists with a mutual love of beauty, and an inclination towards 'Indian thought'—meaning, alas, Mrs Besant —and an income a little under three thousand dollars a year! But what is money? All one wishes to do is to live a full and beautiful life. In Europe, of course, right at the fountain-head of tradition. It might possibly be done in America: in New England, for example. But at a forfeiture of a certain amount of 'beauty.' True beauty takes a long time to mature. The baroque is only half-beautiful, half-matured. No, the real silver bloom, the real golden-sweet bouquet of beauty had its roots in the Renaissance, not in any later or shallower period.

Therefore the two idealists, who were married in New Haven, sailed at once to Paris: Paris of the old days. They had a studio apartment on the Boulevard Montparnasse, and they became real Parisians, in the old, delightful sense, not in the modern, vulgar. It was the shimmer of the pure impressionists, Monet and his followers, the world seen in terms of pure light, light broken and unbroken. How lovely! How lovely the nights, the river, the mornings in the old streets and by the flower-stalls and the book-stalls, the afternoons up on Montmartre or in the Tuileries, the evenings on the boulevards!

They both painted, but not desperately. Art had not taken them by the throat, and they did not take Art by the throat. They painted; that's all. They knew people—nice people, if possible, though one had to take them mixed. And they were happy.

Yet it seems as if human beings must set their claws in *something*. To be 'free,' to be 'living a full and beautiful life,' you must, alas, be attached to something. A 'full and beautiful life' means a tight attachment to *something*—at least, it is so for all idealists—or else a certain boredom supervenes; there is a certain waving of loose ends upon the air, like the waving, yearning tendrils of the vine that spread and rotate, seeking something to clutch, something up which to climb towards the necessary sun. Finding nothing, the vine can only trail, half-fulfilled, upon the ground. Such is freedom! —a clutching of the right pole. And human beings are all vines. But especially the idealist. He is a vine, and he needs to clutch and climb. And he despises the man who is a mere *potato*, or turnip, or lump of wood.

Our idealists were frightfully happy, but they were all the time reaching out for something to cotton on to. At first, Paris was enough. They explored Paris *thoroughly*. And they learned French till they almost felt like French people, they could speak it so glibly.

Still, you know, you never talk French with your *soul*. It can't be done. And though it's very thrilling, at first, talking in French to clever Frenchmen—they seem *so* much cleverer than oneself—still, in the long run, it is not satisfying. The endlessly clever *materialism* of the French leaves you cold, in the end, gives a sense of barrenness and incompatibility with true New England depth. So our two idealists felt.

They turned away from France—but ever so gently. France had disappointed them. 'We've loved it, and we've got a great deal out of it. But after a while, after a considerable while, several years, in fact, Paris leaves one feeling disappointed. It hasn't quite got what one wants.'

'But Paris isn't France.'

'No, perhaps not. France is quite different from Paris. And France is lovely—quite lovely. But *to us*, though we love it, it doesn't say a great deal.'

So, when the War came, the idealists moved to Italy. And they loved Italy. They found it beautiful, and more poignant than France. It seemed much nearer to the New England conception of beauty; something pure, and full of sympathy, without the *materialism* and the *cynicism* of the French. The two idealists seemed to breathe their own true air in Italy.

And in Italy, much more than in Paris, they felt they could thrill to the teachings of the Buddha. They entered the swelling stream of modern Buddhistic emotion, and they read the books, and they practised meditation, and they deliberately set themselves to eliminate from their own souls greed, pain, and sorrow. They did not realize—yet—that Buddha's very eagerness to free himself from pain and sorrow is in itself a sort of greed. No, they dreamed of a perfect world, from which all greed, and nearly all pain, and a great deal of sorrow, were eliminated.

But America entered the War, so the two idealists had to help. They did hospital work. And though their experience made them realize more than ever that greed, pain, and sorrow *should* be eliminated from the world, nevertheless, the Buddhism, or the theosophy, didn't emerge very triumphant from the long crisis. Somehow, somewhere, in some part of themselves, they felt that greed, pain, and sorrow would never be eliminated, because most people don't care about eliminating them, and never will care. Our idealists were far too western to think of abandoning all the world to damnation, while they saved their two selves. They were far too unselfish to sit tight under a bo-tree and reach Nirvana in a mere couple.

It was more than that, though. They simply hadn't enough *Sitzfleisch* to squat under a bo-tree and get to Nirvana by contemplating anything, least of all their own navel. If the whole wide world was not going to be saved, they, personally, were not so very keen on being saved just by themselves. No, it would be so lonesome. They were New Englanders, so it must be all or nothing. Greed, pain, and sorrow must either be eliminated from *all the world*, or else, what was the use of eliminating them from oneself? No use at all! One was just a victim.

And so, although they still *loved* 'Indian thought,' and felt very tender about it: well, to go back to our metaphor, the pole up which the green and anxious vines had clambered so far now proved dry-rotten. It snapped, and the vines came slowly subsiding to earth again. There was no crack and crash. The vines held themselves up by their own foliage, for a while. But they subsided. The beanstalk of 'Indian thought' had given way before Jack and Jill had climbed off the tip of it to a further world.

They subsided with a slow rustle back to earth again. But they made no outcry. They were again 'disappointed.' But they never admitted it. 'Indian thought' had let them down. But they never complained. Even to one another, they never said a word. They were disappointed, faintly but deeply disillusioned, and they both knew it. But the knowledge was tacit.

And they still had so much in their lives. They still had Italy—dear Italy. And they still had freedom, the priceless treasure. And they still had so much 'beauty.' About the fullness of their lives they were not quite so sure. They had one little boy, whom they loved as parents should love their children, but whom they wisely refrained from fastening upon, to build their lives on him. No, no, they must live their own lives! They still had strength of mind to know that.

But they were now no longer so very young. Twenty-five and twenty-seven had become thirty-five and thirty-seven. And though they had had a very wonderful time in Europe, and though they still loved Italy—dear Italy! —yet: they were disappointed. They had got a lot out of it: oh, a very great deal indeed! Still, it hadn't given them quite, not *quite*, what they had expected. Europe was lovely, but it was dead. Living in Europe, you were living on the past. And Europeans, with all their superficial charm, were not *really* charming. They were materialistic, they had no *real* soul. They just did not understand the inner urge of the spirit, because the inner urge was dead in them, they were all survivals. There, that was the truth about Europeans: they were survivals, with no more getting ahead in them.

It was another bean-pole, another vine-support crumbled under the green life of the vine. And very bitter it was, this time. For up the old tree-trunk of Europe the green vine had been clambering silently for more than ten years, ten hugely important years, the years of real living. The two idealists had *lived* in Europe, lived on Europe and on European life and European things as vines in an everlasting vineyard.

They had made their home here; a home such as you could never make in America. Their watchword had been 'beauty.' They had rented, the last four years, the second floor of an old palazzo on the Arno, and here they had all their 'things.' And they derived a profound, profound satisfaction from their apartment; the lofty, silent, ancient rooms with windows on the river, with glistening, dark-red floors, and the beautiful furniture that the idealists had 'picked up.'

Yes, unknown to themselves, the lives of the idealists had been running with a fierce swiftness horizontally, all the time. They had become tense, fierce hunters of 'things' for their home. While their souls were climbing up to the sun of old European culture or old Indian thought, their passions were running horizontally, clutching at 'things.' Of course they did not buy the things for the things' sakes, but for the sake of 'beauty.' They looked upon their home as a place entirely furnished by loveliness, not by 'things' at all. Valerie had some very lovely curtains at the windows of the long *salotto*, looking on the river: curtains of queer ancient material that looked like finely knitted silk, most beautifully faded down from vermilion and orange, and gold, and black, down to a sheer soft glow. Valerie hardly ever came into the *salotto* without mentally

falling on her knees before the curtains. 'Chartres!'
she said. 'To me they are Chartres!' And Melville
never turned and looked at his sixteenth-century
Venetian bookcase, with its two or three dozen of choice
books, without feeling his marrow stir in his bones.
The holy of holies!

The child silently, almost sinisterly, avoided any rude
contact with these ancient monuments of furniture, as if
they had been nests of sleeping cobras, or that 'thing'
most perilous to the touch, the Ark of the Covenant.
His childish awe was silent and cold, but final.

Still, a couple of New England idealists cannot live
merely on the bygone glory of their furniture. At least,
one couple could not. They got used to the marvellous
Bologna cupboard, they got used to the wonderful
Venetian bookcase, and the books, and the Siena
curtains and bronzes, and the lovely sofas and side-
tables and chairs they had 'picked up' in Paris. Oh,
they had been picking things up since the first day they
landed in Europe. And they were still at it. It is the
last interest Europe can offer to an outsider; or to an
insider either.

When people came, and were thrilled by the Melville
interior, then Valerie and Erasmus felt they had not
lived in vain; that they still were living. But in the
long mornings, when Erasmus was desultorily working
at Renaissance Florentine literature, and Valerie was
attending to the apartment; and in the long hours after
lunch; and in the long, usually very cold and oppressive
evenings in the ancient palazzo; then the halo died
from around the furniture, and the things became things,
lumps of matter that just stood there or hung there,
ad infinitum, and said nothing; and Valerie and Erasmus
almost hated them. The glow of beauty, like every
other glow, dies down unless it is fed. The idealists
still dearly loved their things. But they had got them.
And the sad fact is, things that glow vividly while you 're
getting them, go almost quite cold after a year or two.
Unless, of course, people envy them very much, and
the museums are pining for them. And the Melvilles'

'things,' though very good, were not quite so good as that.

So, the glow gradually went out of everything, out of Europe, out of Italy—'the Italians are *dears*'—even out of that marvellous apartment on the Arno. 'Why, if I had this apartment, I'd never, never even want to go out of doors! It's too lovely and perfect.' That was something, of course—to hear that.

And yet Valerie and Erasmus went out of doors; they even went out to get away from its ancient, cold-floored, stone-heavy silence and dead dignity. 'We're living on the past, you know, Dick,' said Valerie to her husband. She called him Dick.

They were grimly hanging on. They did not like to give in. They did not like to own up that they were through. For twelve years, now, they had been 'free' people living a 'full and beautiful life.' And America for twelve years had been their anathema, the Sodom and Gomorrah of industrial materialism.

It wasn't easy to own that you were 'through.' They hated to admit that they wanted to go back. But at last, reluctantly, they decided to go, 'for the boy's sake.'—'We can't *bear* to leave Europe. But Peter is an American, so he had better look at America while he's young.' The Melvilles had an entirely English accent and manner; almost; a little Italian and French here and there.

They left Europe behind, but they took as much of it along with them as possible. Several van-loads, as a matter of fact. All those adorable and irreplaceable 'things.' And all arrived in New York, idealists, child, and the huge bulk of Europe they had lugged along.

Valerie had dreamed of a pleasant apartment, perhaps on Riverside Drive, where it was not so expensive as east of Fifth Avenue, and where all their wonderful things would look marvellous. She and Erasmus house-hunted. But alas! their income was quite under three thousand dollars a year. They found—well, everybody knows what they found. Two small rooms and a kitchenette, and don't let us unpack a *thing*!

The chunk of Europe which they had bitten off went into a warehouse, at fifty dollars a month. And they sat in two small rooms and a kitchenette, and wondered why they 'd done it.

Erasmus, of course, ought to get a job. This was what was written on the wall, and what they both pretended not to see. But it had been the strange, vague threat that the Statue of Liberty had always held over them: 'Thou shalt get a job!' Erasmus had the tickets, as they say. A scholastic career was still possible for him. He had taken his exams brilliantly at Yale, and had kept up his 'researches,' all the time he had been in Europe.

But both he and Valerie shuddered. A scholastic career! The scholastic world! The *American* scholastic world! Shudder upon shudder! Give up their freedom, their full and beautiful life? Never! Never! Erasmus would be forty next birthday.

The 'things' remained in warehouse. Valerie went to look at them. It cost her a dollar an hour, and horrid pangs. The 'things,' poor things, looked a bit shabby and wretched, in that warehouse.

However, New York was not all America. There was the great clean west, so the Melvilles went west, with Peter, but without the things. They tried living the simple life, in the mountains. But doing their own chores became almost a nightmare. 'Things' are all very well to look at, but it 's awful handling them, even when they 're beautiful. To be the slave of hideous things, to keep a stove going, cook meals, wash dishes, carry water, and clean floors; pure horror of sordid anti-life!

In the cabin on the mountains, Valerie dreamed of Florence, the lost apartment; and her Bologna cupboard and Louis-Quinze chairs, above all, her 'Chartres' curtains, stood in New York and costing fifty dollars a month.

A millionaire friend came to the rescue, offering them a cottage on the Californian coast—California! Where the new soul is to be born in man. With joy the idealists moved a little farther west, catching at new vine-props of hope.

And finding them straws! The millionaire cottage was perfectly equipped. It was perhaps as labour-savingly perfect as is possible: electric heating and cooking, a white-and-pearl-enamelled kitchen, nothing to make dirt except the human being himself. In an hour or so the idealists had got through their chores. They were 'free'—free to hear the great Pacific pounding the coast, and to feel a new soul filling their bodies.

Alas! the Pacific pounded the coast with hideous brutality, brute force itself! And the new soul, instead of sweetly stealing into their bodies, seemed only meanly to gnaw the old soul out of their bodies. To feel you are under the fist of the most blind and crunching brute force: to feel that your cherished idealist's soul is being gnawed out of you, and only irritation left in place of it: well, it isn't good enough.

After about nine months, the idealists departed from the Californian west. It had been a great experience, they were glad to have had it. But, in the long run, the west was not the place for them, and they knew it. No, the people who wanted new souls had better get them. They, Valerie and Erasmus Melville, would like to develop the old soul a little further. Anyway, they had not felt any influx of new soul, on the Californian coast. On the contrary.

So, with a slight hole in their material capital, they returned to Massachusetts and paid a visit to Valerie's parents, taking the boy along. The grandparents welcomed the child—poor expatriated boy—and were rather cold to Valerie, but really cold to Erasmus. Valerie's mother definitely said to Valerie, one day, that Erasmus ought to take a job, so that Valerie could live decently. Valerie haughtily reminded her mother of the beautiful apartment on the Arno, and the 'wonderful' things in store in New York, and of the 'marvellous and satisfying life' she and Erasmus had led. Valerie's mother said that she didn't think her daughter's life looked so very marvellous at present: homeless, with a husband idle at the age of forty, a child to educate, and a dwindling capital; looked the reverse of marvellous to her. Let Erasmus take some post in one of the universities.

'What post? What university?' interrupted Valerie.

'That could be found, considering your father's connections and Erasmus's qualifications,' replied Valerie's mother. 'And you could get all your valuable things out of store, and have a really lovely home, which everybody in America would be proud to visit. As it is, your furniture is eating up your income, and you are living like rats in a hole, with nowhere to go to.'

This was very true. Valerie was beginning to pine for a home, with her 'things.' Of course she could have sold her furniture for a substantial sum. But nothing would have induced her to. Whatever else passed away, religions, cultures, continents, and hopes, Valerie would *never* part from the 'things' which she and Erasmus had collected with such passion. To these she was nailed.

But she and Erasmus still would not give up that freedom, that full and beautiful life they had so believed in. Erasmus cursed America. He did not *want* to earn a living. He panted for Europe.

Leaving the boy in charge of Valerie's parents, the two idealists once more set off for Europe. In New York they paid two dollars and looked for a brief, bitter hour at their 'things.' They sailed 'student class'— that is, third. Their income now was less than two thousand dollars, instead of three. And they made straight for Paris—cheap Paris.

They found Europe, this time, a complete failure. 'We have returned like dogs to our vomit,' said Erasmus; 'but the vomit has staled in the meantime.' He found he couldn't stand Europe. It irritated every nerve in his body. He hated America too. But America at least was a darn sight better than this miserable, dirt-eating continent; which was by no means cheap any more, either.

Valerie, with her heart on her things—she had really

burned to get them out of that warehouse, where they had stood now for three years, eating up two thousand dollars—wrote to her mother she thought Erasmus would come back if he could get some suitable work in America. Erasmus, in a state of frustration bordering on rage and insanity, just went round Italy in a poverty-stricken fashion, his coat-cuffs fraying, hating everything with intensity. And when a post was found for him in Cleveland University, to teach French, Italian, and Spanish literature, his eyes grew more beady, and his long, queer face grew sharper and more rat-like, with utter baffled fury. He was forty, and the job was upon him.

'I think you'd better accept, dear. You don't care for Europe any longer. As you say, it's dead and finished. They offer us a house on the college lot, and mother says there's room in it for all our things. I think we'd better cable "Accept."'

He glowered at her like a cornered rat. One almost expected to see rat's whiskers twitching at the sides of the sharp nose.

'Shall I send the cablegram?' she asked.

'Send it!' he blurted.

And she went out and sent it.

He was a changed man, quieter, much less irritable. A load was off him. He was inside the cage.

But when he looked at the furnaces of Cleveland, vast and like the greatest of black forests, with red and white-hot cascades of gushing metal, and tiny gnomes of men, and terrific noises, gigantic, he said to Valerie:

'Say what you like, Valerie, this is the biggest thing the modern world has to show.'

And when they were in their up-to-date little house on the college lot of Cleveland University, and that woebegone debris of Europe, Bologna cupboard, Venice book-shelves, Ravenna bishop's chair, Louis-Quinze side-tables, 'Chartres' curtains, Siena bronze lamps, all were arrayed, and all looked perfectly out of keeping, and therefore very impressive; and when the idealists had had a bunch of gaping people in, and Erasmus had showed off in his best European manner, but still quite cordial and American; and Valerie had been most lady-like, but for all that, 'we prefer America'; then Erasmus said, looking at her with queer sharp eyes of a rat:

'Europe's the mayonnaise all right, but America supplies the good old lobster—what?'

'Every time!' she said, with satisfaction.

And he peered at her. He was in the cage; but it was safe inside. And she, evidently, was her real self at last. She had got the goods. Yet round his nose was a queer, evil, scholastic look, of pure scepticism. But he liked lobster.

THE LOVELY LADY

AT seventy-two, Pauline Attenborough could still sometimes be mistaken, in the half-light, for thirty. She really was a wonderfully preserved woman, of perfect *chic*. Of course, it helps a great deal to have the right frame. She would be an exquisite skeleton, and her skull would be an exquisite skull, like that of some Etruscan woman, with feminine charm still in the swerve of the bone and the pretty naïve teeth.

Mrs Attenborough's face was of the perfect oval, and slightly flat type that wears best. There is no flesh to sag. Her nose rode serenely, in its finely bridged curve. Only her big grey eyes were a tiny bit prominent on the surface of her face, and they gave her away most. The bluish lids were heavy, as if they ached sometimes with the strain of keeping the eyes beneath them arch and bright; and at the corners of the eyes were fine little wrinkles which would slacken with haggardness, then be pulled up tense again, to that bright, gay look like a Leonardo woman who really could laugh outright.

Her niece Cecilia was perhaps the only person in the world who was aware of the invisible little wire which connected Pauline's eye-wrinkles with Pauline's will-power. Only Cecilia *consciously* watched the eyes go haggard and old and tired, and remain so, for hours; until Robert came home. Then ping!—the mysterious little wire that worked between Pauline's will and her face went taut, the weary, haggard, prominent eyes suddenly began to gleam, the eyelids arched, the queer curved eyebrows which floated in such frail arches on Pauline's forehead began to gather a mocking significance, and you had the *real* lovely lady, in all her charm.

She really had the secret of everlasting youth; that is to say, she could don her youth again like an eagle. But she was sparing of it. She was wise enough not to try being young for too many people. Her son Robert, in the evenings, and Sir Wilfred Knipe sometimes in the afternoon to tea; then occasional visitors on Sunday, when Robert was home; for these she was her lovely and changeless self, that age could not wither, nor custom stale; so bright and kindly and yet subtly mocking, like Mona Lisa who knew a thing or two. But Pauline knew more, so she needn't be smug at all, she could laugh that lovely mocking Bacchante laugh of hers, which was at the same time never malicious, always good-naturedly tolerant, both of virtues and vices. The former, of course, taking much more tolerating. So she suggested, roguishly.

Only with her niece Cecilia she did not trouble to keep up the glamour. Ciss was not very observant, anyhow; and more than that, she was plain; more still, she was in love with Robert; and most of all, she was thirty, and dependent on her Aunt Pauline. Oh, Cecilia! Why make music for her!

Cecilia, called by her aunt and by her cousin Robert just Ciss, like a cat spitting, was a big, dark-complexioned pug-faced young woman who rarely spoke, and when she did, couldn't get it out. She was the daughter of a poor Congregational minister who had been, while he lived, brother to Ronald, Aunt Pauline's husband. Ronald and the Congregational minister were both well dead, and Aunt Pauline had had charge of Ciss for the last five years.

They lived all together in a quite exquisite though rather small Queen Anne house some twenty-five miles out of town, secluded in a little dale, and surrounded by small but very quaint and pleasant grounds. It was an ideal place and an ideal life for Aunt Pauline, at the age of seventy-two. When the kingfishers flashed up the little stream in the garden, going under the alders, something still flashed in her heart. She was that kind of woman.

Robert, who was two years older than Ciss, went every day to town, to his chambers in one of the Inns. He was a barrister, and, to his secret but very deep mortification, he earned about a hundred pounds a year. He simple *couldn't* get above that figure, though it was rather easy to get below it. . Of course, it didn't matter. Pauline had money. But then what was Pauline's was Pauline's, and though she could give almost lavishly, still, one was always aware of having a *lovely* and *undeserved* present made to one; presents are so much nicer when they are undeserved, Aunt Pauline would say.

Robert too was plain, and almost speechless. He was medium-sized, rather broad and stout, though not fat. Only his creamy, clean-shaven face was rather fat, and sometimes suggestive of an Italian priest, in its silence and its secrecy. But he had grey eyes like his mother, but very shy and uneasy, not bold like hers. Perhaps Ciss was the only person who fathomed his awful shyness and *malaise*, his habitual feeling that he was in the wrong place; almost like a soul that has got into the wrong body. But he never did anything about it. He went up to his chambers, and read law. It was, however, all the weird old processes that interested him. He had, unknown to everybody but his mother, a quite extraordinary collection of old Mexican legal documents, reports of processes and trials, pleas, accusations, the weird and awful mixture of ecclesiastical law and common law in seventeenth-century Mexico. He had started a study in this direction through coming across a report of a trial of two English sailors, for murder, in Mexico in 1620, and he had gone on, when the next document was an accusation against a Don Miguel Estrada for seducing one of the nuns of the Sacred Heart Convent in Oaxaca in 1680.

Pauline and her son Robert had wonderful evenings with these old papers. The lovely lady knew a little Spanish. She even looked a trifle Spanish herself, with a high comb and a marvellous dark brown shawl embroidered in thick silvery silk embroidery. So she would sit at the perfect old table, soft as velvet in its deep brown surface, a high comb in her hair, ear-rings with drooping pendants in her ears, her arms bare and still beautiful, a few strings of pearls round her throat, a puce velvet dress on and this or another beautiful shawl, and by candlelight she looked, yes, a Spanish high-bred beauty of thirty-two or three. She set the candles to give her face just the chiaroscuro she knew suited her; her high chair that rose behind her face was done in old green brocade, against which her face emerged like a Christmas rose.

They were always three at table; and they always drank a bottle of champagne: Pauline two glasses, Ciss two glasses, Robert the rest. The lovely lady sparkled and was radiant. Ciss, her black hair bobbed, her broad shoulders in a very nice and becoming dress that Aunt Pauline had helped her to make, stared from her aunt to her cousin and back again, with rather confused, mute, hazel eyes, and played the part of an audience suitably impressed. She *was* impressed, somewhere, all the time. And even rendered speechless by Pauline's brilliancy, even after five years. But at the bottom of her consciousness were the data of as weird a document as Robert ever studied; all the things she knew about her aunt and cousin.

Robert was always a gentleman, with an old-fashioned punctilious courtesy that covered his shyness quite completely. He was, and Ciss knew it, more confused than shy. He was worse than she was. Cecilia's own confusion dated from only five years back—Robert's must have started before he was born. In the lovely lady's womb he must have felt *very* confused.

He paid all his attention to his mother, drawn to her as a humble flower to the sun. And yet, priest-like, he was all the time aware, with the tail of his conscious-ness, that Ciss was there, and that she was a bit shut out of it, and that something wasn't right. He was aware of the third consciousness in the room. Whereas to Pauline, her niece Cecilia was an appropriate part of her own setting, rather than a distant consciousness.

Robert took coffee with his mother and Ciss in the warm drawing-room, where all the furniture was so lovely, all collectors' pieces—Mrs Attenborough had made her own money, dealing privately in pictures and furniture and rare things from barbaric countries—and the three talked desultorily till about eight or half-past. It was very pleasant, very cosy, very homely even; Pauline made a real home cosiness out of so much elegant material. The chat was simple, and nearly always bright. Pauline was her *real* self, emanating a friendly mockery and an odd, ironic gaiety. Till there came a little pause.

At which Ciss always rose and said good night and carried out the coffee tray, to prevent Burnett from intruding any more.

And then! Oh, then, the lovely glowing intimacy of the evening, between mother and son, when they deciphered manuscripts and discussed points, Pauline with that eagerness of a girl, for which she was famous. And it was quite genuine. In some mysterious way she had *saved up* her power for being thrilled, in connection with a man. Robert, solid, rather quiet and subdued, seemed like the elder of the two; almost like a priest with a young girl pupil. And that was rather how he felt.

Ciss had a flat for herself just across the courtyard, over the old coach-house and stables. There were no horses. Robert kept his car in the coach-house. Ciss had three very nice rooms up there, stretching along in a row one after another, and she had got used to the ticking of the stable clock.

But sometimes she did not go up to her rooms. In the summer she would sit on the lawn, and from the open window of the drawing-room upstairs she would hear Pauline's wonderful heart-searching laugh. And in the winter the young woman would put on a thick coat and walk slowly to the little balustraded bridge over the stream, and then look back at the three lighted windows of that drawing-room where mother and son were so happy together.

Ciss loved Robert, and she believed that Pauline intended the two of them to marry; when she was dead. But poor Robert, he was so convulsed with shyness already, with man or woman. What would he be when his mother was dead—in a dozen more years? He would be just a shell, the shell of a man who had never lived.

The strange unspoken sympathy of the young with one another, when they are overshadowed by the old, was one of the bonds between Robert and Ciss. But another bond, which Ciss did not know how to draw tight, was the bond of passion. Poor Robert was by nature a passionate man. His silence and his agonized, though hidden, shyness were both the result of a secret physical passionateness. And how Pauline could play on this! Ah, Ciss was not blind to the eyes which he fixed on his mother, eyes fascinated yet humiliated, full of shame. He was ashamed that he was not a man. And he did not love his mother. He was fascinated by her. Completely fascinated. And for the rest, paralysed in a life-long confusion.

Ciss stayed in the garden till the lights leapt up in Pauline's bedroom—about ten o'clock. The lovely lady had retired. Robert would now stay another hour or so, alone. Then he too would retire. Ciss, in the dark outside, sometimes wished she could creep up to him and say: 'Oh, Robert! It's all wrong!' But Aunt Pauline would hear. And anyhow, Ciss couldn't do it. She went off to her own rooms, once more, and so for ever.

In the morning coffee was brought up on a tray to each of the three relatives. Ciss had to be at Sir Wilfred Knipe's at nine o'clock, to give two hours' lessons to his little granddaughter. It was her sole serious occupation, except that she played the piano for the love of it. Robert set off to town about nine. And, as a rule, Aunt Pauline appeared to lunch, though sometimes not until tea-time. When she appeared, she looked fresh and young. But she was inclined to fade rather quickly, like a flower without water, in the day-time. Her hour was the candle-hour.

So she always rested in the afternoon. When the sun shone, if possible she took a sun-bath. This was one of her secrets.   Her lunch was very light, she could take her sun-and-air-bath before noon or after, as it pleased her.   Often it was in the afternoon, when the sun shone very warmly into a queer little yew-walled square just behind the stables.   Here Ciss stretched out the lying-chair and rugs, and put the light parasol handy in the silent little enclosure of thick dark yew-hedges beyond the red walls of the unused stables.   And hither came the lovely lady with her book.   Ciss then had to be on guard in one of her own rooms, should her aunt, who was very keen-eared, hear a footstep.

One afternoon it occurred to Cecilia that she herself might while away this rather long afternoon by taking a sun bath.   She was growing restive.   The thought of the flat roof of the stable buildings, to which she could climb from a loft at the end, started her on a new adventure.   She often went on to the roof; she had to, to wind up the stable clock, which was a job she had assumed to herself.   Now she took a rug, climbed out under the heavens, looked at the sky and the great elm-tops, looked at the sun, then took off her things and lay down perfectly serenely, in a corner of the roof under the parapet, full in the sun.

It was rather lovely, to bask all one's length like this in warm sun and air.   Yes, it was very lovely!   It even seemed to melt some of the hard bitterness of her heart, some of that core of unspoken resentment which never dissolved.   Luxuriously, she spread herself, so that the sun should touch her limbs fully, fully.   If she had no other lover, she should have the sun!   She rolled voluptuously.   And suddenly, her heart stood still in her body, and her hair almost rose on end as a voice said very softly, musingly in her ear:

'No, Henry dear!   It was not my fault you died instead of marrying that Claudia.   No, darling, I was quite, quite willing for you to marry her, unsuitable though she was.'

Cecilia sank down on her rug powerless and perspiring with dread.   That awful voice, so soft, so musing, yet so unnatural.   Not a human voice at all.   Yet there must, there must be someone on the roof! Oh! how unspeakably awful!

She lifted her weak head and peeped across the sloping leads. Nobody! The chimneys were far too narrow to shelter anybody. There was nobody on the roof. Then it must be someone in the trees, in the elms. Either that, or terror unspeakable, a bodiless voice! She reared her head a little higher.

And as she did so, came the voice again:

'No, darling! I told you you would tire of her in six months. And you see, it was true, dear. It was true, true, true! I wanted to spare you that. So it wasn't I who made you feel weak and disabled, wanting that very silly Claudia; poor thing, she looked so woebegone afterwards! Wanting her and not wanting her, you got *yourself* into that perplexity, my dear. I only warned you. What else could I do? And you lost your spirit and died without ever knowing me again. It was bitter, bitter——'

The voice faded away. Cecilia subsided weakly on to her rug, after the anguished tension of listening. Oh, it was awful. The sun shone, the sky was blue, all seemed so lovely and afternoony and summery. And yet, oh, horror!—she was going to be forced to believe in the supernatural! And she loathed the supernatural, ghosts and voices and rappings and all the rest.

But that awful creepy bodiless voice, with its rusty sort of whisper of an overtone! It had something so fearfully familiar in it too! and yet was so utterly uncanny. Poor Cecilia could only lie there unclothed, and so all the more agonizingly helpless, inert, collapsed in sheer dread.

And then she heard the thing sigh! A deep sigh that seemed weirdly familiar, yet was not human. 'Ah, well; ah, well, the heart must bleed! Better it should bleed than break. It is grief, grief! But it wasn't my fault, dear. And Robert could marry our poor dull Ciss to-morrow, if he wanted her. But he doesn't care about it, so why force him into anything!' The sounds were very uneven, sometimes only a husky sort of whisper. Listen! Listen!

Cecilia was about to give vent to loud and piercing screams of hysteria, when the last two sentences arrested her. All her caution and her cunning sprang alert. It was Aunt Pauline! It must be Aunt Pauline, practising ventriloquism or something like that! What a devil she was!

Where was she? She must be lying down there, right below where Cecilia herself was lying. And it was either some fiend's trick of ventriloquism, or else thought transference that conveyed itself like sound. The sounds were very uneven. Sometimes quite inaudible, sometimes only a brushing sort of noise. Ciss listened intently. No, it could not be ventriloquism. It was worse, some form of thought transference. Some horror of that sort. Cecilia still lay weak and inert, terrified to move, but she was growing calmer with suspicion. It was some diabolic trick of that unnatural woman.

But *what a devil* of a woman! She even knew that she, Cecilia, had mentally accused her of killing her son Henry. Poor Henry was Robert's elder brother, twelve years older than Robert. He had died suddenly when he was twenty-two, after an awful struggle with himself, because he was passionately in love with a young and very good-looking actress, and his mother had humorously despised him for the attachment. So he had caught some sudden ordinary disease, but the poison had gone to his brain and killed him, before he ever regained consciousness. Ciss knew the few facts from her own father. And lately, she had been thinking that Pauline was going to kill Robert as she had killed Henry. It was clear murder: a mother murdering her sensitive sons, who were fascinated by her: the Circe!

'I suppose I may as well get up,' murmured the dim unbreaking voice. 'Too much sun is as bad as too little. Enough sun, enough love thrill, enough proper food, and not too much of any of them, and a woman might live for ever. I verily believe for ever. If she absorbs as much vitality as she expends! Or perhaps a trifle more!'

It was certainly Aunt Pauline! How, how horrible!
She, Ciss, was hearing Aunt Pauline's thoughts. Oh,
how horrible! She, Ciss, was hearing Aunt Pauline's
thoughts. Oh, how ghastly! Aunt Pauline was sending out her thoughts in a sort of radio, and she, Ciss,
had to *hear* what her aunt was thinking. How ghastly!
How insufferable! One of them would surely have to
die.

She twisted and she lay inert and crumpled, staring
vacantly in front of her. Vacantly! Vacantly! And
her eyes were staring almost into a hole. She was staring
into it unseeing, a hole going down in the corner from
the lead gutter. It meant nothing to her. Only it
frightened her a little more.

When suddenly out of the hole came a sigh and a last
whisper. 'Ah, well! Pauline! Get up, it's enough
for to-day!' Good God! Out of the hole of the rain-
pipe! The rain-pipe was acting as a speaking-tube!
Impossible! No, quite possible. She had read of it
even in some book. And Aunt Pauline, like the old and
guilty woman she was, talked aloud to herself. That
was it!

A sullen exultance sprang into Ciss's breast. *That*
was why she would never have anybody, not even
Robert, in her bedroom. That was why she never dozed
in a chair, never sat absent-minded anywhere, but went
to her room, and kept to her room, except when she
roused herself to be alert. When she slackened off, she
talked to herself! She talked in a soft little crazy voice,
to herself. But she was not crazy. It was only her
thoughts murmuring themselves aloud.

So she had qualms about poor Henry! Well she
might have! Ciss believed that Aunt Pauline had
loved her big, handsome, brilliant first-born much more
than she loved Robert, and that his death had been a
terrible blow and a chagrin to her. Poor Robert had
been only ten years old when Henry died. Since then
he had been the substitute.

Ah, how awful!

But Aunt Pauline was a strange woman. She had

left her husband when Henry was a small child, some years even before Robert was born. There was no quarrel. Sometimes she saw her husband again, quite amicably, but a little mockingly. And she even gave him money.

For Pauline earned all her own. Her father had been a consul in the east and in Naples; and a devoted collector of beautiful and exotic things. When he died, soon after his grandson Henry was born, he left his collection of treasures to his daughter. And Pauline, who had really a passion and a genius for loveliness, whether in texture or form or colour, had laid the basis of her fortune on her father's collection. She had gone on collecting, buying where she could, and selling to collectors and to museums. She was one of the first to sell old, weird African wooden figures to the museums, and ivory carvings from New Guinea. She bought Renoir as soon as she saw his pictures. But not Rousseau. And all by herself, she made a fortune.

After her husband died, she had not married again. She was not even *known* to have had lovers. If she did have lovers, it was not among the men who had admired her most and paid her devout and open attendance. To these she was a 'friend.'

Cecilia slipped on her clothes and caught up her rug, hastened carefully down the ladder to the loft. As she descended she heard the ringing musical call: 'All right, Ciss!' which meant that the lovely lady was finished, and returning to the house. Even her voice was marvellously young and sonorous, beautifully balanced and self-possessed. So different from the little voice in which she talked to herself. *That* was much more the voice of an old woman.

Ciss hastened round to the yew enclosure, where lay the comfortable chaise-longue with the various delicate rugs. Everything Pauline had was choice, to the fine straw mat on the floor. The great yew walls were beginning to cast long shadows. Only in the corner, where the rugs tumbled their delicate colours, was there hot, still sunshine.

The rugs folded up, the chair lifted away, Cecilia stooped to look at the mouth of the rain-pipe. There it was, in the corner, under a little hood of masonry and just projecting from the thick leaves of the creeper on the wall. If Pauline, lying there, turned her face towards the wall, she would speak into the very mouth of the hole. Cecilia was reassured. She had heard her aunt's thoughts indeed, but by no uncanny agency.

That evening, as if aware of something, Pauline was a little quicker than usual, though she looked her own serene, rather mysterious self. And after coffee she said to Robert and Ciss: 'I'm so sleepy. The sun has made me so sleepy. I feel full of sunshine like a bee. I shall go to bed, if you don't mind. You two sit and have a talk.'

Cecilia looked quickly at her cousin.

'Perhaps you would rather be alone,' she said to him.

'No, no,' he replied. 'Do keep me company for a while, if it doesn't bore you.'

The windows were open, the scent of the honeysuckle wafted in, with the sound of an owl. Robert smoked in silence. There was a sort of despair in the motionless, rather squat body. He looked like a caryatid bearing a weight.

'Do you remember Cousin Henry?' Cecilia asked him suddenly.

He looked up in surprise.

'Yes, very well,' he said.

'What did he look like?' she said, glancing into her cousin's big, secret-troubled eyes, in which there was so much frustration.

'Oh, he was handsome; tall and fresh-coloured, with mother's soft brown hair.' As a matter of fact, Pauline's hair was grey. 'The ladies admired him very much; he was at all the dances.'

'And what kind of character had he?'

'Oh, very good-natured and jolly. He liked to be amused. He was rather quick and clever, like mother, and very good company.'

'And did he love your mother?'

'Very much. She loved him too—better than she does me, as a matter of fact. He was so much more nearly her idea of a man.'

'Why was he more her idea of a man?'

'Tall—handsome—attractive, and very good company—and would, I believe, have been very successful at law. I'm afraid I am merely negative in all those respects.'

Ciss looked at him attentively, with her slow-thinking hazel eyes. Under his impassive mask, she knew he suffered.

'Do you think you are so much more negative than he?' she said.

He did not lift his face. But after a few moments he replied:

'My life, certainly, is a negative affair.'

She hesitated before she dared ask him:

'And do you mind?'

He did not answer her at all. Her heart sank.

'You see, I am afraid my life is as negative as yours is,' she said. 'And I'm beginning to mind bitterly. I'm thirty.'

She saw his creamy, well-bred hand tremble.

'I suppose,' he said, without looking at her, 'one will rebel when it is too late.'

That was queer, from him.

'Robert,' she said, 'do you like me at all?'

She saw his dusky, creamy face, so changeless in its folds, go pale.

'I am very fond of you,' he murmured.

'Won't you kiss me? Nobody ever kisses me,' she said pathetically.

He looked at her, his eyes strange with fear and a certain haughtiness. Then he rose and came softly over to her, and kissed her gently on the cheek.

'It's an awful shame, Ciss!' he said softly.

She caught his hand and pressed it to her breast.

'And sit with me some time in the garden,' she said, murmuring with difficulty. 'Won't you?'

He looked at her anxiously and searchingly.

'What about mother?' he said.

Ciss smiled a funny little smile, and looked into his eyes. He suddenly flushed crimson, turning aside his face. It was a painful sight.

'I know,' he said, 'I am no lover of women.'

He spoke with sarcastic stoicism against himself, but even she did not know the shame it was to him.

'You never try to be!' she said.

Again his eyes changed uncannily.

'Does one have to try?' he said.

'Why, yes! One never does anything if one doesn't try.'

He went pale again.

'Perhaps you are right,' he said.

In a few minutes she left him, and went to her rooms. At least, she had tried to take off the everlasting lid from things.

The weather continued sunny, Pauline continued her sun-baths, and Ciss lay on the roof eavesdropping in the literal sense of the word. But Pauline was not to be heard. No sound came up the pipe. She must be lying with her face away into the open. Ciss listened with all her might. She could just detect the faintest, faintest murmur away below, but no audible syllable.

And at night, under the stars, Cecilia sat and waited in silence, on the seat which kept in view the drawing-room windows and the side-door into the garden. She saw the light go up in her aunt's room. She saw the lights at last go out in the drawing-room. And she waited. But he did not come. She stayed on in the darkness half the night, while the owl hooted. But she stayed alone.

Two days she heard nothing, her aunt's thoughts were not revealed and at evening nothing happened. Then the second night, as she sat with heavy, helpless persistence in the garden, suddenly she started. He had come out. She rose and went softly over the grass to him.

'Don't speak,' he murmured.

And in silence, in the dark, they walked down the

garden and over the little bridge to the paddock, where the hay, cut very late, was in cock. There they stood disconsolate under the stars.

'You see,' he said, 'how can I ask for love, if I don't feel any love in myself? You know I have a real regard for you——'

'How can you feel any love, when you never feel anything?' she said.

'That is true,' he replied.

And she waited for what next.

'And how can I marry?' he said. 'I am a failure even at making money. I can't ask my mother for money.'

She sighed deeply.

'Then don't bother yet about marrying,' she said. 'Only love me a little. Won't you?'

He gave a short laugh.

'It sounds atrocious, to say it is hard to begin,' he said.

She sighed again. He was so stiff to move.

'Shall we sit down a minute,' she said. And then as they sat on the hay, she added: 'May I touch you? Do you mind?'

'Yes, I mind! But do as you wish,' he replied, with that mixture of shyness and queer candour which made him a little ridiculous, as he knew quite well. But in his heart there was almost murder.

She touched his black, always tidy hair with her fingers.

'I suppose I shall rebel one day,' he said again, suddenly.

They sat some time, till it grew chilly. And he held her hand fast, but he never put his arms round her. At last she rose and went indoors, saying good night.

The next day, as Cecilia lay stunned and angry on the roof, taking her sun-bath, and becoming hot and fierce with sunshine, suddenly she started. A terror seized her in spite of herself. It was the voice.

'*Caro, caro, tu non l' hai visto!*' it was murmuring away, in a language Cecilia did not understand. She lay and writhed her limbs in the sun, listening intently to words she could not follow. Softly, whisperingly, with infinite caressiveness and yet with that subtle, insidious arrogance under its velvet, came the voice, murmuring in Italian: *'Bravo, si molto bravo, poverino, ma uomo come te non lo sarà mai, mai, mai!'* Oh, especially in Italian Cecilia heard the poisonous charm of the voice, so caressive, so soft and flexible, yet so utterly egoistic. She hated it with intensity as it sighed and whispered out of nowhere. Why, why should it be so delicate, so subtle and flexible and beautifully controlled, while she herself was so clumsy! Oh, poor Cecilia, she writhed in the afternoon sun, knowing her own clownish clumsiness and lack of suavity, in comparison.

'No, Robert dear, you will never be the man your father was, though you have some of his looks. He was a marvellous lover, soft as a flower yet piercing as a humming-bird. No, Robert dear, you will never know how to serve a woman as Monsignor Mauro did. *Cara, cara mia bellissima, ti ho aspettato come l'agonizzante aspetta la morte, morte deliziosa, quasi quasi troppo deliziosa per un' anima humana*—Soft as a flower, yet probing like a humming-bird. He gave himself to a woman as he gave himself to God. Mauro! Mauro! How you loved me!'

The voice ceased in reverie, and Cecilia knew what she had guessed before, that Robert was not the son of her Uncle Ronald, but of some Italian.

'I am disappointed in you, Robert. There is no poignancy in you. Your father was a Jesuit, but he was the most perfect and poignant lover in the world. You are a Jesuit like a fish in a tank. And that Ciss of yours is the cat fishing for you. It is less edifying even than poor Henry.'

Cecilia suddenly bent her mouth down to the tube, and said in a deep voice:

'Leave Robert alone! Don't kill him as well.'

There was a dead silence, in the hot July afternoon that was lowering for thunder. Cecilia lay prostrate, her heart beating in great thumps. She was listening as if her whole soul were an ear. At last she caught the whisper:

'Did someone speak?'

She leaned again to the mouth of the tube.

'Don't kill Robert as you killed me,' she said with slow enunciation, and a deep but small voice.

'Ah!' came the sharp little cry. 'Who is that speaking?'

'Henry!' said the deep voice.

There was a dead silence. Poor Cecilia lay with all the use gone out of her. And there was dead silence. Till at last came the whisper:

'I didn't kill Henry. No, NO! Henry, surely you can't blame me! I loved you, dearest. I only wanted to help you.'

'You killed me!' came the deep, artificial, accusing voice. 'Now, let Robert live. Let him go! Let him marry!'

There was a pause.

'How very, very awful!' mused the whispering voice. 'Is it possible, Henry, you are a spirit, and you condemn me?'

'Yes! I condemn you!'

Cecilia felt all her pent-up rage going down that rain-pipe. At the same time, she almost laughed. It was awful.

She lay and listened and listened. No sound! As if time had ceased, she lay inert in the weakening sun. The sky was yellowing. Quickly she dressed herself, went down, and out to the corner of the stables.

'Aunt Pauline!' she called discreetly. 'Did you hear thunder?'

'Yes! I am going in. Don't wait,' came a feeble voice.

Cecilia retired, and from the loft watched, spying, as the figure of the lovely lady, wrapped in a lovely wrap of old blue silk, went rather totteringly to the house.

The sky gradually darkened, Cecilia hastened in with the rugs. Then the storm broke. Aunt Pauline did not appear for tea. She found the thunder trying. Robert also did not arrive till after tea, in the pouring rain. Cecilia went down the covered passage to her own house, and dressed carefully for dinner, putting some white columbines at her breast.

The drawing-room was lit with a softly shaded lamp. Robert, dressed, was waiting, listening to the rain. He too, seemed strangely crackling and on edge. Cecilia came in, with the white flowers nodding at her breast. Robert was watching her curiously, a new look on his face. Cecilia went to the bookshelves near the door, and was peering for something, listening acutely. She heard a rustle, then the door softly opening. And as it opened, Ciss suddenly switched on the strong electric light by the door.

Her aunt, in a dress of black lace over ivory colour, stood in the doorway. Her face was made up, but haggard with a look of unspeakable irritability, as if years of suppressed exasperation and dislike of her fellow-men had suddenly crumpled her into an old witch.

'Oh, aunt!' cried Cecilia.

'Why, mother, you're a little old lady!' came the astounded voice of Robert; like an astonished boy; as if it were a joke.

'Have you only just found it out?' snapped the old woman venomously.

'Yes! Why, I thought——' His voice tailed out in misgiving.

The haggard, old Pauline, in a frenzy of exasperation, said:

'Aren't we going down?'

She had never even noticed the excess of light, a thing she shunned.   And she went downstairs almost tottering.

At table she sat with her face like a crumpled mask of unspeakable irritability.   She looked old, very old, and like a witch.   Robert and Cecilia fetched furtive glances at her.   And Ciss, watching Robert, saw that he was so astonished and repelled by his mother's looks, that he was another man.

'What kind of a drive home did you have?' snapped Pauline, with an almost gibbering irritability.

'It rained, of course,' he said.

'How clever of you to have found that out!' said his mother, with the grisly grin of malice that had succeeded her arch smirk.

'I don't understand,' he said with quiet suavity.

'It's apparent,' said his mother, rapidly and sloppily eating her food.

She rushed through the meal like a crazy dog, to the utter consternation of the servant. And the moment it was over, she darted in a queer, crab-like way upstairs. Robert and Cecilia followed her, thunderstruck, like two conspirators.

'You pour the coffee. I loathe it! I'm going! Good night!' said the old woman, in a succession of sharp shots. And she scrambled out of the room.

There was a dead silence. At last he said:

'I'm afraid mother isn't well. I must persuade her to see a doctor.'

'Yes!' said Cecilia.

The evening passed in silence. Robert and Ciss stayed on in the drawing-room, having lit a fire. Outside was cold rain. Each pretended to read. They did not want to separate. The evening passed with ominous mysteriousness, yet quickly.

At about ten o'clock, the door suddenly opened, and Pauline appeared, in a blue wrap. She shut the door behind her, and came to the fire. Then she looked at the two young people in hate, real hate.

'You two had better get married quickly,' she said in an ugly voice. 'It would look more decent; such a passionate pair of lovers!'

Robert looked up at her quietly.

'I thought you believed that cousins should not marry, mother,' he said.

'I do! But you're not cousins. Your father was an Italian priest.' Pauline held her daintily slippered foot to the fire, in an old coquettish gesture. Her body tried to repeat all the old graceful gestures. But the nerve had snapped, so it was a rather dreadful caricature.

'Is that really true, mother?' he asked.

'True! What do you think? He was a distinguished man, or he wouldn't have been my lover. He was far too distinguished a man to have had you for a son. But that joy fell to me.'

'How unfortunate all round,' he said slowly.

'Unfortunate for you? *You* were lucky. It was *my* misfortune,' she said acidly to him.

She was really a dreadful sight, like a piece of lovely Venetian glass that has been dropped, and gathered up again in horrible, sharp-edged fragments.

Suddenly she left the room again.

For a week it went on. She did not recover. It was as if every nerve in her body had suddenly started screaming in an insanity of discordance. The doctor came, and gave her sedatives, for she never slept. Without drugs, she never slept at all, only paced back and forth in her room, looking hideous and evil, reeking with malevolence. She could not bear to see either her son or her niece. Only when either of them came, she asked in pure malice:

'Well! When's the wedding? Have you celebrated the nuptials yet?'

At first Cecilia was stunned by what she had done. She realized vaguely that her aunt, once a definite thrust of condemnation had penetrated her beautiful armour, had just collapsed squirming inside her shell. It was too terrible. Ciss was almost terrified into repentance. Then she thought: This is what she always was. Now let her live the rest of her days in her true colours.

But Pauline would not live long. She was literally shrivelling away. She kept her room, and saw no one. She had her mirrors taken away.

Robert and Cecilia sat a good deal together. The jeering of the mad Pauline had not driven them apart, as she had hoped. But Cecilia dared not confess to him what she had done.

'Do you think your mother ever loved anybody?' Ciss asked him tentatively, rather wistfully, one evening.

He looked at her fixedly.

'Herself!' he said at last.

'She didn't even *love* herself,' said Ciss. 'It was something else—what was it?' She lifted a troubled, utterly puzzled face to him.

'Power!' he said curtly.

'But what power?' she asked. 'I don't understand.'

'Power to feed on other lives,' he said bitterly. 'She was beautiful, and she fed on life. She has fed on me as she fed on Henry. She put a sucker into one's soul, and sucked up one's essential life.'

'And don't you forgive her?'

'No.'

'Poor Aunt Pauline!'

But even Ciss did not mean it. She was only aghast.

'I *know* I've got a heart,' he said, passionately striking his breast. 'But it's almost sucked dry. I *know* people who want power over others.'

Ciss was silent; what was there to say?

And two days later, Pauline was found dead in her bed, having taken too much veronal, for her heart was weakened. From the grave even she hit back at her son and her niece. She left Robert the noble sum of one thousand pounds; and Ciss one hundred. All the rest, with the nucleus of her valuable antiques, went to form the 'Pauline Attenborough Museum.'

SKETCHES AND ESSAYS

1958

ADOLF

When we were children our father often worked on the night shift. Once it was springtime, and he used to arrive home, black and tired, just as we were downstairs in our night-dresses. Then night met morning face to face, and the contact was not always happy. Perhaps it was painful to my father to see us gaily entering upon the day into which he dragged himself soiled and weary. He didn't like going to bed in the spring morning sunshine.

But sometimes he was happy, because of his long walk through the dewy fields in the first daybreak. He loved the open morning, the crystal and the space, after a night down pit. He watched every bird, every stir in the trembling grass, answered the whinnying of the pewits and tweeted to the wrens. If he could, he also would have whinnied and tweeted and whistled in a native language that was not human. He liked non-human things best.

One sunny morning we were all sitting at table when we heard his heavy slurring walk up the entry. We became uneasy. His was always a disturbing presence, trammelling. He passed the window darkly, and we heard him go into the scullery and put down his tin bottle. But directly he came into the kitchen. We felt at once that he had something to communicate. No one spoke. We watched his black face for a second.

'Give me a drink,' he said.

My mother hastily poured out his tea. He went to pour it out into his saucer. But instead of drinking he suddenly put something on the table among the teacups. A tiny brown rabbit! A small rabbit, a mere morsel, sitting against the bread as still as if it were a made thing.

'A rabbit! A young one! Who gave it you, father?'

But he laughed enigmatically, with a sliding motion of his yellow-grey eyes, and went to take off his coat.   We pounced on the rabbit.

'Is it alive?   Can you feel its heart beat?'

My father came back and sat down heavily in his armchair.   He dragged his saucer to him, and blew his tea, pushing out his red lips under his black moustache.

'Where did you get it, father?'

'I picked it up,' he said, wiping his naked forearm over his mouth and beard.

'Where?'

'It is a wild one!' came my mother's quick voice.

'Yes, it is.'

'Then why did you bring it?' cried my mother.

'Oh, we wanted it,' came our cry.

'Yes, I 've no doubt you did——' retorted my mother. But she was drowned in our clamour of questions.

On the field path my father had found a dead mother rabbit and three dead little ones—this one alive, but unmoving.

'But what had killed them, daddy?'

'I couldn't say, my child.   I s'd think she 'd aten something.'

'Why did you bring it!' again my mother's voice of condemnation.   'You know what it will be.'

My father made no answer, but we were loud in protest.

'He must bring it.   It 's not big enough to live by itself.   It would die,' we shouted.

'Yes, and it will die now.   And then there 'll be *another* outcry.'

My mother set her face against the tragedy of dead pets.   Our hearts sank.

'It won't die, father, will it?   Why will it?   It won't.'

'I s'd think not,' said my father.

'You know well enough it will.   Haven't we had it all before!' said my mother.

'They dunna always pine,' replied my father testily.

But my mother reminded him of other little wild animals he had brought, which had sulked and refused to live, and brought storms of tears and trouble in our house of lunatics.

Trouble fell on us. The little rabbit sat on our lap, unmoving, its eye wide and dark. We brought it milk, warm milk, and held it to its nose. It sat as still as if it was far away, retreated down some deep burrow, hidden, oblivious. We wetted its mouth and whiskers with drops of milk. It gave no sign, did not even shake off the wet white drops. Somebody began to shed a few secret tears.

'What did I say?' cried my mother. 'Take it and put it down in the field.'

Her command was in vain. We were driven to get dressed for school. There sat the rabbit. It was like a tiny obscure cloud. Watching it, the emotions died out of our breast. Useless to love it, to yearn over it. Its little feelings were all ambushed. They must be circumvented. Love and affection were a trespass upon it. A little wild thing, it became more mute and asphyxiated still in its own arrest, when we approached with love. We must not love it. We must circumvent it, for its own existence.

So I passed the order to my sister and my mother. The rabbit was not to be spoken to, nor even looked at. Wrapping it in a piece of flannel I put it in an obscure corner of the cold parlour, and put a saucer of milk before its nose. My mother was forbidden to enter the parlour whilst we were at school.

'As if I should take any notice of your nonsense,' she cried, affronted. Yet I doubt if she ventured into the parlour.

At midday, after school, creeping into the front room, there we saw the rabbit still and unmoving in the piece of flannel. Strange grey-brown neutralization of life, still living! It was a sore problem to us.

'Why won't it drink its milk, mother?' we whispered. Our father was asleep.

'It prefers to sulk its life away, silly little thing.' A profound problem. Prefers to sulk its life away! We put young dandelion leaves to its nose. The sphinx was not more oblivious. Yet its eye was bright.

At tea-time, however, it had hopped a few inches, out of its flannel, and there it sat again, uncovered, a little solid cloud of muteness, brown, with unmoving whiskers. Only its side palpitated slightly with life.

Darkness came; my father set off to work. The rabbit was still unmoving. Dumb despair was coming over the sisters, a threat of tears before bedtime. Clouds of my mother's anger gathered as she muttered against my father's wantonness.

Once more the rabbit was wrapped in the old pit singlet. But now it was carried into the scullery and put under the copper fire-place, that it might imagine itself inside a burrow. The saucers were placed about, four or five, here and there on the floor, so that if the little creature *should* chance to hop abroad, it could not fail to come upon some food. After this my mother was allowed to take from the scullery what she wanted and then she was forbidden to open the door.

When morning came and it was light, I went downstairs. Opening the scullery door, I heard a slight scuffle. Then I saw dabbles of milk all over the floor and tiny rabbit-droppings in the saucers. And there was the miscreant, the tips of his ears showing behind a pair of boots. I peeped at him. He sat bright-eyed and askance, twitching his nose and looking at me while not looking at me.

He was alive—very much alive. But still we were afraid to trespass much on his confidence.

'Father!' My father was arrested at the door. 'Father, the rabbit's alive.'

'Back your life it is,' said my father.

'Mind how you go in.'

By evening, however, the little creature was tame, quite tame. He was christened Adolf. We were enchanted by him. We couldn't really love him, because he was wild and loveless to the end. But he was an unmixed delight.

We decided he was too small to live in a hutch—he must live at large in the house. My mother protested, but in vain. He was so tiny. So we had him upstairs, and he dropped his tiny pills on the bed and we were enchanted.

Adolf made himself instantly at home. He had the run of the house, and was perfectly happy, with his tunnels and his holes behind the furniture.

We loved him to take meals with us. He would sit on the table humping his back, sipping his milk, shaking his whiskers and his tender ears, hopping off and hobbling back to his saucer, with an air of supreme unconcern. Suddenly he was alert. He hobbled a few tiny paces, and reared himself up inquisitively at the sugar basin. He fluttered his tiny fore-paws, and then reached and laid them on the edge of the basin, whilst he craned his thin neck and peeped in. He trembled his whiskers at the sugar, then did his best to lift down a lump.

'*Do* you think I will have it! Animals in the sugar pot!' cried my mother, with a rap of her hand on the table.

Which so delighted the electric Adolf that he flung his hindquarters and knocked over a cup.

'It's your own fault, mother. If you left him alone——'

He continued to take tea with us. He rather liked warm tea. And he loved sugar. Having nibbled a lump, he would turn to the butter. There he was shooed off by our parent. He soon learned to treat her shooing with indifference. Still, she hated him to put his nose in the food. And he loved to do it. And one day between them they overturned the cream-jug. Adolf deluged his little chest, bounced back in terror, was seized by his little ears by my mother and bounced down on the hearth-rug. There he shivered in momentary discomfort, and suddenly set off in a wild flight to the parlour.

This last was his happy hunting ground. He had cultivated the bad habit of pensively nibbling certain bits of cloth in the hearth-rug. When chased from this pasture he would retreat under the sofa. There he would twinkle in Buddhist meditation until suddenly, no one knew why, he would go off like an alarm clock. With a sudden bumping scuffle he would whirl out of the room, going through the doorway with his little ears flying. Then we would hear his thunderbolt hurtling in the parlour, but before we could follow, the wild streak of Adolf would flash past us, on an electric wind that swept him round the scullery and carried him back, a little mad thing, flying possessed like a ball round the parlour. After which ebullition he would sit in a corner composed and distant, twitching his whiskers in abstract meditation. And it was in vain we questioned him about his outbursts. He just went off like a gun, and was as calm after it as a gun that smokes placidly.

Alas, he grew up rapidly. It was almost impossible to keep him from the outer door.

One day, as we were playing by the stile, I saw his brown shadow loiter across the road and pass into the field that faced the houses. Instantly a cry of 'Adolf!' —a cry he knew full well. And instantly a wind swept him away down the sloping meadow, his tail twinkling and zigzagging through the grass. After him we pelted. It was a strange sight to see him, ears back, his little loins so powerful, flinging the world behind him. We ran ourselves out of breath, but could not catch him. Then somebody headed him off, and he sat with sudden unconcern, twitching his nose under a bunch of nettles.

His wanderings cost him a shock. One Sunday morning my father had just been quarrelling with a pedlar, and we were hearing the aftermath indoors, when there came a sudden unearthly scream from the yard. We flew out. There sat Adolf cowering under a bench, whilst a great black and white cat glowered intently at him, a few yards away. Sight not to be forgotten. Adolf rolling back his eyes and parting his strange muzzle in another scream, the cat stretching forward in a slow elongation.

Ha, how we hated that cat! How we pursued him over the chapel wall and across the neighbours' gardens.

Adolf was still only half grown.

'Cats!' said my mother. 'Hideous detestable animals, why do people harbour them?'

But Adolf was becoming too much for her. He dropped too many pills. And suddenly to hear him clumping downstairs when she was alone in the house was startling. And to keep him from the door was impossible. Cats prowled outside. It was worse than having a child to look after.

Yet we would not have him shut up. He became more lusty, more callous than ever. He was a strong kicker, and many a scratch on face and arms did we owe to him. But he brought his own doom on himself. The lace curtains in the parlour—my mother was rather proud of them—fell on the floor very full. One of Adolf's joys was to scuffle wildly through them as though through some foamy undergrowth. He had already torn rents in them.

One day he entangled himself altogether. He kicked, he whirled round in a mad nebulous inferno. He screamed—and brought down the curtain-rod with a smash, right on the best beloved pelargonium, just as my mother rushed in. She extricated him, but she never forgave him. And he never forgave either. A heartless wildness had come over him.

Even we understood that he must go. It was decided, after a long deliberation, that my father should carry him back to the wildwoods. Once again he was stowed into the great pocket of the pit jacket.

'Best pop him i' th' pot,' said my father, who enjoyed raising the wind of indignation.

And so, next day, our father said that Adolf, set down on the edge of the coppice, had hopped away with utmost indifference, neither elated nor moved. We heard it and believed. But many, many were the heart-searchings. How would the other rabbits receive him? Would they smell his tameness, his humanized degradation, and rend him? My mother pooh-poohed the extravagant idea.

However, he was gone, and we were rather relieved. My father kept an eye open for him. He declared that several times passing the coppice in the early morning,

he had seen Adolf peeping through the nettle-stalks.
He had called him, in an odd, high-voiced, cajoling
fashion. But Adolf had not responded. Wildness gains
so soon upon its creatures. And they become so contemptuous then of our tame presence. So it seemed to
me. I myself would go to the edge of the coppice, and
call softly. I myself would imagine bright eyes between
the nettle-stalks, flash of a white, scornful tail past the
bracken. That insolent white tail, as Adolf turned his
flank on us! It reminded me always of a certain rude
gesture, and a certain unprintable phrase, which may not
even be suggested.

But when naturalists discuss the meaning of the rabbit's white tail, that rude gesture and still ruder phrase
always come to my mind. Naturalists say that the rabbit shows his white tail in order to guide his young safely
after him, as a nursemaid's flying strings are the signal to
her toddling charges to follow on. How nice and naïve!
I only know that my Adolf wasn't naïve. He used to
whisk his flank at me, push his white feather in my eye,
and say: '*Merde!*' It's a rude word—but one which
Adolf was always semaphoring at me, flag-wagging it
with all the derision of his narrow haunches.

That's a rabbit all over—insolence, and the white flag
of spiteful derision. Yes, and he keeps his flag flying to
the bitter end, sporting, insolent little devil that he is.
See him running for his life. Oh, how his soul is fanned
to an ecstasy of fright, a fugitive whirlwind of panic.
Gone mad, he throws the world behind him, with
astonishing hind legs. He puts back his head and lays
his ears on his sides and rolls the white of his eyes in
sheer ecstatic agony of speed. He knows the awful
approach behind him; bullet or stoat. He knows! He
knows, his eyes are turned back almost into his head. It
is agony. But it is also ecstasy. Ecstasy! See the insolent white flag bobbing. He whirls on the magic wind
of terror. All his pent-up soul rushes into agonized electric emotion of fear. He flings himself on, like a falling
star swooping into extinction. White heat of the agony
of fear. And at the same time, bob! bob! bob! goes the

white tail, *merde! merde! merde!* it says to the pursuer. The rabbit can't help it. In his utmost extremity he still flings the insult at the pursuer. He is the unconquerable fugitive, the indomitable meek. No wonder the stoat becomes vindictive.

And if he escapes, this precious rabbit! Don't you see him sitting there, in his earthly nook, a little ball of silence and rabbit triumph? Don't you see the glint on his black eye? Don't you see, in his very immobility, how the whole world is *merde* to him? No conceit like the conceit of the meek. And if the avenging angel in the shape of the ghostly ferret steals down on him, there comes a shriek of terror out of that little hump of self-satisfaction sitting motionless in a corner. Falls the fugitive. But even fallen, his white feather floats. Even in death it seems to say: 'I am the meek, I am the righteous, I am the rabbit. All you rest, you are evil doers, and you shall be *bien emmerdés!*'

SAN GAUDENZIO

IN the autumn the little rosy cyclamens blossom in the shade of this west side of the lake. They are very cold and fragrant, and their scent seems to belong to Greece, to the Bacchae. They are real flowers of the past. They seem to be blossoming in the landscape of Phaedra and Helen. They bend down, they brood like little chill fires. They are little living myths that I cannot understand.

After the cyclamens the Christmas roses are in bud. It is at this season that the cacchi are ripe on the trees in the garden, whole naked trees full of lustrous, orange-yellow, paradisal fruit, gleaming against the wintry blue sky. The monthly roses still blossom frail and pink, there are still crimson and yellow roses. But the vines are bare and the lemon houses shut. And then, in mid-winter, the lowest buds of the Christmas roses appear under the hedges and rocks and by the streams. They are very lovely, these first, large, cold, pure buds, like violets, like magnolias, but cold, lit up with the light from the snow.

The days go by, through the brief silence of winter, when the sunshine is so still and pure, like iced wine, and the dead leaves gleam brown, and water sounds hoarse in the ravines. It is so still and transcendent, the cypress-trees poise like flames of forgotten darkness, that should have been blown out at the end of the summer. For as we have candles to light the darkness of night, so the cypresses are candles to keep the darkness aflame in the full sunshine.

Meanwhile, the Christmas roses become many. They rise from their budded, intact humbleness near the ground, they rise up, they throw up their crystal, they become handsome, they are heaps of confident, mysterious whiteness in the shadow of a rocky stream. It is almost uncanny to see them. They are the flowers of darkness, white and wonderful beyond belief.

Then their radiance becomes soiled and brown, they thaw, break, and scatter and vanish away. Already the primroses are coming out, and the almond is in bud. The winter is passing away. On the mountains the fierce snow gleams apricot gold as evening approaches, golden, apricot, but so bright that it is almost frightening. What can be so fiercely gleaming when all is shadowy? It is something inhuman and unmitigated between heaven and earth.

The heavens are strange and proud all the winter, their progress goes on without reference to the dim earth. The dawns come white and translucent, the lake is a moonstone in the dark hills, then across the lake there stretches a vein of fire, then a whole, orange, flashing track over the whiteness. There is the exquisite silent passage of the day, and then at evening the afterglow, a huge incandescence of rose, hanging above and gleaming, as if it were the presence of a host of angels in rapture. It gleams like a rapturous chorus, then passes away, and the stars appear, large and flashing.

Meanwhile, the primroses are dawning on the ground, their light is growing stronger, spreading over the banks and under the bushes. Between the olive roots the violets are out, large, white, grave violets, and less serious blue ones. And looking down the hill, among the grey smoke of olive leaves, pink puffs of smoke are rising up. It is the almond- and the apricot-trees, it is the spring.

Soon the primroses are strong on the ground. There is a bank of small, frail crocuses shooting the lavender into this spring. And then the tussocks and tussocks of primroses are fully out, there is full morning everywhere on the banks and roadsides and stream-sides, and around the olive roots, a morning of primroses underfoot, with an invisible threading of many violets, and then the lovely blue clusters of hepatica, really like pieces of blue sky showing through a clarity of primrose. The few birds are piping thinly and shyly, the streams sing again, there is a strange flowering shrub full of incense, over-turned flowers of crimson and gold, like Bohemian glass. Between the olive roots new grass is coming, day is leap-ing all clear and coloured from the earth, it is full spring, full first rapture.

Does it pass away, or does it only lose its pristine quality? It deepens and intensifies, like experience. The days seem to be darker and richer, there is a sense of power in the strong air. On the banks by the lake the orchids are out, many, many pale bee-orchids stand-ing clear from the short grass over the lake. And in the hollows are the grape hyacinths, purple as noon, with the heavy, sensual fragrance of noon. They are many-breasted, and full of milk, and ripe, and sun-darkened, like many-breasted Diana.

We could not bear to live down in the village any more, now that the days opened large and spacious and the evenings drew out in sunshine. We could not bear the indoors, when above us the mountains shone in clear air. It was time to go up, to climb with the sun.

So after Easter we went to San Gaudenzio. It was three miles away, up the winding mule track that climbed higher and higher along the lake. Leaving the last house of the village, the path wound on the steep, cliff-like side of the lake, curving into the hollow where the landslip had tumbled the rocks in chaos, then out again on to the bluff of a headland that hung over the lake.

Thus we came to the tall barred gate of San Gaudenzio, on which was the usual little fire-insurance tablet, and then the advertisements for beer, 'Birra, Verona,' which is becoming a more and more popular drink.

Through the gate, inside the high wall, is the little Garden of Eden, a property of three or four acres fairly level upon a headland over the lake. The high wall girds it on the land side, and makes it perfectly secluded. On the lake side it is bounded by the sudden drops of the land, in sharp banks and terraces, overgrown with ilex and with laurel bushes, down to the brink of the cliff, so that the thicket of the first declivities seems to safeguard the property.

The pink farm-house stands almost in the centre of the little territory, among the olive-trees. It is a solid, six-roomed place, about fifty years old, having been rebuilt by Paolo's uncle. Here we came to live for a time with the Fiori, Maria and Paolo, and their three children, Giovanni and Marco and Felicina.

Paolo had inherited, or partly inherited, San Gaudenzio, which had been in his family for generations. He was a peasant of fifty-three, very grey and wrinkled and worn-looking, but at the same time robust, with full strong limbs and a powerful chest. His face was old, but his body was solid and powerful. His eyes were blue like upper ice, beautiful. He had been a fair-haired man, now he was almost white.

He was strangely like the pictures of peasants in the northern Italian pictures, with the same curious nobility, the same aristocratic, eternal look of motionlessness, something statuesque. His head was hard and fine, the bone finely constructed, though the skin of his face was loose and furrowed with work. His temples had that fine, hard clarity which is seen in Mantegna, an almost jewel-like quality.

We all loved Paolo, he was so finished in his being, detached, with an almost classic simplicity and gentleness, and eternal kind of sureness. There was also something concluded and unalterable about him, something inaccessible.

Maria Fiori was different. She was from the plain, like Enrico Persevalli and the bersaglieri from the Venetian district. She reminded me again of oxen, broad-boned and massive in physique, dark-skinned, slow in her soul. But, like the oxen of the plain, she knew her work, she knew the other people engaged in the work. Her intelligence was attentive and purposive. She had been a housekeeper, a servant, in Venice and Verona, before her marriage. She had got the hang of this world of commerce and activity, she wanted to master it. But she was weighted down by her heavy animal blood.

Paolo and she were the opposite sides of the universe,

the light and the dark. Yet they lived together now without friction, detached, each subordinated in their common relationship. With regard to Maria, Paolo omitted himself; Maria omitted herself with regard to Paolo. Their souls were silent and detached, completely apart, and silent, quite silent. They shared the physical relationship of marriage as if it were something beyond them, a third thing.

They had suffered very much in the earlier stages of their connection. Now the storm had gone by, leaving them, as it were, spent. They were both by nature passionate, vehement. But the lines of their passion were opposite. Hers was the primitive, crude, violent flux of the blood, emotional and undiscriminating, but wanting to mix and mingle. His was the hard, clear, invulnerable passion of the bones, finely tempered and unchangeable. She was the flint and he the steel. But in continual striking together they only destroyed each other. The fire was a third thing, belonging to neither of them.

She was still heavy and full of desire. She was much younger than he.

'How long did you know your signora before you were married?' she asked me.

'Six weeks,' I said.

'Il Paolo e me, venti giorni, tre settimani,' she cried vehemently. Three weeks they had known each other when they married. She still triumphed in the fact. So did Paolo. But it was past, strangely and rather terribly past.

What did they want when they came together, Paolo and she? He was a man over thirty, she was a woman of twenty-three. They were both violent in desire and of strong will. They came together at once, like two wrestlers almost matched in strength. Their meetings must have been splendid. Giovanni, the eldest child, was a tall lad of sixteen, with soft brown hair and grey eyes, and a clarity of brow, and the same calm simplicity of bearing which made Paolo so complete; but the son had at the same time a certain brownness of skin, a

heaviness of blood, which he had from his mother.
Paolo was so clear and translucent.

In Giovanni the fusion of the parents was perfect, he
was a perfect spark from the flint and steel. There was
in Paolo a subtle intelligence in feeling, a delicate appreciation of the other person. But the mind was un-
intelligent, he could not grasp a new order. Maria
Fiori was much sharper and more adaptable to the ways
of the world. Paolo had an almost glass-like quality,
fine and clear and perfectly tempered; but he was also
finished and brittle. Maria was much coarser, more vulgar, but also she was more human, more fertile, with
crude potentiality. His passion was too fixed in its
motion, hers too loose and overwhelming.

But Giovanni was beautiful, gentle, and courtly like
Paolo, but warm, like Maria, ready to flush like a girl
with anger or confusion. He stood straight and tall,
and seemed to look into the far distance with his clear
grey eyes. Yet also he could look at one and touch one
with his look, he could meet one. Paolo's blue eyes
were like the eyes of the old spinning-woman, clear and
blue and belonging to the mountains, their vision seemed
to end in space, abstract. They reminded me of the
eyes of the eagle, which looks into the sun, and which
teaches its young to do the same, although they are
unwilling.

Marco, the second son, was thirteen years old. He
was his mother's favourite. Giovanni loved his father
best. But Marco was his mother's son, with the same
brown-gold and red complexion, like a pomegranate, and
coarse black hair, and brown eyes like pebble, like agate,
like an animal's eyes. He had the same broad, bovine
figure, though he was only a boy. But there was some
discrepancy in him. He was not unified, he had no
identity.

He was strong and full of animal life, but always aimless, as though his wits scarcely controlled him. But he
loved his mother with a fundamental, generous, un-
distinguishing love. Only he always forgot what he was
going to do. He was much more sensitive than Maria,

more shy and reluctant. But his shyness, his sensitiveness only made him more aimless and awkward, a tiresome clown, slack and uncontrolled, witless. All day long his mother shouted and shrilled and scolded at him, or hit him angrily. He did not mind, he came up like a cork, warm and roguish and curiously appealing. She loved him with a fierce protective love, grounded on pain. There was such a split, a contrariety in his soul, one part reacting against the other, which landed him always into trouble.

It was when Marco was a baby that Paolo had gone to America. They were poor on San Gaudenzio. There were the few olive-trees, the grapes, and the fruit; there was the one cow. But these scarcely made a living. Neither was Maria content with the real peasants' lot any more, polenta at midday and vegetable soup in the evening, and no way out, nothing to look forward to, no future, only this eternal present. She had been in service, and had eaten bread and drunk coffee, and known the flux and variable chance of life. She had departed from the old static conception. She knew what one might be, given a certain chance. The fixture was the thing she militated against. So Paolo went to America, to California, into the gold mines.

Maria wanted the future, the endless possibility of life on earth. She wanted her sons to be freer, to achieve a new plane of living. The peasant's life was a slave's life, she said, railing against the poverty and the drudgery. And it was quite true, Paolo and Giovanni worked twelve and fourteen hours a day at heavy laborious work that would have broken an Englishman. And there was nothing at the end of it. Yet Paolo was even happy so. This was the truth to him.

It was the mother who wanted things different. It was she who railed and railed against the miserable life of the peasants. When we were going to throw to the fowls a dry broken penny roll of white bread, Maria said, with anger and shame and resentment in her voice: 'Give it to Marco, he will eat it. It isn't too dry for him.'

White bread was a treat for them even now, when

everybody eats bread. And Maria Fiori hated it, that bread should be a treat to her children, when it was the meanest food of all the rest of the world. She was in opposition to this order. She did not want her sons to be peasants, fixed and static as posts driven in the earth. She wanted them to be in the great flux of life, in the midst of all possibilities. So she at length sent Paolo to America to the gold-mines. Meanwhile, she covered the wall of her parlour with picture post cards, to bring the outer world of cities and industries into her house.

Paolo was entirely remote from Maria's world. He had not yet even grasped the fact of money, not thoroughly. He reckoned in land and olive-trees. So he had the old fatalistic attitude to his circumstances, even to his food. The earth was the Lord's and the fullness thereof: also the leanness thereof. Paolo could only do his part and leave the rest. If he ate in plenty, having oil and wine and sausage in the house, and plenty of maize meal, he was glad with the Lord. If he ate meagrely, of poor polenta, that was fate, it was the skies that ruled these things, and no man ruled the skies. He took his fate as it fell from the skies.

Maria was exorbitant about money. She would charge us all she could for what we had and for what was done for us.

Yet she was not mean in her soul. In her soul she was in a state of anger because of her own closeness. It was a violation to her strong animal nature. Yet her mind had wakened to the value of money. She knew she could alter her position, the position of her children, by virtue of money. She knew it was only money that made the difference between master and servant. And this was all the difference she would acknowledge. So she ruled her life according to money. Her supreme passion was to be mistress rather than servant, her supreme aspiration for her children was that in the end they might be masters and not servants.

Paolo was untouched by all this. For him there was some divinity about a master which even America had not destroyed. If we came in for supper whilst the family was still at table he would have the children at once take their plates to the wall, he would have Maria at once set the table for us, though their own meal were never finished.   And this was not servility, it was the dignity of a religious conception.   Paolo regarded us as belonging to the Signoria, those who are elect, near to God.   And this was part of his religious service.   His life was a ritual.   It was very beautiful, but it made me unhappy, the purity of his spirit was so sacred and the actual facts seemed such a sacrilege to it.   Maria was nearer to the actual truth when she said that money was the only distinction. · But Paolo had hold of an eternal truth, where hers was temporal.   Only Paolo misapplied this eternal truth.   He should not have given Giovanni the inferior status and a fat, mean Italian tradesman the superior.   That was false, a real falsity.   Maria knew it and hated it.   But Paolo could not distinguish between the accident of riches and the aristocracy of the spirit. So Maria rejected him altogether, and went to the other extreme.   We were all human beings like herself; naked, there was no distinction between us, no higher nor lower. But we were possessed of more money than she.   And she had to steer her course between these two conceptions.   The money alone made the real distinction, the separation; the being, the life made the common level.

Paolo had the curious peasants' avarice also, but it was not meanness.   It was a sort of religious conservation of his own power, his own self.   Fortunately he could leave all business transactions on our account to Maria, so that his relation with us was purely ritualistic.   He would have given me anything, trusting implicitly that I would fulfil my own nature as signore, one of those more godlike, nearer the light of perfection than himself, a peasant.   It was pure bliss to him to bring us the first fruit of the garden, it was like laying it on an altar.

And his fulfilment was in a fine, subtle, exquisite relationship, not of manners, but subtle interappreciation.   He worshipped a finer understanding and a subtler tact.   A further fineness and dignity and freedom in bearing was to him an approach towards the divine, so he

loved men best of all, they fulfilled his soul. A woman
was always a woman, and sex was a low level whereon he
did not esteem himself. But a man, a doer, the instrument of God, he was really godlike.

Paolo was a conservative. For him the world was
established and divine in its establishment. His vision
grasped a small circle. A finer nature, a higher understanding, took in a greater circle, comprehended the
whole. So that when Paolo was in relation to a man of
further vision, he himself was extended towards the
whole. Thus he was fulfilled. And his initial assumption was that every signore, every gentleman, was a man
of further, purer vision than himself. This assumption
was false. But Maria's assumption, that no one had a
further vision, no one was more elect than herself, that
we are all one flesh and blood and being, was even more
false. Paolo was mistaken in actual life, but Maria was
ultimately mistaken.

Paolo, conservative as he was, believing that a priest
must be a priest of God, yet very rarely went to church.
And he used the religious oaths that Maria hated, even
Porca-Maria. He always used oaths, either Bacchus or
God or Mary or the Sacrament. Maria was always
offended. Yet it was she who, in her soul, jeered at the
Church and at religion. She wanted the human society
as the absolute, without religious abstractions. So
Paolo's oaths enraged her, because of their profanity, she
said. But it was really because of their subscribing to
another superhuman order. She jeered at the clerical
people. She made a loud clamour of derision when the
parish priest of the village above went down to the big
village on the lake, and across the piazza, the quay, with
two pigs in a sack on his shoulder. This was a real
picture of the sacred minister to her.

One day, when a storm had blown down an olive-tree
in front of the house, and Paolo and Giovanni were
beginning to cut it up, this same priest of Mugiano came
to San Gaudenzio. He was an iron-grey, thin, disreput-
able-looking priest, very talkative and loud and queer.
He seemed like an old ne'er-do-well in priest's black, and

he talked loudly, almost to himself, as drunken people do. At once *he* must show the Fiori how to cut up the tree, he must have the axe from Paolo. He shouted to Maria for a glass of wine. She brought it out to him with a sort of insolent deference, insolent contempt of the man and traditional deference to the cloth. The priest drained the tumblerful of wine at one drink, his thin throat with its Adam's apple working. And he did not pay the penny.

Then he stripped off his cassock and put away his hat, and, a ludicrous figure in ill-fitting black knee-breeches and a not very clean shirt, a red handkerchief round his neck, he proceeded to give great extravagant blows at the tree. He was like a caricature. In the doorway Maria was encouraging him rather jeeringly, whilst she winked at me. Marco was stifling his hysterical amusement in his mother's apron, and prancing with glee. Paolo and Giovanni stood by the fallen tree, very grave and unmoved, inscrutable, abstract. Then the youth came away to the doorway, with a flush mounting on his face and a grimace distorting its youngness. Only Paolo, unmoved and detached, stood by the tree with unchanging, abstract face, very strange, his eyes fixed in the ageless stare which is so characteristic.

Meanwhile the priest swung drunken blows at the tree, his thin buttocks bending in the green-black broadcloth, supported on thin shanks, and thin throat growing dull purple in the red knotted kerchief. Nevertheless he was doing the job. His face was wet with sweat. He wanted another glass of wine.

He took no notice of us. He was strangely a local, even a mountebank figure, but entirely local, an appurtenance of the district.

It was Maria who jeeringly told us the story of the priest, who shrugged her shoulders to imply that he was a contemptible figure. Paolo sat with the abstract look on his face, as of one who hears and does not hear, is not really concerned. He never opposed or contradicted her, but stayed apart. It was she who was violent and brutal in her ways. But sometimes Paolo went into a rage, and then Maria, everybody, was afraid. It was a white heavy rage, when his blue eyes shone unearthly, and his mouth opened with a curious drawn blindness of the old Furies. There was something of the cruelty of a falling mass of snow, heavy, horrible. Maria drew away, there was a silence. Then the avalanche was finished.

They must have had some cruel fights before they learned to withdraw from each other so completely. They must have begotten Marco in hatred, terrible disintegrated opposition and otherness. And it was after this, after the child of their opposition was born, that Paolo went away to California, leaving his San Gaudenzio, travelling with several companions, like blind beasts, to Havre, and thence to New York, then to California. He stayed five years in the gold mines, in a wild valley, living with a gang of Italians in a town of corrugated iron.

All the while he had never really left San Gaudenzio. I asked him: 'Used you to think of it, the lake, the Monte Baldo, the laurel-trees down the slope?' He tried to see what I wanted to know. Yes, he said—but uncertainly. I could see that he had never been really homesick. It had been very wretched on the ship going from Havre to New York. That he told me about. And he told me about the gold mines, the galleries, the valley, the huts in the valley. But he had never really fretted for San Gaudenzio whilst he was in California.

In real truth he was at San Gaudenzio all the time, his fate was riveted there. His going away was an excursion from reality, a kind of sleep-walking. He left his own reality there in the soil above the lake of Garda. That his body was in California, what did it matter? It was merely for a time, and for the sake of his own earth, his land. He would pay off the mortgage. But the gate at home was his gate all the time, his hand was on the latch.

As for Maria, he had felt his duty towards her. She was part of his little territory, the rooted centre of the world. He sent her home the money. But it did not occur to him, in his soul, to miss her. He wanted her to be safe with the children, that was all. In his flesh perhaps he missed the woman.   But his spirit was even more completely isolated since marriage.   Instead of having united with each other, they had made each other more terribly distinct and separate.   He could live alone eternally.   It was his condition.   His sex was functional, like eating and drinking.   To take a woman, a prostitute at the camp, or not to take her, was no more vitally important than to get drunk or not to get drunk of a Sunday.   And fairly often on Sunday Paolo got drunk. His world remained unaltered.

But Maria suffered more bitterly.   She was a young, powerful, passionate woman, and she was unsatisfied body and soul.   Her soul's unsatisfaction became a bodily unsatisfaction.   Her blood was heavy, violent, anarchic, insisting on the equality of the blood in all, and therefore on her own absolute right to satisfaction.

She took a wine licence for San Gaudenzio, and she sold wine.   There were many scandals about her. Somehow it did not matter very much, outwardly. The authorities were too divided among themselves to enforce public opinion.   Between the clerical party and the radicals and the socialists, what canons were left that were absolute?   Besides, these wild villages had always been ungoverned.

Yet Maria suffered.   Even she, according to her conviction, belonged to Paolo.   And she felt betrayed, betrayed and deserted.   The iron had gone deep into her soul.   Paolo had deserted her, she had been betrayed to other men for five years.   There was something cruel and implacable in life.   She sat sullen and heavy, for all her quick activity.   Her soul was sullen and heavy.

I could never believe Felicina was Paolo's child.   She was an unprepossessing little girl, affected, cold, selfish, foolish.   Maria and Paolo, with real Italian greatness, were warm and natural towards the child in her.   But they did not love her in their very souls, she was the fruit of ash to them.   And this must have been the reason that she was so self-conscious and foolish and affected, small child that she was.

Paolo had come back from America a year before she

was born—a year before she was born, Maria insisted. The husband and wife lived together in a relationship of complete negation. In his soul he was sad for her, and in her soul she felt annulled. He sat at evening in the chimney-seat, smoking, always pleasant and cheerful, not for a moment thinking he was unhappy. It has all taken place in his sub-consciousness. But his eyebrows and eyelids were lifted in a kind of vacancy, his blue eyes were round and somehow finished, though he was so gentle and vigorous in body. But the very quick of him was killed. He was like a ghost in the house, with his loose throat and powerful limbs, his open, blue, extinct eyes, and his musical, slightly husky voice, that seemed to sound out of the past.

And Maria, stout and strong and handsome like a peasant woman, went about as if there were a weight on her, and her voice was high and strident. She, too, was finished in her life. But she remained unbroken, her will was like a hammer that destroys the old form.

Giovanni was patiently labouring to learn a little English. Paolo knew only four or five words, the chief of which were 'a' right,' 'boss,' 'bread,' and 'day.' The youth had these by heart, and was studying a little more. He was very graceful and lovable, but he found it difficult to learn. A confused light, like hot tears, would come into his eyes when he had again forgotten the phrase. But he carried the paper about with him, and he made steady progress.

He would go to America, he also. Not for anything would he stay in San Gaudenzio. His dream was to be gone. He would come back. The world was not San Gaudenzio to Giovanni.

The old order, the order of Paolo and of Pietro di Paoli, the aristocratic order of the supreme God, God the Father, the Lord, was passing away from the beautiful little territory. The household no longer receives its food, oil and wine and maize, from out of the earth in the motion of fate. The earth is annulled, and money takes its place. The landowner, who is the lieutenant of God and of Fate, like Abraham, he, too, is annulled. There

is now the order of the rich, which supersedes the order
of the Signoria.

It is passing away from Italy as it has passed from
England. The peasant is passing away, the workman is
taking his place. The stability is gone. Paolo is a
ghost, Maria is the living body. And the new order
means sorrow for the Italian more even than it has
meant for us. But he will have the new order.

San Gaudenzio is already becoming a thing of the past.
Below the house, where the land drops in sharp slips to
the sheer cliff's edge, over which it is Maria's constant
fear that Felicina will tumble, there are the deserted
lemon gardens of the little territory, snug down below.
They are invisible till one descends by tiny paths, sheer
down into them. And there they stand, the pillars and
walls erect, but a dead emptiness prevailing, lemon-trees
all dead, gone, a few vines in their place. It is only
twenty years since the lemon-trees finally perished
of a disease and were not renewed. But the deserted
terraces, shut between great walls, descending in their
openness full to the south, to the lake and the mountain
opposite, seem more terrible than Pompeii in their silence
and utter seclusion. The grape hyacinths flower in the
cracks, the lizards run, this strange place hangs suspended and forgotten, forgotten for ever, its erect pillars
utterly meaningless.

I used to sit and write in the great loft of the lemon
house, high up, far, far from the ground, the open front
giving across the lake and the mountain snow opposite
flush with twilight. The old matting and boards, the
old disused implements of lemon culture made shadows
in the deserted place. Then there would come the call
from the back, away above: 'Venga, venga mangiare.'

We ate in the kitchen, where the olive and laurel wood
burned in the open fire-place. It was always soup in the
evening. Then we played games or cards, all playing;
or there was singing, with the accordion, and sometimes
a rough mountain peasant with a guitar.

But it is all passing away. Giovanni is in America,
unless he has come back to the War. He will not want

to live in San Gaudenzio when he is a man, he says. He and Marco will not spend their lives wringing a little oil and wine out of the rocky soil, even if they are not killed in the fighting which is going on at the end of the lake. In my loft by the lemon houses now I should hear the guns. And Giovanni kissed me with a kind of supplication when I went on to the steamer, as if he were beseeching for a soul. His eyes were bright and clear and lit up with courage. He will make a good fight for the new soul he wants—that is, if they do not kill him in this War.

MAN IS A HUNTER

IT is a very nice law which forbids shooting in England on Sundays. Here in Italy, on the contrary, you would think there was a law ordering every Italian to let off a gun as often as possible. Before the eyelids of dawn have come apart, long before the bells of the tiny church jangle to announce daybreak, there is a sputter and crackle as of irritating fireworks, scattering from the olive gardens and from the woods. You sigh in your bed. The Holy Day has started: the huntsmen are abroad; they will keep at it till heaven sends the night, and the little birds are no more.

The very word *cacciatore*, which means hunter, stirs one's bile. Oh, Nimrod, oh, Bahram, put by your arrows:

> And Bahrám, that great Hunter—the Wild Ass
> Stamps o'er his Head, but cannot break his Sleep.

Here, an infinite number of tame asses shoot over my head, if I happen to walk in the wood to look at the arbutus berries, and they never fail to rouse my ire, no matter how fast asleep it may have been.

Man is a hunter! *L' uomo è cacciatore:* the Italians are rather fond of saying it. It sounds so virile. One sees Nimrod surging through the underbrush, with his spear, in the wake of a bleeding lion. And if it is a question of a man who has got a girl into trouble: '*L' uomo è cacciatore*'—'man is a hunter'—what can you expect? It behoves the 'game' to look out for itself. Man is a hunter!

There used to be a vulgar song: 'If the missis wants to go for a row, let 'er go.' Here it should be: 'If the master wants to run, with a gun, let him run.' For the pine-wood is full of them, as a dog's back with fleas in summer. They crouch, they lurk, they stand erect,

268

motionless as virile statues, with gun on the alert. Then *bang!* they have shot something, with an astonishing amount of noise. And then they run, with fierce and predatory strides, to the spot.

There is nothing there! Nothing! The game! *La caccia!*—where is it? If they had been shooting at the ghost of Hamlet's father, there could not be a blanker and more spooky emptiness. One expects to see a wounded elephant lying on its side, writhing its trunk; at the very least, a wild boar ploughing the earth in his death agony. But no! There is nothing, just nothing at all. Man, being a hunter, is, fortunately for the rest of creation, a very bad shot.

Nimrod, in velveteen corduroys, bandolier, cartridges, game-bag over his shoulder and gun in his hand, stands with feet apart *virilissimo*, on the spot where the wild boar should be, and gazes downwards at some imaginary point in underworld space. So! Man is a hunter. He casts a furtive glance around, under the arbutus bush, and a tail of his eye in my direction, knowing I am looking on in raillery. Then he hitches his game-bag more determinedly over his shoulder, grips his gun, and strides off uphill, large strides, virile as Hector. Perhaps even he is a Hector, Italianized into Ettore. Anyhow, he's going to be the death of something or somebody, if only he can shoot straight.

A Tuscan pine-wood is by no means a jungle. The trees are umbrella pines, with the umbrellas open, and bare handles. They are rather parsimoniously scattered. The undergrowth, moreover, is allowed to grow only for a couple of years or so; then it is most assiduously reaped, gleaned, gathered, cleaned up clean as a lawn, for cooking Nimrod's macaroni. So that, in a *pineta*, you have a piny roof over your head, and for the rest a pretty clear run for your money. So where can the game lurk? There is hardly cover for a bumble-bee. Where can the game be that is worth all this powder? The lions and wolves and boars that must prowl perilously round all these Nimrods?

You will never know. Or not until you are going

home, between the olive-trees. The hunters have been burning powder in the open, as well as in the wood: a proper fusillade. Then, on the path between the olives, you may pick up a warm, dead bullfinch, with a bit of blood on it. The little grey bird lies on its side, with its frail feet closed, and its red breast ruffled. Nimrod, having hit for once, has failed to find his quarry.

So you will know better when the servant comes excitedly and asks: 'Signore, do you want any game?' Game! Splendid idea! A couple of partridges? a hare? even a wild rabbit? Why, of course! So she arrives in triumph with a knotted red handkerchief, and the not very bulky game inside it. Untie the knots! Aha!— Alas! There, in a little heap on the table, three robins, two finches, four hedge sparrows, and two starlings, in a fluffy, coloured, feathery little heap, all the small heads rolling limp. 'Take them away,' you say. 'We don't eat little birds.' 'But these,' she says, tipping up the starlings roughly, 'these are big ones.' 'Not these, either, do we eat.' 'No?' she exclaims, in a tone which means: '*More fools you !*' And, disgusted, disappointed at not having sold the goods, she departs with the game.

You will know best of all if you go to the market, and see whole yard-lengths of robins, like coral and onyx necklaces, and strings of bullfinches, goldfinches, larks, sparrows, nightingales, starlings, temptingly offered along with strings of sausages, these last looking like the strings of pearls in the show. If one bought the birds to wear as ornament, barbaric necklaces, it would be more conceivable. You can get quite a string of different-coloured ones for tenpence. But imagine the small mouthful of little bones each of these tiny carcasses must make!

But, after all, a partridge and a pheasant are only a bit bigger than a sparrow and a finch. And compared to a flea, a robin is big game. It is all a question of dimensions. Man is a hunter. 'If the master wants to hunt, don't you grunt; let him hunt!'

FLOWERY TUSCANY

I

EACH country has its own flowers, that shine out specially there. In England it is daisies and buttercups, hawthorn and cowslips. In America, it is golden-rod, stargrass, June daisies, Mayapple and asters, that we call Michaelmas daisies. In India, hibiscus and datura and champac flowers, and in Australia, mimosa, that they call wattle, and sharp-tongued strange heath-flowers. In Mexico, it is cactus flowers, that they call roses of the desert, lovely and crystalline among many thorns; and also the dangling yard-long clusters of the cream bells of the yucca, like dropping froth.

But by the Mediterranean, now as in the days of the argosy, and, we hope, for ever, it is narcissus and anemone, asphodel, and myrtle. Narcissus and anemone, asphodel, crocus, myrtle, and parsley, they leave their sheer significance only by the Mediterranean. There are daisies in Italy too: at Paestum there are white little carpets of daisies, in March, and Tuscany is spangled with celandine. But for all that, the daisy and the celandine are English flowers, their best significance is for us and for the north.

The Mediterranean has narcissus and anemone, myrtle and asphodel, and grape hyacinth. These are the flowers that speak and are understood in the sun round the Middle Sea.

Tuscany is especially flowery, being wetter than Sicily and more homely than the Roman hills. Tuscany manages to remain so remote, and secretly smiling to itself in its many sleeves. There are so many hills popping up, and they take no notice of one another. There are so many little deep valleys with streams that seem to go their own little way entirely, regardless of

river or sea. There are thousands, millions, of utterly
secluded little nooks, though the land has been under
cultivation these thousands of years. But the intensive
culture of vine and olive and wheat, by the ceaseless
industry of naked human hands and winter-shod feet,
and slow-stepping, soft-eyed oxen, does not devastate a
country, does not denude it, does not lay it bare, does
not uncover its nakedness, does not drive away either
Pan or his children. The streams run and rattle over
wild rocks of secret places, and murmur through black-
thorn thickets where the nightingales sing all together,
unruffled and undaunted.

It is queer that a country so perfectly cultivated as
Tuscany, where half the produce of five acres of land will
have to support ten human mouths, still has so much
room for the wild flowers and the nightingale. When
little hills heave themselves suddenly up, and shake
themselves free of neighbours, man has to build his
garden and his vineyard, and sculp his landscape. Talk
of hanging gardens of Babylon, all Italy, apart from the
plains, is a hanging garden. For centuries upon centuries man has been patiently modelling the surface of
the Mediterranean countries, gently rounding the hills,
and graduating the big slopes and the little slopes into
the almost invisible levels of terraces. Thousands of
square miles of Italy have been lifted in human hands,
piled and laid back in tiny little flats, held up by the
drystone walls, whose stones came from the lifted earth.
It is a work of many, many centuries. It is the gentle
sensitive sculpture of all the landscape. And it is the
achieving of the peculiar Italian beauty which is so
exquisitely natural, because man, feeling his way sensitively to the fruitfulness of the earth, has moulded the
earth to his necessity without violating it.

Which shows that it *can* be done. Man *can* live on the
earth and by the earth without disfiguring the earth. It
has been done here, on all these sculptured hills and
softly, sensitively terraced slopes.

But, of course, you can't drive a steam plough on
terraces four yards wide, terraces that dwindle and

broaden and sink and rise a little, all according to the
pitch and the breaking outline of the mother hill. Corn
has got to grow on these little shelves of earth, where
already the grey olive stands semi-invisible, and the
grape-vine twists upon its own scars. If oxen can step
with that lovely pause at every little stride, they can
plough the narrow field. But they will have to leave a
tiny fringe, a grassy lip over the drystone wall below.
And if the terraces are too narrow to plough, the peasant
digging them will still leave the grassy lip, because it
helps to hold the surface in the rains.

And here the flowers take refuge. Over and over and
over and over has this soil been turned, twice a year,
sometimes three times a year, for several thousands of
years. Yet the flowers have never been driven out.
There is a very rigorous digging and sifting, the little
bulbs and tubers are flung away into perdition, not a
weed shall remain.

Yet spring returns, and on the terrace lips, and in the
stony nooks between terraces, up rise the aconites, the
crocuses, the narcissus and the asphodel, the inextin-
guishable wild tulips. There they are, for ever hanging
on the precarious brink of an existence, but for ever
triumphant, never quite losing their footing. In
England, in America, the flowers get rooted out, driven
back. They become fugitive. But in the intensive
cultivation of ancient Italian terraces, they dance round
and hold their own.

Spring begins with the first narcissus, rather cold and
shy and wintry. They are the little bunchy, creamy
narcissus with the yellow cup like the yolk of the flower.
The natives call these flowers *tazzette*, little cups. They
grow on the grassy banks rather sparse, or push up
among thorns.

To me they are winter flowers, and their scent is
winter. Spring starts in February, with the winter
aconite. Some icy day, when the wind is down from
the snow of the mountains, early in February, you will
notice on a bit of fallow land, under the olive-trees,
tight, pale-gold little balls, clenched tight as nuts, and

resting on round ruffs of green near the ground.   It is the winter aconite suddenly come.

The winter aconite is one of the most charming flowers. Like all the early blossoms, once her little flower emerges it is quite naked.   No shutting a little green sheath over herself, like the daisy or the dandelion.   Her bubble of frail, pale, pure gold rests on the round frill of her green collar, with the snowy wind trying to blow it away.

But without success.   The *tramontana* ceases, comes a day of wild February sunshine.   The clenched little nuggets of the aconite puff out, they become light bubbles, like small balloons, on a green base.   The sun blazes on, with February splendour.   And by noon, all under the olives are wide-open little suns, the aconites spreading all their rays; and there is an exquisitely sweet scent, honey-sweet, not narcissus-frosty; and there is a February humming of little brown bees.

· Till afternoon, when the sun slopes, and the touch of snow comes back into the air.

But at evening, under the lamp on the table, the aconites are wide and excited, and there is a perfume of sweet spring that makes one almost start humming and trying to be a bee.

Aconites don't last very long.   But they turn up in all odd places—on clods of dug earth, and in land where the broad beans are thrusting up, and along the lips of terraces.   But they like best land left fallow for one winter.   There they throng, showing how quick they are to seize on an opportunity to live and shine forth.

In a fortnight, before February is over, the yellow bubbles of the aconite are crumpling to nothingness. But already in a cosy nook the violets are dark purple, and there is a new little perfume in the air.

Like the debris of winter stand the hellebores, in all the wild places, and the butcher's broom is flaunting its last bright red berry.   Hellebore is Christmas roses, but in Tuscany the flowers never come white.   They emerge out of the grass towards the end of December, flowers wintry of winter, and they are delicately pale green, and of a lovely shape, with yellowish stamens.   They have a peculiar wintry quality of invisibility, so lonely rising from the sere grass, and pallid green, held up like a little hand-mirror that reflects nothing. At first they are single upon a stem, short and lovely, and very wintry-beautiful, with a will not to be touched, not to be noticed. One instinctively leaves them alone. But as January draws towards February, these hellebores, these greenish Christmas roses become more assertive. Their pallid water - green becomes yellower, pale sulphur-yellow-green, and they rise up, they are in tufts, in throngs, in veritable bushes of greenish open flowers, assertive, bowing their faces with a hellebore assertiveness. In some places they throng among the bushes and above the water of the stream, giving the peculiar pale glimmer almost of primroses, as you walk among them. Almost of primroses, yet with a coarse hellebore leaf and an uprearing hellebore assertiveness, like snakes in winter.

And as one walks among them, one brushes the last scarlet off the butcher's broom. This low little shrub is the Christmas holly of Tuscany, only a foot or so high, with a vivid red berry stuck on in the middle of its sharp hard leaf. In February the last red ball rolls off the prickly plume, and winter rolls with it. The violets already are emerging from the moisture.

But before the violets make any show, there are the crocuses. If you walk up through the pine-wood, that lifts its umbrellas of pine so high, up till you come to the brow of the hill at the top, you can look south, due south, and see snow on the Apennines, and on a blue afternoon, seven layers of blue-hilled distance.

Then you sit down on that southern slope, out of the wind, and there it is warm, whether it be January or February, *tramontana* or not. There the earth has been baked by innumerable suns, baked and baked again; moistened by many rains, but never wetted for long. Because it is rocky, and full to the south, and sheering steep in the slope.

And there, in February, in the sunny baked desert of that crumbly slope, you will find the first crocuses. On the sheer aridity of crumbled stone you see a queer, alert little star, very sharp and quite small. It has opened out rather flat, and looks like a tiny freesia flower, creamy, with a smear of yellow yolk. It has no stem, seems to have been just lightly dropped on the crumbled, baked rock. It is the first hill crocus.

II

North of the Alps, the everlasting winter is interrupted by summers that struggle and soon yield; south of the Alps, the everlasting summer is interrupted by spasmodic and spiteful winters that never get a real hold, but that are mean and dogged. North of the Alps, you may have a pure winter's day in June. South of the Alps, you may have a midsummer day in December or January or even February. The in-between, in either case, is just as it may be. But the lands of the sun are south of the Alps, for ever.

Yet things, the flowers especially, that belong to both sides of the Alps, are not much earlier south than north of the mountains. Through all the winter there are roses in the garden, lovely creamy roses, more pure and mysterious than those of summer, leaning perfect from the stem. And the narcissus in the garden are out by the end of January, and the little simple hyacinths early in February.

But out in the fields, the flowers are hardly any sooner than English flowers. It is mid-February before the first violets, the first crocus, the first primrose. And in mid-February one may find a violet, a primrose, a crocus in England, in the hedgerows and the garden corner.

And still there is a difference. There are several kinds of wild crocus in this region of Tuscany: little spiky mauve ones, and spiky little creamy ones, that grow among the pine-trees of the bare slopes. But the beautiful ones are those of a meadow in the corner of the woods, the low hollow meadow below the steep, shadowy pine-slopes, the secretive grassy dip where the water seeps through the turf all winter, where the stream runs between thick bushes, where the nightingale sings his mightiest in May, and where the wild thyme is rosy and full of bees, in summer.

Here the lavender crocuses are most at home—here sticking out of the deep grass, in a hollow like a cup, a bowl of grass, come the lilac-coloured crocuses, like an innumerable encampment. You may see them at twilight, with all the buds shut, in the mysterious stillness of the grassy underworld, palely glimmering like myriad folded tents. So the Apaches still camp, and close their tepees, in the hollows of the great hills of the west, at night.

But in the morning it is quite different. Then the sun shines strong on the horizontal green cloud-puffs of the pines, the sky is clear and full of life, the water runs hastily, still browned by the last juice of crushed olives. And there the earth's bowl of crocuses is amazing. You cannot believe that the flowers are really still. They are open with such delight, and their pistil-thrust is so red-orange, and they are so many, all reaching out wide and marvellous, that it suggests a perfect ecstasy of radiant, thronging movement, lit-up violet and orange, and surging in some invisible rhythm of concerted, delightful movement. You cannot believe they do not move, and make some sort of crystalline sound of delight. If you sit still and watch, you begin to move with them, like moving with the stars, and you feel the sound of their radiance. All the little cells of the flowers must be leaping with flowery life and utterance.

And the small brown honey bees hop from flower to flower, dive down, try, and off again. The flowers have been already rifled, most of them. Only sometimes a bee stands on his head, kicking slowly inside the flower, for some time. He has found something. And all the bees have little loaves of pollen, bee-bread, in their elbow joints.

The crocuses last in their beauty for a week or so, and as they begin to lower their tents and abandon camp, the violets begin to thicken. It is already March. The violets have been showing like tiny dark hounds for some weeks. But now the whole pack comes forth, among the grass and the tangle of wild thyme, till the air all sways subtly scented with violets, and the banks above where the crocuses had their tents are now swarming brilliant purple with violets. They are the sweet violets of early spring, but numbers have made them bold, for they flaunt and ruffle till the slopes are a bright blue-purple blaze of them, full in the sun, with an odd late crocus still standing wondering and erect amongst them.

And now that it is March, there is a rush of flowers. Down by the other stream, which turns sideways to the sun, and has tangles of brier and bramble, down where the hellebore has stood so wan and dignified all winter, there are now white tufts of primroses, suddenly come. Among the tangle and near the water-lip, tufts and bunches of primroses, in abundance. Yet they look more wan, more pallid, more flimsy than English primroses. They lack some of the full wonder of the northern flowers. One tends to overlook them, to turn to the great, solemn-faced purple violets that rear up from the bank, and above all, to the wonderful little towers of the grape hyacinth.

I know no flower that is more fascinating, when it first appears, than the blue grape hyacinth. And yet, because it lasts so long, and keeps on coming so repeatedly, for at least two months, one tends later on to ignore it, even to despise it a little. Yet that is very unjust.

The first grape hyacinths are flowers of blue, thick and rich and meaningful, above the unrenewed grass. The upper buds are pure blue, shut tight; round balls of pure, perfect warm blue, blue, blue; while the lower bells are darkish blue-purple, with the spark of white at the mouth. As yet, none of the lower bells has withered, to leave the greenish, separate sparseness of fruiting that spoils the grape hyacinth later on, and makes it seem naked and functional. All hyacinths are like that in the seeding.

But, at first, you have only a compact tower of night-blue clearing to dawn, and extremely beautiful. If we were tiny as fairies, and lived only a summer, how lovely these great trees of bells would be to us, towers of night and dawn-blue globes. They would rise above us thick and succulent, and the purple globes would push the blue ones up, with white sparks of ripples, and we should see a god in them.

As a matter of fact, someone once told me they were the flowers of the many-breasted Artemis; and it is true, the Cybele of Ephesus, with her clustered breasts, was like a grape hyacinth at the bosom.

This is the time, in March, when the sloe is white and misty in the hedge-tangle by the stream, and on the slope of land the peach - tree stands pink and alone. The almond blossom, silvery pink, is passing, but the peach, deep-toned, bluey, not at all ethereal, this reveals itself like flesh, and the trees are like isolated individuals, the peach and the apricot.

A man said this spring: 'Oh, I *don't* care for peach blossom! It is such a vulgar pink!' One wonders what anybody means by a 'vulgar' pink. I think pink flannelette is rather vulgar. But probably it's the flannelette's fault, not the pink. And peach blossom has a beautiful sensual pink, far from vulgar, most rare and private. And pink is so beautiful in a landscape, pink houses, pink almond, pink peach and purply apricot, pink asphodels.

It is so conspicuous and so individual, that pink among the coming green of spring, because the first flowers that emerge from winter seem always white or yellow or purple. Now the celandines are out, and along the edges of the *podere*, the big, sturdy, black-purple anemones, with black hearts.

They are curious, these great, dark-violet anemones. You may pass them on a grey day, or at evening or early morning, and never see them. But as you come along in the full sunshine, they seem to be baying at you with all their throats, baying deep purple into the air. It is because they are hot and wide open now, gulping the sun. Whereas when they are shut, they have a silkiness and a curved head, like the curve of an umbrella handle, and a peculiar outward colourlessness, that makes them quite invisible. They may be under your feet, and you will not see them.

Altogether anemones are odd flowers. On these last hills above the plain, we have only the big black-purple ones, in tufts here and there, not many. But two hills away, the young green corn is blue with the lilac-blue kind, still the broad-petalled sort with the darker heart. But these flowers are smaller than our dark-purple, and frailer, more silky. Ours are substantial, thickly vegetable flowers, and not abundant. The others are lovely and silky-delicate, and the whole corn is blue with them. And they have a sweet, sweet scent, when they are warm.

Then on the priest's *podere* there are the scarlet, Adonis-blood anemones: only in one place, in one long fringe under a terrace, and there by a path below. These flowers above all you will never find unless you look for them in the sun. Their silver silk outside makes them quite invisible, when they are shut up.

Yet, if you are passing in the sun, a sudden scarlet faces on to the air, one of the loveliest scarlet apparitions in the world. The inner surface of the Adonis-blood anemone is as fine as velvet, and yet there is no suggestion of pile, not as much as on a velvet rose. And from this inner smoothness issues the red colour, perfectly pure and unknown of earth, no earthiness, and yet solid, not transparent. How a colour manages to be perfectly strong and impervious, yet of a purity that suggests condensed light, yet not luminous, at least, not transparent, is a problem. The poppy in her radiance is translucent, and the tulip in her utter redness has a touch of opaque earth. But the Adonis-blood anemone is neither translucent nor opaque. It is just pure condensed red, of a velvetiness without velvet, and a scarlet without glow.

This red seems to me the perfect premonition of summer—like the red on the outside of apple blossom —and later, the red of the apple. It is the premonition in redness of summer and of autumn.

The red flowers are coming now. The wild tulips are in bud, hanging their grey leaves like flags. They come up in myriads, wherever they get a chance. But they are holding back their redness till the last days of March, the early days of April.

Still, the year is warming up. By the high ditch the common magenta anemone is hanging its silky tassels or opening its great magenta daisy-shape to the hot sun. It is much nearer to red than the big-petalled anemones are; except the Adonis-blood. They say these anemones sprang from the tears of Venus, which fell as she went looking for Adonis. At that rate, how the poor lady must have wept, for the anemones by the Mediterranean are common as daisies in England.

The daisies are out here too, in sheets, and they too are red-mouthed. The first ones are big and handsome. But as March goes on, they dwindle to bright little things, like tiny buttons, clouds of them together. That means summer is nearly here.

The red tulips open in the corn like poppies, only with a heavier red. And they pass quickly, without repeating themselves. There is little lingering in a tulip.

In some places there are odd yellow tulips, slender, spiky, and Chinese - looking. They are very lovely, pricking out their dulled yellow in slim spikes. But they too soon lean, expand beyond themselves, and are gone like an illusion.

And when the tulips are gone, there is a moment's pause, before summer. Summer is the next move.

A LETTER FROM GERMANY

WE are going back to Paris to-morrow, so this is the last moment to write a letter from Germany. Only from the fringe of Germany, too.

It is a miserable journey from Paris to Nancy, through that Marne country, where the country still seems to have had the soul blasted out of it, though the dreary fields are ploughed and level, and the pale wire trees stand up. But it is all void and null. And in the villages, the smashed houses in the street rows, like rotten teeth between good teeth.

You come to Strasbourg, and the people still talk Alsatian German, as ever, in spite of French shop-signs. The place feels dead. And full of cotton goods, white goods, from Mülhausen, from the factories that once were German. Such cheap white cotton goods, in a glut.

The cathedral front rearing up high and flat and fanciful, a sort of darkness in the dark, with round rose windows and long, long prisms of stone. Queer, that men should have ever wanted to put stone upon fanciful stone to such a height, without having it fall down. The Gothic! I was always glad when my card-castle fell. But these Goths and Alemans seemed to have a craze for peaky heights.

The Rhine is still the Rhine, the great divider. You feel it as you cross. The flat, frozen, watery places. Then the cold and curving river. Then the other side, seeming so cold, so empty, so frozen, so forsaken. The train stands and steams fiercely. Then it draws through the flat Rhine plain, past frozen pools of flood-water, and frozen fields, in the emptiness of this bit of occupied territory.

Immediately you are over the Rhine, the spirit of place has changed. There is no more attempt at the bluff of geniality. The marshy places are frozen. The fields are vacant. There seems nobody in the world.

It is as if the life had retreated eastwards. As if the Germanic life were slowly ebbing away from contact with western Europe, ebbing to the deserts of the east. And there stand the heavy, ponderous, round hills of the Black Forest, black with an inky blackness of Germanic trees, and patched with a whiteness of snow. They are like a series of huge, involved black mounds, obstructing the vision eastwards. You look at them from the Rhine plain, and know that you stand on an actual border, up against something.

The moment you are in Germany, you know. It feels empty, and, somehow, menacing. So must the Roman soldiers have watched those black, massive round hills: with a certain fear, and with the knowledge that they were at their own limit. A fear of the invisible natives. A fear of the invisible life lurking among the woods. A fear of their own opposite.

So it is with the French: this almost mystic fear. But one should not insult even one's fears.

Germany, this bit of Germany, is very different from what it was two and a half years ago, when I was here. Then it was still open to Europe. Then it still looked to western Europe for a reunion, for a sort of reconciliation. Now that is over. The inevitable, mysterious barrier has fallen again, and the great leaning of the Germanic spirit is once more eastwards, towards Russia, towards Tartary. The strange vortex of Tartary has become the positive centre again, the positivity of western Europe is broken. The positivity of our civilization has broken. The influences that come, come invisibly out of Tartary. So that all Germany reads *Beasts*, *Men*, *and Gods* with a kind of fascination. Returning again to the fascination of the destructive east, that produced Attila.

So it is at night. Baden-Baden is a little quiet place, all its guests gone. No more Turgenevs or Dostoevskys or Grand Dukes or King Edwards coming to drink the waters. All the outward effect of a world-famous watering-place. But empty now, a mere Black Forest village with the wagon-loads of timber going through, to the French.

The Rentenmark, the new gold mark of Germany, is abominably dear. Prices are high in England, but English money buys less in Baden than it buys in London, by a long chalk. And there is no work—consequently no money. Nobody buys anything, except absolute necessities. The shopkeepers are in despair. And there is less and less work.

Everybody gives up the telephone—can't afford it. The tram-cars don't run, except about three times a day to the station. Up to the Annaberg, the suburb, the lines are rusty, no trams ever go. The people can't afford the ten pfennigs for the fare. Ten pfennigs is an important sum now: one penny. It is really a hundred milliards of marks.

Money becomes insane, and people with it.

At night the place is almost dark, economizing light. Economy, economy, economy—that too becomes an insanity. Luckily the Government keeps bread fairly cheap.

But at night you feel strange things stirring in the darkness, strange feelings stirring out of this still unconquered Black Forest. You stiffen your backbone and you listen to the night. There is a sense of danger. It is not the people. They don't seem dangerous. Out of the very air comes a sense of danger, a queer, *bristling* feeling of uncanny danger.

Something has happened. Something has happened which has not yet eventuated. The old spell of the old world has broken, and the old, bristling, savage spirit has set in. The war did not break the old peace-and-production hope of the world, though it gave it a severe wrench. Yet the old peace-and-production hope still governs, at least the consciousness. Even in Germany it has not quite gone.

But it feels as if, virtually, it were gone. The last two years have done it. The hope in peace-and-production is broken. The old flow, the old adherence is ruptured. And a still older flow has set in. Back, back to the savage polarity of Tartary, and away from the polarity of civilized Christian Europe. This, it seems to me, has already happened. And it is a happening of far more profound import than any actual *event*. It is the father of the next phase of events.

And the feeling never relaxes. As you travel up the Rhine valley, still the same latent sense of danger, of silence, of suspension. Not that the people are actually planning or plotting or preparing. I don't believe it for a minute. But something has happened to the human soul, beyond all help. The human soul recoiling now from unison, and making itself strong elsewhere. The ancient spirit of prehistoric Germany coming back, at the end of history.

The same in Heidelberg, Heidelberg full, full, full of people. Students the same, youths with rucksacks the same, boys and maidens in gangs come down from the hills. The same, and not the same. These queer gangs of Young Socialists, youths and girls, with their non-materialistic professions, their half-mystic assertions, they strike one as strange. Something primitive, like loose, roving gangs of broken, scattered tribes, so they affect one. And the swarms of people somehow produce an impression of silence, of secrecy, of stealth. It is as if everything and everybody recoiled away from the old unison, as barbarians lurking in a wood recoil out of sight. The old habits remain. But the bulk of the people have no money. And the whole stream of feeling is reversed.

So you stand in the woods above the town and see the Neckar flowing green and swift and slippery out of the gulf of Germany, to the Rhine. And the sun sets slow and scarlet into the haze of the Rhine valley. And the old, pinkish stone of the ruined castle across looks sultry, the marshalry is in shadow below, the peaked roofs of old, tight Heidelberg compressed in its river gateway glimmer and glimmer out. There is a blue haze.

And it all looks as if the years were wheeling swiftly backwards, no more onwards. Like a spring that is broken, and whirls swiftly back, so time seems to be whirling with mysterious swiftness to a sort of death.

Whirling to the ghost of the old Middle Ages of Germany, then to the Roman days, then to the days of the silent forest and the dangerous, lurking barbarians.

Something about the Germanic races is unalterable. White-skinned, elemental, and dangerous. Our civilization has come from the fusion of the dark-eyes with the blue. The meeting and mixing and mingling of the two races has been the joy of our ages. And the Celt has been there, alien, but necessary as some chemical reagent to the fusion. So the civilization of Europe rose up. So these cathedrals and these thoughts.

But now the Celt is the disintegrating agent. And the Latin and southern races are falling out of association with the northern races, the northern Germanic impulse is recoiling towards Tartary, the destructive vortex of Tartary.

It is a fate; nobody now can alter it. It is a fate. The very blood changes. Within the last three years, the very constituency of the blood has changed, in European veins. But particularly in Germanic veins.

At the same time, we have brought it about ourselves —by a Ruhr occupation, by an English nullity, and by a German false will. We have done it ourselves. But apparently it was not to be helped.

Quos vult perdere Deus, dementat prius.

THE MOZO

ROSALINO really goes with the house, though he has been in service here only two months. When we went to look at the place, we saw him lurking in the *patio*, and glancing furtively under his brows. He is not one of the erect, bantam little Indians that stare with a black, incomprehensible, but somewhat defiant stare. It may be Rosalino has a distant strain of other Indian blood, not Zapotec. Or it may be he is only a bit different. The difference lies in a certain sensitiveness and aloneness, as if he were a mother's boy. The way he drops his head and looks sideways under his black lashes, apprehensive, apprehending, feeling his way, as it were. Not the bold male glare of most of the Indians, who seem as if they had never, never had mothers at all.

The Aztec gods and goddesses are, as far as we have known anything about them, an unlovely and unlovable lot. In their myths there is no grace or charm, no poetry. Only this perpetual grudge, grudge, grudging, one god grudging another, the gods grudging men their existence, and men grudging the animals. The goddess of love is goddess of dirt and prostitution, a dirt-eater, a horror, without a touch of tenderness. If the god wants to make love to her, she has to sprawl down in front of him, blatant and accessible.

And then, after all, when she conceives and brings forth, what is it she produces? What is the infant-god she tenderly bears? Guess, all ye people, joyful and triumphant!

You never could.

It is a stone knife.

It is a razor-edged knife of blackish-green flint, the knife of all knives, the veritable Paraclete of knives. It is the sacrificial knife with which the priest makes a gash in his victim's breast, before he tears out the heart, to hold it smoking to the sun. And the Sun, the Sun behind the sun, is supposed to suck the smoking heart greedily with insatiable appetite.

This, then, is a pretty Christmas Eve. Lo, the goddess is gone to bed, to bring forth her child. Lo! ye people, await the birth of the saviour, the wife of a god is about to become a mother.

Tarumm-tarah! Tarumm-tarah! blow the trumpets. The child is born. Unto us a son is given. Bring him forth, lay him on a tender cushion. Show him, then, to all the people. See! See! See him upon the cushion, tenderly new-born and reposing! Ah, *qué bonito!* Oh, what a nice, blackish, smooth, keen stone knife!

And to this day, most of the Mexican Indian women seem to bring forth stone knives. Look at them, these sons of incomprehensible mothers, with their black eyes like flints, and their stiff little bodies as taut and as keen as knives of obsidian. Take care they don't rip you up.

Our Rosalino is an exception. He drops his shoulders just a little. He is a bit bigger, also, than the average Indian down here. He must be about five feet four inches. And he hasn't got the big, obsidian, glaring eyes. His eyes are smaller, blacker, like the quick black eyes of the lizard. They don't look at one with the obsidian stare. They are just a bit aware that there is another being, unknown, at the other end of the glance. Hence he drops his head with a little apprehension, screening himself as if he were vulnerable.

Usually, these people have no correspondence with one at all. To them a white man or white woman is a sort of phenomenon, just as a monkey is a sort of phenomenon; something to watch, and wonder at, and laugh at, but not to be taken on one's own plane.

Now the white man is a sort of extraordinary white monkey that, by cunning, has learnt lots of semi-magical secrets of the universe, and made himself boss of the show. Imagine a race of big white monkeys got up in fantastic clothes, and able to kill a man by hissing at him; able to leap through the air in great hops, covering a mile in each leap; able to transmit his thoughts by a moment's effort of concentration to some great white monkey or monkeyess, a thousand miles away: and you have, from our point of view, something of the picture that the Indian has of us.

The white monkey has curious tricks. He knows, for example, the time. Now to a Mexican, and an Indian, time is a vague, foggy reality. There are only three times: *en la mañana, en la tarde, en la noche :* in the morning, in the afternoon, in the night. There is even no midday, and no evening.

But to the white monkey, horrible to relate, there are exact spots of time, such as five o'clock, half-past nine. The day is a horrible puzzle of exact spots of time.

The same with distance: horrible invisible distances called two miles, ten miles. To the Indians, there is near and far, and very near and very far. There is two days or one day. But two miles are as good as twenty to him, for he goes entirely by his feeling. If a certain two miles feels far to him, then it *is* far, it is *muy lejos !* But if a certain twenty miles *feels* near and familiar, then it is not far. Oh, no, it is just a little distance. And he will let you set off in the evening, for night to overtake you in the wilderness, without a qualm. It is not far.

But the white man has a horrible, truly horrible, monkey-like passion for invisible exactitudes. *Mañana*, to the native, may mean to-morrow, three days hence, six months hence, and never. There are no fixed points in life, save birth, and death, and the *fiestas*. The fixed points of birth and death evaporate spontaneously into vagueness. And the priests fix the *fiestas*. From time immemorial priests have fixed the *fiestas*, the festivals of the gods, and men have had no more to do with time. What should men have to do with time?

The same with money. These *centavos* and these *pesos*, what do they mean, after all? Little disks that have no charm. The natives insist on reckoning in invisible coins, coins that don't exist here, like *reales* or *pesetas*. If you buy two eggs for a *real*, you have to pay twelve and a half *centavos*. Since also half a *centavo* doesn't exist, you or the vendor forfeit the non-existent.

The same with honesty, the *meum* and the *tuum*. The white man has a horrible way of remembering, even to a *centavo*, even to a thimbleful of *mescal*. Horrible! The Indian, it seems to me, is not naturally dishonest. He is not naturally avaricious, has not even any innate cupidity. In this he is unlike the old people of the Mediterranean, to whom possessions have a mystic meaning, and a silver coin a mystic white halo, a *lueur* of magic.

To the real Mexican, no! He doesn't care. He doesn't even *like* keeping money. His deep instinct is to spend it at once, so that he needn't have it. He doesn't really want to keep anything, not even his wife and children. Nothing that he has to be responsible for. Strip, strip, strip away the past and the future, leave the naked moment of the present disentangled. Strip away memory, strip away forethought and care; leave the moment, stark and sharp and without consciousness, like the obsidian knife. The before and the after are the stuff of consciousness. The instant moment is for ever keen with a razor edge of oblivion, like the knife of sacrifice.

But the great white monkey has got hold of the keys of the world, and the black-eyed Mexican has to serve the great white monkey, in order to live. He has to learn the tricks of the white monkey-show: time of the day, coin of money, machines that start at a second, work that is meaningless and yet is paid for with exactitude, in exact coin. A whole existence of monkey-tricks and monkey-virtues. The strange monkey-virtue of charity, the white monkeys nosing round to *help*, to *save*! Could any trick be more unnatural? Yet it is one of the tricks of the great white monkey.

If an Indian is poor, he says to another: I have no food; give me to eat. Then the other hands the hungry one a couple of *tortillas*. That is natural. But when the white monkeys come round, they peer at the house,

at the woman, at the children. They say: Your child
is sick. *Si, señor.* What have you done for it?—
Nothing. What is to be done?—You must make a
poultice. I will show you how.

Well, it was very amusing, this making hot dough to
dab on the baby. Like plastering a house with mud.
But why do it twice? Twice is not amusing. The child
will die. Well, then, it will be in paradise. How nice
for it! That's just what God wants of it, that it shall
be a cheerful little angel among the roses of paradise.
What could be better?

How tedious of the white monkey coming with the
trick of salvation, to rub oil on the baby, and put
poultices on it, and make you give it medicine in a spoon
at morning, noon, and night. Why morning and noon
and night? Why not just any time, anywhen? It will
die to-morrow if you don't do these things to-day! But
to-morrow is another day, and it is not dead now, so
if it dies at another time, it must be because the other
times are out of hand.

Oh, the tedious, exacting white monkeys, with their
yesterdays and to-days and to-morrows! To-morrow
is always another day, and yesterday is part of the en-
circling never. Why think outside the moment? And
inside the moment one does not think. So why pretend
to think? It is one of the white monkey-tricks. He is
a clever monkey. But he is ugly, and he has nasty
white flesh. We are not ugly, with screwed-up faces,
and we have good warm-brown flesh. If we have to
work for the white monkey, we don't care. His tricks
are half-amusing. And one may as well amuse oneself
that way as any other. So long as one is amused.

So long as the devil does not rouse in us, seeing the
white monkeys for ever mechanically bossing, with their
incessant tick-tack of work. Seeing them get the work
out of us, the sweat, the money, and then taking the
very land from us, the very oil and metal out of our
soil.

They do it! They do it all the time. Because they
can't help it. Because grasshoppers can but hop, and

ants can carry little sticks, and white monkeys can go tick-tack, tick-tack, do this, do that, time to work, time to eat, time to drink, time to sleep, time to walk, time to ride, time to wash, time to look dirty, tick-tack, tick-tack, time, time, time, time, time! Oh, cut off his nose and make him swallow it.

For the *moment* is as changeless as an obsidian knife, and the heart of the Indian is keen as the moment that divides past from future, and sacrifices them both.

To Rosalino, too, the white monkey-tricks are amusing. He is ready to work for the white monkeys, to learn some of their tricks, their monkey-speech of Spanish, their tick-tack ways. He works for four *pesos* a month, and his food: a few *tortillas*. Four *pesos* are two American dollars: about nine shillings. He owns two cotton shirts, two pairs of calico pantaloons, two blouses, one of pink cotton, one of darkish flannelette, and a pair of sandals. Also, his straw hat that he has curled up to look very jaunty, and a rather old, factory-made, rather cheap shawl, or plaid rug with fringe. *Et praeterea nihil.*

His duty is to rise in the morning and sweep the street in front of the house, and water it. Then he sweeps and waters the broad, brick-tiled verandas, and flicks the chairs with a sort of duster made of fluffy reeds. After which he walks behind the cook—she is very superior, had a Spanish grandfather, and Rosalino must address her as *Señora*—carrying the basket to market. Returned from the market, he sweeps the whole of the *patio*, gathers up the leaves and refuse, fills the pannier-basket, hitches it up on to his shoulders, and holds it by a band across his forehead, and thus, a beast of burden, goes out to deposit the garbage at the side of one of the little roads leading out of the city. Every *little* road leaves the town between heaps of garbage, an avenue of garbage blistering in the sun.

Returning, Rosalino waters the whole of the garden and sprinkles the whole of the *patio*. This takes most of the morning. In the afternoon, he sits without much to do. If the wind has blown or the day was hot, he starts again at about three o'clock, sweeping up leaves, and sprinkling everywhere with an old watering-can.

Then he retreats to the entrance-way, the *zaguán*, which, with its big doors and its cobbled track, is big enough to admit an ox-wagon. The *zaguán* is his home: just the doorway. In one corner is a low wooden bench about four feet long and eighteen inches wide. On this he screws up and sleeps, in his clothes as he is, wrapped in the old *serape*.

But this is anticipating. In the obscurity of the *zaguán* he sits and pores, pores, pores over a school-book, learning to read and write. He can read a bit, and write a bit. He filled a large sheet of foolscap with writing: quite nice. But I found out that what he had written was a Spanish poem, a love-poem, with *no puedo olvidar* and *voy a cortar*—the rose, of course. He had written the thing straight ahead, without verse-lines or capitals or punctuation at all, just a vast string of words, a whole foolscap sheet full. When I read a few lines aloud, he writhed and laughed in an agony of confused feelings. And of what he had written he understood a small, small amount, parrot-wise, from the top of his head. Actually, it meant just words, sound, noise, to him: noise called *Castellano*, Castilian. Exactly like a parrot.

From seven to eight he goes to the night-school, to cover a bit more of the foolscap. He has been going for two years. If he goes two years more he will perhaps really be able to read and write six intelligible sentences: but only Spanish, which is as foreign to him as Hindustani would be to an English farm-boy. Then if he can speak his quantum of Spanish, and read it and write it to a very uncertain extent, he will return to his village two days' journey on foot into the hills, and then, in time, he may even rise to be an *alcalde*, or headman of the village, responsible to the Government. If he were *alcalde* he would get a little salary. But far more important to him is the glory: being able to boss.

He has a *paisano*, a fellow-countryman, to sleep with him in the *zaguán*, to guard the doors. Whoever gets into the house or *patio* must get through these big doors. There is no other entrance, not even a needle's eye. The windows to the street are heavily barred. Each house is its own small fortress. Ours is a double square, the trees and flowers in the first square, with the two wings of the house. And in the second *patio*, the chickens, pigeons, guinea-pigs, and the big heavy earthenware dish or tub, called an *apaxtle*, in which all the servants can bathe themselves, like chickens in a saucer.

By half-past nine at night Rosalino is lying on his little bench, screwed up, wrapped in his shawl, his sandals, called *huaraches*, on the floor. Usually he takes off his *huaraches* when he goes to bed. That is all his preparation. In another corner, wrapped up, head and all, like a mummy in his thin old blanket, the *paisano*, another lad of about twenty, lies asleep on the cold stones. And at an altitude of five thousand feet, the nights can be cold.

Usually everybody is in by half-past nine in our very quiet house. If not, you may thunder at the big doors. It is hard to wake Rosalino. You have to go close to him, and call. That will wake him. But don't touch him. That would startle him terribly. No one is touched unawares, except to be robbed or murdered.

'Rosalino! *están tocando!*'—'Rosalino! they are knocking!'

At last there starts up a strange, glaring, utterly lost Rosalino. Perhaps he just has enough wit to pull the door-catch. One wonders where he was, and what he was, in his sleep, he starts up so strange and wild and lost.

The first time he had anything to do for me was when the van was come to carry the bit of furniture to the house. There was Aurelio, the dwarf *mozo* of our friends, and Rosalino, and the man who drove the wagon. But there *should* have been also a *cargador*—a porter. 'Help them,' said I to Rosalino. 'You give a hand to help.' But he winced away, muttering, '*No quiero!*—I don't want to.'

The fellow, I thought to myself, is a fool. He thinks it's not his job, and perhaps he is afraid of smashing the furniture. Nothing to be done but to leave him alone.

We settled in, and Rosalino seemed to like doing things for us. He liked learning his monkey-tricks from the white monkeys. And since we started feeding him from our own meals, and for the first time in his life he had real soups, meat stews, or a fried egg, he loved to do things in the kitchen. He would come with sparkling black eyes: '*He comido el caldo. Grazias!*' ('I have eaten the soup. Thank you.')—And he would give a strange, excited little yelp of a laugh.

Came the day when we walked to Huayapa, on the Sunday, and he was very thrilled. But at night, in the evening when we got home, he lay mute on his bench —not that he was really tired. The Indian gloom, which settles on them like a black marsh-fog, had settled on him. He did not bring in the water—let me carry it by myself.

Monday morning, the same black, reptilian gloom, and a sense of hatred. He hated us. This was a bit flabbergasting, because he had been so thrilled and happy the day before. But the revulsion had come. He didn't forgive himself for having felt free and happy with us. He had eaten what we had eaten, hard-boiled eggs and sardine sandwiches and cheese; he had drunk out of the orange-peel *taza*, which delighted him so much. He had had a bottle of *gazoosa*, fizz, with us, on the way home, in San Felipe.

And now, the reaction. The flint knife. He had been happy, *therefore* we were scheming to take another advantage of him. We had some devilish white-monkey trick up our sleeve; we wanted to get at his *soul*, no doubt, and do it the white monkey's damage. We wanted to get at his heart, did we? But his heart was an obsidian knife.

He hated us, and gave off a black steam of hate,

that filled the *patio* and made one feel sick. He did not come to the kitchen, he did not carry the water. Leave him alone.

At lunch-time on Monday he said he wanted to leave. Why? He said he wanted to go back to his village.

Very well. He was to wait just a few days, till another *mozo* was found.

At this a glance of pure, reptilian hate from his black eyes.

He sat motionless on his bench all the afternoon, in the Indian stupor of gloom and profound hate. In the evening, he cheered up a little and said he would stay on, at least till Easter.

Tuesday morning. More stupor and gloom and hate. He wanted to go back to his village at once. All right! No one wanted to keep him against his will. Another *mozo* would be found at once.

He went off in the numb stupor of gloom and hate, a very potent hate that could affect one in the pit of one's stomach with nausea.

Tuesday afternoon, and he thought he would stay.

Wednesday morning, and he wanted to go.

Very good. Inquiries made; another *mozo* was coming on Friday morning. It was settled.

Thursday was *fiesta*. Wednesday, therefore, we would go to market, the Niña—that is the mistress—myself, and Rosalino with the basket. He loved to go to market with the *patrones*. We would give him money and send him off to bargain for oranges, *pitahayas*, potatoes, eggs, a chicken, and so forth. This he simply loved to do. It put him into a temper to see us buying without bargaining, and paying ghastly prices.

He bargained away, silent almost, muttering darkly. It took him a long time, but he had far greater success than even Natividad, the cook. And he came back in triumph, with much stuff and little money spent.

So again that afternoon, he was staying on. The spell was wearing off.

The Indians of the hills have a heavy, intense sort of attachment to their villages; Rosalino had not been out of the little city for two years. Suddenly finding himself in Huayapa, a real Indian hill-village, the black Indian gloom of nostalgia must have made a crack in his spirits. But he had been perfectly cheerful—perhaps too cheerful—till we got home.

Again, the Señorita had taken a photograph of him. They are all crazy to have their photographs taken. I had given him an envelope and a stamp, to send a photograph to his mother. Because in his village he had a widow mother, a brother, and a married sister. The family owned a bit of land, with orange-trees. The best oranges come from the hills, where it is cooler. Seeing the photograph, the mother, who had completely forgotten her son, as far as any keen remembering goes, suddenly, like a cracker going off inside her, wanted him: at that very moment. So she sent an urgent message.

But already it was Wednesday afternoon. Arrived a little fellow in white clothes, smiling hard. It was the brother from the hills. Now, we thought, Rosalino will have someone to walk back with. On Friday, after the *fiesta*, he would go.

Thursday, he escorted us with the basket to the *fiesta*. He bargained for flowers, and for a *serape* which he didn't get, for a carved *jicara* which he did get, and for a number of toys. He and the Niña and the Señorita ate a great wafer of a pancake with sweet stuff on it. The basket grew heavy. The brother appeared, to carry the hen and the extra things. Bliss.

He was perfectly happy again. He didn't want to go on Friday; he didn't want to go at all. He wanted to stay with us and come with us to England when we went home.

So, another trip to the friend, the Mexican, who had found us the other *mozo*. Now to put off the other boy again: but then, they are like that.

And the Mexican, who had known Rosalino when he first came down from the hills and could speak no Spanish, told us another thing about him.

In the last revolution—a year ago—the revolutionaries

of the winning side wanted more soldiers from the hills. The *alcalde* of the hill-village was told to pick out young men and send them down to the barracks in the city. Rosalino was among the chosen.

But Rosalino refused, said again *No quiero!* He is one of those, like myself, who have a horror of serving in a mass of men, or even being mixed up with a mass of men. He obstinately refused. Whereupon the recruiting soldiers beat him with the butt of their rifles till he lay unconscious, apparently dead.

Then, because they wanted him at once, and he would now be no good for some time, with his injured back, they left him, to get the revolution over without him.

This explains his fear of furniture-carrying, and his fear of being 'caught.'

Yet that little Aurelio, the friend's *mozo*, who is not above four feet six in height, a tiny fellow, fared even worse. He, too, is from the hills. In his village, a cousin of his gave some information to the *losing* side in the revolution. The cousin wisely disappeared.

But in the city, the winning side seized Aurelio, since he was the *cousin* of the delinquent. In spite of the fact that he was the faithful *mozo* of a foreign resident, he was flung into prison. Prisoners in prison are not fed. Either friends or relatives bring them food, or they go very, very thin. Aurelio had a married sister in town, but *she* was afraid to go to the prison, lest she and her husband should be seized. The master, then, sent his new *mozo* twice a day to the prison with a basket; the huge, huge prison, for this little town of a few thousands.

Meanwhile the master struggled and struggled with the 'authorities'—friends of the people—for Aurelio's release. Nothing to be done.

One day the new *mozo* arrived at the prison with the basket, to find no Aurelio. A friendly soldier gave the message Aurelio had left. '*Adios a mi patrón. Me llevan.*' Oh, fatal words: '*Me llevan*'—They are taking me off. The master rushed to the train: it had gone, with the dwarf, plucky little *mozo*, into the void.

Months later, Aurelio reappeared. He was in rags, haggard, and his dark throat was swollen up to the ears. He had been taken off, two hundred miles into Vera Cruz State. He had been hung up by the neck, with a fixed knot, and left hanging for hours. Why? To make the cousin come and save his relative: put his own neck into a running noose. To make the absolutely innocent fellow confess: what? Everybody knew he was innocent. At any rate, to teach everybody better next time. Oh, brotherly teaching!

Aurelio escaped, and took to the mountains. Sturdy little dwarf of a fellow, he made his way back, begging *tortillas* at the villages, and arrived, haggard, with a great swollen neck, to find his master waiting, and another 'party' in power. More friends of the people.

To-morrow is another day. The master nursed Aurelio well, and Aurelio is a strong, if tiny, fellow, with big, brilliant black eyes that for the moment will trust a foreigner, but none of his own people. A dwarf in stature, but perfectly made, and very strong. And very intelligent, far more quick and intelligent than Rosalino.

Is it any wonder that Aurelio and Rosalino, when they see the soldiers with guns on their shoulders marching towards the prison with some blanched prisoner between them—and one sees it every few days—stand and gaze in a blank kind of horror, and look at the *patrón*, to see if there is any refuge?

Not to be *caught*! Not to be *caught*! It must have been the prevailing motive of Indian-Mexico life since long before Montezuma marched his prisoners to sacrifice.

EDGAR ALLAN POE

POE has no truck with Indians or Nature. He makes no bones about Red Brothers and Wigwams.

He is absolutely concerned with the disintegration processes of his own psyche. As we have said, the rhythm of American art activity is dual.

1. A disintegrating and sloughing of the old consciousness.

2. The forming of a new consciousness underneath.

Fenimore Cooper has the two vibrations going on together. Poe has only one, only the disintegrative vibration. This makes him almost more a scientist than an artist.

Moralists have always wondered helplessly why Poe's 'morbid' tales need have been written. They need to be written because old things need to die and disintegrate, because the old white psyche has to be gradually broken down before anything else can come to pass.

Man must be stripped even of himself. And it is a painful, sometimes a ghastly process.

Poe had a pretty bitter doom. Doomed to seethe down his soul in a great continuous convulsion of disintegration, and doomed to register the process. And then doomed to be abused for it, when he had performed some of the bitterest tasks of human experience that can be asked of a man. Necessary tasks, too. For the human soul must suffer its own disintegration, *consciously*, if ever it is to survive.

But Poe is rather a scientist than an artist. He is reducing his own self as a scientist reduces a salt in a crucible. It is an almost chemical analysis of the soul and consciousness. Whereas in true art there is always the double rhythm of creating and destroying.

This is why Poe calls his things 'tales.' They are a concatenation of cause and effect.

His best pieces, however, are not tales. They are more. They are ghastly stories of the human soul in its disruptive throes.

Moreover, they are 'love' stories.

Ligeia and *The Fall of the House of Usher* are really love stories.

Love is the mysterious vital attraction which draws things together, closer, closer together. For this reason sex is the actual crisis of love. For in sex the two blood-systems, in the male and female, concentrate and come into contact, the merest film intervening. Yet if the intervening film breaks down, it is death.

So there you are. There is a limit to everything. There is a limit to love.

The central law of all organic life is that each organism is intrinsically isolate and single in itself.

The moment its isolation breaks down, and there comes an actual mixing and confusion, death sets in.

This is true of every individual organism, from man to amoeba.

But the secondary law of all organic life is that each organism only lives through contact with other matter, assimilation, and contact with other life, which means assimilation of new vibrations, non-material. Each individual organism is vivified by intimate contact with fellow organisms: up to a certain point.

So man. He breathes the air into him, he swallows food and water. But more than this. He takes into him the life of his fellow-men, with whom he comes into contact, and he gives back life to them. This contact draws nearer and nearer, as the intimacy increases. When it is a whole contact, we call it love. Men live by food, but die if they eat too much. Men live by love, but die, or cause death, if they love too much.

There are two loves: sacred and profane, spiritual and sensual.

In sensual love, it is the two blood-systems, the man's

and the woman's, which sweep up into pure contact, and *almost* fuse. Almost mingle. Never quite. There is always the finest imaginable wall between the two blood-waves, through which pass unknown vibrations, forces, but through which the blood itself must never break, or it means bleeding.

In spiritual love, the contact is purely nervous. The nerves in the lovers are set vibrating in unison like two instruments. The pitch can rise higher and higher. But carry this too far, and the nerves begin to break, to bleed, as it were, and a form of death sets in.

The trouble about man is that he insists on being master of his own fate, and he insists on *oneness*. For instance, having discovered the ecstasy of spiritual love, he insists that he shall have this all the time, and nothing but this, for this is life. It is what he calls 'heightening' life. He wants his nerves to be set vibrating in the intense and exhilarating unison with the nerves of another being, and by this means he acquires an ecstasy of vision, he finds himself in glowing unison with all the universe.

But as a matter of fact this glowing unison is only a temporary thing, because the first law of life is that each organism is isolate in itself, it must return to its own isolation.

Yet man has tried the glow of unison, called love, and he *likes* it. It gives him his highest gratification. He wants it. He wants it all the time. He wants it and he will have it. He doesn't want to return to his own isolation. Or if he must, it is only as a prowling beast returns to its lair to rest and set out again.

This brings us to Edgar Allan Poe. The clue to him lies in the motto he chose for *Ligeia*, a quotation from the mystic Joseph Glanvill: 'And the will therein lieth, which dieth not. Who knoweth the mysteries of the will, with its vigour? For God is but a great Will pervading all things by nature of its intentness. Man doth not yield himself to the angels, nor unto death utterly, save only through the weakness of his feeble will.'

It is a profound saying: and a deadly one.

Because if God is a great will, then the universe is but an instrument.

I don't know what God is. But He is not simply a will. That is too simple. Too anthropomorphic. Because a man wants his own will, and nothing but his will, he needn't say that God is the same will, magnified *ad infinitum*.

For me, there may be one God, but He is nameless and unknowable.

For me, there are also many gods, that come into me and leave me again. And they have very various wills, I must say.

But the point is Poe.

Poe had experienced the ecstasies of extreme spiritual love. And he wanted those ecstasies and nothing but those ecstasies. He wanted that great gratification, the sense of flowing, the sense of unison, the sense of heightening of life. He had experienced this gratification. He was told on every hand that this ecstasy of spiritual, nervous love was the greatest thing in life, was life itself. And he had tried it for himself, he knew that for him it *was* life itself. So he wanted it. And he *would have* it. He set up his will against the whole of the limitations of nature.

This is a brave man, acting on his own belief, and his own experience. But it is also an arrogant man, and a fool.

Poe was going to get the ecstasy and the heightening, cost what it might. He went on in a frenzy, as characteristic American women nowadays go on in a frenzy, after the very same thing: the heightening, the flow, the ecstasy. Poe tried alcohol, and any drug he could lay his hand on. He also tried any human being he could lay his hands on.

His grand attempt and achievement was with his wife; his cousin, a girl with a singing voice. With her he went in for the intensest flow, the heightening, the prismatic shades of ecstasy. It was the intensest nervous vibration of unison, pressed higher and higher in pitch, till the blood-vessels of the girl broke, and the blood began to flow out loose. It was love. If you call it love.

Love can be terribly obscene.

It is love that causes the neuroticism of the day. It is love that is the prime cause of tuberculosis.

The nerves that vibrate most intensely in spiritual unisons are the sympathetic ganglia of the breast, of the throat, and the hind brain. Drive this vibration over-intensely, and you weaken the sympathetic tissues of the chest—the lungs—or of the throat, or of the lower brain, and the tubercles are given a ripe field.

But Poe drove the vibrations beyond any human pitch of endurance.

Being his cousin, she was more easily keyed to him.

Ligeia is the chief story. Ligeia! A mental-derived name. To him the woman, his wife, was not Lucy. She was Ligeia. No doubt she even preferred it thus.

Ligeia is Poe's love-story, and its very fantasy makes it more truly his own story.

It is a tale of love pushed over a verge. And love pushed to extremes is a battle of wills between the lovers.

Love is become a battle of wills.

Which shall first destroy the other, of the lovers? Which can hold out longest, against the other?

Ligeia is still the old-fashioned woman. Her will is still to submit. She wills to submit to the vampire of her husband's consciousness. Even death.

'In stature she was tall, somewhat slender, and, in her latter days, even emaciated. I would in vain attempt to portray the majesty, the quiet ease, of her demeanour, or the incomprehensible lightness and elasticity of her footfall. I was never made aware of her entrance into my closed study save by the dear music of her low, sweet voice, as she placed her marble hand on my shoulder.'

Poe has been so praised for his style. But it seems to me a meretricious affair. 'Her marble hand' and 'the elasticity of her footfall' seem more like chair-springs and mantelpieces than a human creature. She never was quite a human creature to him. She was an instrument from which he got his extremes of sensation. His *machine à plaisir*, as somebody says.

All Poe's style, moreover, has this mechanical quality, as his poetry has a mechanical rhythm. He never sees anything in terms of life, almost always in terms of matter, jewels, marble, etc., — or in terms of force, scientific. And his cadences are all managed mechanically. This is what is called 'having a style.'

What he wants to do with Ligeia is to analyse her, till he knows all her component parts, till he has got her all in his consciousness. She is some strange chemical salt which he must analyse out in the test-tubes of his brain, and then—when he's finished the analysis— *È finita la commedia !*

But she won't be quite analysed out. There is something, something he can't get. Writing of her eyes, he says: 'They were, I must believe, far larger than the ordinary eyes of our race'—as if anybody would want eyes 'far larger' than other folks'. 'They were even fuller than the fullest of the gazelle eyes of the tribe of the valley of Nourjahad'—which is blarney. 'The hue of the orbs was the most brilliant of black and, far over them, hung jetty lashes of great length'—suggests a whip-lash. 'The brows, slightly irregular in outline, had the same tint. The *strangeness*, which I found in the eyes, was of a nature distinct from the formation, or the colour, or the brilliancy of the features, and must, after all, be referred to as the *expression*.'—Sounds like an anatomist anatomizing a cat.—'Ah, word of no meaning! behind whose vast latitude of sound we entrench our ignorance of so much of the spiritual. The expression of the eyes of Ligeia! How for long hours have I pondered upon it! How have I, through the whole of a midsummer night, struggled to fathom it! What was it — that something more profound than the well of Democritus —which lay far within the pupils of my beloved? What *was* it ? I was possessed with a passion to discover. . . .'

It is easy to see why each man kills the thing he loves. To *know* a living thing is to kill it. You have to kill a thing to know it satisfactorily. For this reason, the desirous consciousness, the SPIRIT, is a vampire.

One should be sufficiently intelligent and interested to know a good deal *about* any person one comes into close contact with. *About* her. Or *about* him.

But to try to *know* any living being is to try to suck the life out of that being.

Above all things, with the woman one loves. Every sacred instinct teaches one that one must leave her unknown. You know your woman darkly, in the blood. To try to *know* her mentally is to try to kill her. Beware, oh woman, of the man who wants to *find out what you are*. And, oh man, beware a thousand times more of the woman who wants to *know* you, or *get* you, what you are.

It is the temptation of a vampire fiend, is this knowledge.

Man does so horribly want to master the secret of life and of individuality *with his mind*. It is like the analysis of protoplasm. You can only analyse *dead* protoplasm, and know its constituents. It is a death process.

Keep KNOWLEDGE for the world of matter, force, and function. It has got nothing to do with being.

But Poe wanted to know—wanted to know what was the strangeness in the eyes of Ligeia. She might have told him it was horror at his probing, horror at being vamped by his consciousness.

But she wanted to be vamped. She wanted to be probed by his consciousness, to be KNOWN. She paid for wanting it, too.

Nowadays it is usually the man who wants to be vamped, to be KNOWN.

Edgar Allan probed and probed. So often he seemed on the verge. But she went over the verge of death before he came over the verge of knowledge. And it is always so.

He decided, therefore, that the clue to the strange-

ness lay in the mystery of will. 'And the will therein
lieth, which dieth not. . . .'

Ligeia had a 'gigantic volition. . . . An intensity
in thought, action, or speech was possibly, in her, a
result, or at least an index' (he really meant indication)
'of that gigantic volition which, during our long inter-
course, failed to give other and more immediate evidence
of its existence.'

I should have thought her long submission to him
was chief and ample 'other evidence.'

'Of all the women whom I have ever known, she, the
outwardly calm, the ever-placid Ligeia, was the most
violently a prey to the tumultuous vultures of stern
passion. And of such passion I could form no estimate,
save by the miraculous expansion of those eyes which
at once so delighted and appalled me—by the almost
magical melody, modulation, distinctness, and placidity
of her very low voice—and by the fierce energy (rendered
doubly effective by contrast with her manner of utterance) of the wild words which she habitually uttered.'

Poor Poe, he had caught a bird of the same feather as
himself. One of those terrible cravers, who crave the
further sensation. Crave to madness or death. 'Vultures
of stern passion' indeed! Condors.

But having recognized that the clue was in her
gigantic volition, he should have realized that the process of this loving, this craving, this knowing, was a
struggle of wills. But Ligeia, true to the great tradition and mode of womanly love, by her will kept herself
submissive, recipient. She is the passive body who is
explored and analysed into death. And yet, at times,
her great female will must have revolted. 'Vultures of
stern passion'! With a convulsion of desire she desired
his further probing and exploring. To any lengths.
But then, 'tumultuous vultures of stern passion.' She
had to fight with herself.

But Ligeia wanted to go on and on with the craving,
with the love, with the sensation, with the probing,
with the knowing, on and on to the end.

There is no end. There is only the rupture of death.

That's where men, and women, are 'had.' Man is always sold, in his search for final KNOWLEDGE.

'That she loved me I should not have doubted; and I might have been easily aware that, in a bosom such as hers, love would have reigned no ordinary passion. But in death only was I fully impressed with the strength of her affection.   For long hours, detaining my hand, would she pour out before me the overflowing of a heart whose more than passionate devotion amounted to idolatry.'   (Oh, the indecency of all this endless intimate talk!)   'How had I deserved to be blessed by such confessions?'   (Another man would have felt himself cursed.)   'How had I deserved to be cursed with the removal of my beloved in the hour of her making them? But upon this subject I cannot bear to dilate.   Let me say only that in Ligeia's more than womanly abandonment to a love, alas! all unmerited, all unworthily bestowed, I at length recognized the principle of her longing with so wildly earnest a desire for the life which was now fleeing so rapidly away.   It is this wild longing—it is this eager vehemence of desire for life—*but* for life—that I have no power to portray—no utterance capable of expressing.'

Well, that is ghastly enough, in all conscience.

'And from them that have not shall be taken away even that which they have.'

'To him that hath life shall be given life, and from him that hath not life shall be taken away even that life which he hath.'

Or her either.

These terribly conscious birds, like Poe and his Ligeia, deny the very life that is in them; they want to turn it all into talk, into *knowing*.   And so life, which will *not* be known, leaves them.

But poor Ligeia, how could she help it?   It was her doom. All the centuries of the SPIRIT, all the years of American rebellion against the Holy Ghost, had done it to her.

She dies, when she would rather do anything than die.   And when she dies the clue, which he only lived to grasp, dies with her.

Foiled!

Foiled!

No wonder she shrieks with her last breath.

On the last day Ligeia dictates to her husband a poem. As poems go, it is rather false, meretricious. But put yourself in Ligeia's place, and it is real enough, and ghastly beyond bearing.

> Out, out are the lights—out all!
>   And over each quivering form
> The curtain, a funeral pall,
>   Comes down with the rush of a storm,
> And the angels, all pallid and wan,
>   Uprising, unveiling, affirm
> That the play is the tragedy 'Man,'
>   And its hero the Conqueror Worm.

Which is the American equivalent for a William Blake poem. For Blake, too, was one of these ghastly, obscene 'Knowers.'

'"O God!" half shrieked Ligeia, leaping to her feet and extending her arms aloft with a spasmodic movement, as I made an end of these lines. "O God! O Divine Father!—shall these things be undeviatingly so? Shall this conqueror be not once conquered? Are we not part and parcel in Thee? Who—who knoweth the mysteries of the will with its vigour? Man doth not yield him to the angels, *nor unto death utterly,* save only through the weakness of his feeble will."'

So Ligeia dies. And yields to death at least partly. *Anche troppo.*

As for her cry to God—has not God said that those who sin against the Holy Ghost shall not be forgiven?

And the Holy Ghost is within us. It is the thing that prompts us to be real, not to push our own cravings too far, not to submit to stunts and high-falutin, above all, not to be too egoistic and wilful in our conscious self, but to change as the spirit inside us bids us change, and leave off when it bids us leave off, and laugh when we must laugh, particularly at ourselves, for in deadly earnestness there is always something a bit ridiculous. The Holy Ghost bids us never be too deadly in our earnestness, always to laugh in time, at ourselves and everything. Particularly at our sublimities. Everything has its hour of ridicule—everything.

Now Poe and Ligeia, alas, couldn't laugh. They were frenziedly earnest. And frenziedly they pushed on this vibration of consciousness and unison in consciousness. They sinned against the Holy Ghost that bids us all laugh and forget, bids us know our own limits. And they weren't forgiven.

Ligeia needn't blame God. She had only her own will, her 'gigantic volition' to thank, lusting after more consciousness, more beastly KNOWING.

Ligeia dies. The husband goes to England, vulgarly buys or rents a gloomy, grand old abbey, put it into some sort of repair, and furnishes it with exotic, mysterious, theatrical splendour. Never anything open and real. This theatrical 'volition' of his. The bad taste of sensationalism.

Then he marries the fair-haired, blue-eyed Lady Rowena Trevanion, of Tremaine. That is, she would be a sort of Saxon-Cornish blue-blood damsel. Poor Poe!

'In halls such as these—in a bridal chamber such as this—I passed, with the Lady of Tremaine, the unhallowed hours of the first month of our marriage—passed them with but little disquietude. That my wife dreaded the fierce moodiness of my temper—that she shunned me, and loved me but little—I could not help perceiving, but it gave me rather pleasure than otherwise. I loathed her with a hatred belonging more to demon than to man. My memory flew back (oh, with what intensity of regret!) to Ligeia, the beloved, the august, the beautiful, the entombed. I revelled in recollections of her purity . . .' etc.

Now the vampire lust is consciously such.

In the second month of the marriage the Lady Rowena fell ill. It is the shadow of Ligeia hangs over her. It is the ghostly Ligeia who pours poison into Rowena's cup. It is the spirit of Ligeia, leagued with the spirit of the husband, that now lusts in the slow destruction of Rowena. The two vampires, dead wife and living husband.

For Ligeia has not yielded unto death *utterly*. Her fixed, frustrated will comes back in vindictiveness. She could not have her way in life. So she, too, will find victims in life. And the husband, all the time, only uses Rowena as a living body on which to wreak his vengeance for his being thwarted with Ligeia. Thwarted from the final KNOWING her.

And at last from the corpse of Rowena, Ligeia rises. Out of her death, through the door of a corpse they have destroyed between them, reappears Ligeia, still trying to have her will, to have more love and knowledge, the final gratification which is never final, with her husband.

For it is true, as William James and Conan Doyle and the rest allow, that a spirit can persist in the after-death. Persist by its own volition. But usually, the evil persistence of a thwarted will, returning for vengeance on life. Lemures, vampires.

It is a ghastly story of the assertion of the human will, the will - to - love and the will - to - consciousness, asserted against death itself. The pride of human conceit in KNOWLEDGE.

There are terrible spirits, ghosts, in the air of America.

Eleonora, the next story, is a fantasy revealing the sensational delights of the man in his early marriage with the young and tender bride. They dwelt, he, his cousin and her mother, in the sequestered Valley of the Many-coloured Grass, the valley of prismatic sensation, where everything seems spectrum-coloured. They looked down at their *own images* in the River of Silence, and drew the god Eros from that wave: out of their own self-consciousness, that is. This is a description of the life of introspection and of the love which is begotten by the self in the self, the self-made love. The trees are like serpents worshipping the sun. That is, they represent the phallic passion in its poisonous or mental activity. Everything runs to consciousness: serpents worshipping the sun. The embrace of love, which should bring darkness and oblivion, would with these lovers be a daytime thing bringing more heightened consciousness, visions, spectrum-visions, prismatic. The evil thing that daytime love-making is, and all sex-palaver.

In *Berenice* the man must go down to the sepulchre of his beloved and pull out her thirty-two small white teeth, which he carries in a box with him. It is repulsive and gloating. The teeth are the instruments of biting, of resistance, of antagonism. They often become symbols of opposition, little instruments or entities of crushing and destroying. Hence the dragon's teeth in the myth. Hence the man in *Berenice* must take possession of the irreducible part of his mistress. 'Toutes ses dents étaient des idées,' he says. Then they are little fixed ideas of mordant hate, of which he possesses himself.

The other great story linking up with this group is *The Fall of the House of Usher*. Here the love is between brother and sister. When the self is broken, and the mystery of the recognition of *otherness* fails, then the longing for identification with the beloved becomes a lust. And it is this longing for identification, utter merging, which is at the base of the incest problem. In psycho-analysis almost every trouble in the psyche is traced to an incest-desire. But it won't do. Incest-desire is only one of the modes by which men strive to get their gratification of the intensest vibration of the spiritual nerves, without any resistance. In the family, the natural vibration is most nearly in unison. With a stranger, there is greater resistance. Incest is the getting of gratification and the avoiding of resistance.

The root of all evil is that we all want this spiritual gratification, this flow, this apparent heightening of life, this knowledge, this valley of many-coloured grass, even grass and light prismatically decomposed, giving ecstasy. We want all this *without resistance*. We want it continually. And this is the root of all evil in us.

We ought to pray to be resisted, and resisted to the bitter end. We ought to decide to have done at last with craving.

The motto to *The Fall of the House of Usher* is a couple of lines from Béranger.

> Son cœur est un luth suspendu;
> Sitôt qu'on le touche il résonne.

We have all the trappings of Poe's rather overdone, vulgar fantasy. 'I reined my horse to the precipitous brink of a black and lurid tarn that lay in unruffled lustre by the dwelling, and gazed down—but with a shudder even more thrilling than before—upon the re-modelled and inverted images of the grey sedge, and the ghastly tree-stems, and the vacant and eye-like windows.' The House of Usher, both dwelling and family, was very old. Minute fungi overspread the exterior of the house, hanging in festoons from the eaves. Gothic archways, a valet of stealthy step, sombre tapestries, ebon black floors, a profusion of tattered and antique furniture, feeble gleams of encrimsoned light through latticed panes, and over all 'an air of stern, deep, irredeemable gloom'—this makes up the interior.

The inmates of the house, Roderick and Madeline Usher, are the last remnants of their incomparably ancient and decayed race. Roderick has the same large, luminous eye, the same slightly arched nose of delicate Hebrew model, as characterized Ligeia. He is ill with the nervous malady of his family. It is he whose nerves are so strung that they vibrate to the unknown quiver-ings of the ether. He, too, has lost his self, his living soul, and become a sensitized instrument of the external influences; his nerves are verily like an aeolian harp which must vibrate. He lives in 'some struggle with the grim phantasm, Fear,' for he is only the physical, post-mortem reality of a living being.

It is a question how much, once the true centrality of the self is broken, the instrumental consciousness of man can register. When man becomes selfless, wafting instrumental like a harp in an open window, how much can his elemental consciousness express? The blood as it runs has its own sympathies and responses to the material world, quite apart from seeing. And the nerves we know vibrate all the while to unseen presences, unseen forces. So Roderick Usher quivers on the edge of material existence.

It is this mechanical consciousness which gives 'the fervid facility of his impromptus.' It is the same thing that gives Poe his extraordinary facility in versification. The absence of real central or impulsive being in himself leaves him inordinately, mechanically sensitive to sounds and effects, associations of sounds, associations of rhyme, for example—mechanical, facile, having no root in any passion. It is all a secondary, meretricious process. So we get Roderick Usher's poem, *The Haunted Palace*, with its swift yet mechanical subtleties of rhyme and rhythm, its vulgarity of epithet. It is all a sort of dream-process, where the association between parts is mechanical, accidental as far as passional meaning goes.

Usher thought that all vegetable things had sentience. Surely all material things have a *form* of sentience, even the inorganic: surely they all exist in some subtle and complicated tension of vibration which makes them sensitive to external influence and causes them to have an influence on other external objects, irrespective of contact. It is of this vibration or inorganic consciousness that Poe is master: the sleep-consciousness. Thus Roderick Usher was convinced that his whole surroundings, the stones of the house, the fungi, the water in the tarn, the very reflected image of the whole, was woven into a physical oneness with the family, condensed, as it were, into one atmosphere—the special atmosphere in which alone the Ushers could live. And it was this atmosphere which had moulded the destinies of his family.

But while ever the soul remains alive, it is the moulder and not the moulded. It is the souls of living men that subtly impregnate stones, houses, mountains, continents, and give these their subtlest form. People only become subject to stones after having lost their integral souls.

In the human realm, Roderick had one connection: his sister Madeline. She, too, was dying of a mysterious disorder, nervous, cataleptic. The brother and sister loved each other passionately and exclusively. They were twins, almost identical in looks. It was the same absorbing love between them, this process of unison in nerve-vibration, resulting in more and more extreme exaltation and a sort of consciousness, and a gradual break-down into death. The exquisitely sensitive Roger, vibrating without resistance with his sister Madeline, more and more exquisitely, and gradually devouring her, sucking her life like a vampire in his anguish of extreme love. And she asking to be sucked.

Madeline died and was carried down by her brother into the deep vaults of the house. But she was not dead. Her brother roamed about in incipient madness —a madness of unspeakable terror and guilt. After eight days they were suddenly startled by a clash of metal, then a distinct, hollow, metallic, and clangorous, yet apparently muffled, reverberation. Then Roderick Usher, gibbering, began to express himself: '*We have put her living into the tomb!* Said I not that my senses were acute? I *now* tell you that I heard her first feeble movements in the hollow coffin. I heard them—many, many days ago—yet I dared not — *I dared not speak.*'

It is the same old theme of 'each man kills the thing he loves.' He knew his love had killed her. He knew she died at last, like Ligeia, unwilling and unappeased. So, she rose again upon him. 'But then without those doors there *did* stand the lofty and enshrouded figure of the Lady Madeline of Usher. There was blood upon her white robes, and the evidence of some bitter struggle upon every portion of her emaciated frame. For a moment she remained trembling and reeling to and fro upon the threshold, then, with a low moaning cry, fell heavily inward upon the person of her brother, and in her violent and now final death-agonies bore him to the floor a corpse, and a victim to the terrors he had anticipated.'

It is lurid and melodramatic, but it is true. It is a ghastly psychological truth of what happens in the last stages of this beloved love, which cannot be separate, cannot be isolate, cannot listen in isolation to the iso-late Holy Ghost. For it is the Holy Ghost we must live by. The next era is the era of the Holy Ghost. And the Holy Ghost speaks individually inside each individual: always, for ever a ghost. There is no mani-festation to the general world. Each isolate individual listening in isolation to the Holy Ghost within him.

The Ushers, brother and sister, betrayed the Holy Ghost in themselves. They would love, love, love, with-out resistance. They would love, they would merge, they would be as one thing. So they dragged each other down into death. For the Holy Ghost says you must *not* be as one thing with another being. Each must abide by itself, and correspond only within certain limits.

The best tales all have the same burden. Hate is as inordinate as love, and as slowly consuming, as secret, as underground, as subtle. All this underground vault business in Poe only symbolizes that which takes place *beneath* the consciousness. On top, all is fair-spoken. Beneath, there is awful murderous extremity of burying alive. Fortunato, in *The Cask of Amontillado*, is buried alive out of perfect hatred, as the Lady Madeline of Usher is buried alive out of love. The lust of hate is the inordinate desire to consume and unspeakably possess the soul of the hated one, just as the lust of love is the desire to possess, or to be possessed by, the beloved, utterly. But in either case the result is the dissolu-tion of both souls, each losing itself in transgressing its own bounds.

The lust of Montresor is to devour utterly the soul of Fortunato. It would be no use killing him outright. If a man is killed outright his soul remains integral, free to return into the bosom of some beloved, where it can enact itself. In walling up his enemy in the vault, Montresor seeks to bring about the indescribable capitu-lation of the man's soul, so that he, the victor, can possess himself of the very being of the vanquished.

Perhaps this can actually be done. Perhaps, in the attempt, the victor breaks the bonds of his own identity, and collapses into nothingness, or into the infinite. Becomes a monster.

What holds good for inordinate hate holds good for inordinate love. The motto, *Nemo me impune lacessit*, might just as well be *Nemo me impune amat*.

In *William Wilson* we are given a rather unsubtle account of the attempt of a man to kill his own soul. William Wilson the mechanical, lustful ego succeeds in killing William Wilson the living self. The lustful ego lives on, gradually reducing itself towards the dust of the infinite.

In *The Murders in the Rue Morgue* and *The Gold Bug* we have those mechanical tales where the interest lies in the following out of a subtle chain of cause and effect. The interest is scientific rather than artistic, a study in psychologic reactions.

The fascination of murder itself is curious. Murder is not just killing. Murder is a lust to get at the very quick of life itself, and kill it—hence the stealth and the frequent morbid dismemberment of the corpse, the attempt to get at the very quick of the murdered being, to find the quick and to possess it. It is curious that the two men fascinated by the art of murder, though in different ways, should have been De Quincey and Poe, men so different in ways of life, yet perhaps not so widely different in nature. In each of them is traceable that strange lust for extreme love and extreme hate, possession by mystic violence of the other soul, or violent deathly surrender of the soul in the self: an absence of manly virtue, which stands alone and accepts limits.

Inquisition and torture are akin to murder: the same lust. It is a combat between inquisitor and victim as to whether the inquisitor shall get at the quick of life itself, and pierce it. Pierce the very quick of the soul. The evil will of man tries to do this. The brave soul of man refuses to have the life-quick pierced in him. It is strange: but just as the thwarted will can persist evilly, after death, so can the brave spirit preserve, even through torture and death, the quick of life and truth.

Nowadays society is evil. It finds subtle ways of torture, to destroy the life-quick, to get at the life-quick in a man. Every possible form. And still a man can hold out, if he can laugh and listen to the Holy Ghost. —but society is evil, evil, and love is evil. And evil breeds evil, more and more.

So the mystery goes on. La Bruyère says that all our human unhappiness *viennent de ne pouvoir être seuls*. As long as man lives he will be subject to the yearning of love or the burning of hate, which is only inverted love.

But he is subject to something more than this. If we do not live to eat, we do not live to love either.

We live to stand alone, and listen to the Holy Ghost. The Holy Ghost, who is inside us, and who is many gods. Many gods come and go, some say one thing and some say another, and we have to obey the God of the innermost hour. It is the multiplicity of gods within us make up the Holy Ghost.

But Poe knew only love, love, love, intense vibrations and heightened consciousness. Drugs, women, self-destruction, but anyhow the prismatic ecstasy of heightened consciousness and sense of love, of flow. The human soul in him was beside itself. But it was not lost. He told us plainly how it was, so that we should know.

He was an adventurer into vaults and cellars and horrible underground passages of the human soul. He sounded the horror and the warning of his own doom.

Doomed he was. He died wanting more love, and love killed him. A ghastly disease, love. Poe telling us of his disease: trying even to make his disease fair and attractive. Even succeeding.

Which is the inevitable falseness, duplicity of art, American art in particular.

POEMS

LOVE ON THE FARM

WHAT large, dark hands are those at the window
Grasping in the golden light
Which weaves its way through the evening wind
  At my heart's delight?

Ah, only the leaves! But in the west
I see a redness suddenly come
Into the evening's anxious breast—
  'Tis the wound of love goes home!

The woodbine creeps abroad
Calling low to her lover:
  The sun-lit flirt who all the day
  Has poised above her lips in play
  And stolen kisses, shallow and gay,
  Of pollen, now has gone away—
    She woos the moth with her sweet, low word;
And when above her his moth-wings hover
Then her bright breast she will uncover
And yield her honey-drop to her lover.

Into the yellow, evening glow
Saunters a man from the farm below;
Leans, and looks in at the low-built shed
Where the swallow has hung her marriage bed.
  The bird lies warm against the wall.
  She glances quick her startled eyes
  Towards him, then she turns away
  Her small head, making warm display
  Of red upon the throat. Her terrors sway
  Her out of the nest's warm, busy ball,
  Whose plaintive cry is heard as she flies
  In one blue stoop from out the sties
  Into the twilight's empty hall.

Oh, water-hen, beside the rushes
Hide your quaintly scarlet blushes,
Still your quick tail, lie still as dead,
Till the distance folds over his ominous tread!

The rabbit presses back her ears,
Turns back her liquid, anguished eyes
And crouches low; then with wild spring
Spurts from the terror of *his* oncoming;
To be choked back, the wire ring
Her frantic effort throttling:
  Piteous brown ball of quivering fears!
Ah, soon in his large, hard hands she dies,
And swings all loose from the swing of his walk!
Yet calm and kindly are his eyes
And ready to open in brown surprise
Should I not answer to his talk
Or should he my tears surmise.

I hear his hand on the latch, and rise from my chair
Watching the door open; he flashes bare
His strong teeth in a smile, and flashes his eyes
In a smile like triumph upon me; then careless-wise
He flings the rabbit soft on the table board
And comes towards me: ah! the uplifted sword
Of his hand against my bosom! and oh, the broad
Blade of his glance that asks me to applaud
His coming! With his hand he turns my face to him
And caresses me with his fingers that still smell grim
Of the rabbit's fur! God, I am caught in a snare!
I know not what fine wire is round my throat;
I only know I let him finger there
My pulse of life, and let him nose like a stoat
Who sniffs with joy before he drinks the blood.

And down his mouth comes to my mouth! and down
His bright dark eyes come over me, like a hood
Upon my mind! his lips meet mine, and a flood
Of sweet fire sweeps across me, so I drown
Against him, die, and find death good.

BALLAD OF ANOTHER OPHELIA

O THE green glimmer of apples in the orchard,
Lamps in a wash of rain!
O the wet walk of my brown hen through the stack-
    yard!
O tears on the window-pane!

Nothing now will ripen the bright green apples
Full of disappointment and of rain;
Blackish they will taste, of tears, when the yellow
    dapples
Of autumn tell the withered tale again.

All round the yard it is cluck! my brown hen.
Cluck! and the rain-wet wings;
Cluck! my marigold bird, and again
Cluck! for your yellow darlings.

For a grey rat found the gold thirteen
Huddled away in the dark.
Flutter for a moment, oh, the beast is quick and keen,
Extinct one yellow-fluffy spark!

Once I had a lover bright like running water,
Once his face was open like the sky,
Open like the sky looking down in all its laughter
On the buttercups, and the buttercups was I.

What then is hidden in the skirts of all the blossom?
What is peeping from your skirts, O mother hen?
'Tis the sun that asks the question, in a lovely haste
    for wisdom;
What a lovely haste for wisdom is in men!

Yea, but it is cruel when undressed is all the blossom
And her shift is lying white upon the floor,
That a grey one, like a shadow, like a rat, a thief, a
    rainstorm,
Creeps upon her then and ravishes her store!

O the grey garner that is full of half-grown apples!
O the golden sparkles laid extinct!
And O, behind the cloud-leaves, like yellow autumn
    dapples,
Did you see the wicked sun that winked?

VIOLETS

SISTER, tha knows while we was on th' planks
    Aside o' t' grave, an' th' coffin set
On th' yaller clay, wi' th' white flowers top of it
    Waitin' ter be buried out o' th' wet?

An' t' parson makin' haste, an' a' t' black
    Huddlin' up i' t' rain,
Did t' 'appen ter notice a bit of a lass way back
    Hoverin', lookin' poor an' plain?

    —How should I be lookin' round!
      An' me standin' there on th' plank,
    An' our Ted's coffin set on th' ground,
      Waitin' to be sank!

    I 'd as much as I could do, to think
      Of 'im bein' gone
    That young, an' a' the fault of drink
      An' carryin's on!—

Let that be; 'appen it worna th' drink, neither,
  Nor th' carryin' on as killed 'im.
               —No, 'appen not,
My sirs! But I say 'twas! For a blither
Lad never stepped, till 'e got in with your lot.—

All right, all right, it 's my fault! But let
Me tell about that lass. When you 'd all gone
Ah stopped behind on t' pad, i' t' pourin' wet,
An' watched what 'er 'ad on.

Tha should ha' seed 'er slive up when yer 'd gone!
Tha should ha' seed 'er kneel an' look in
At th' sloppy grave! an' 'er little neck shone
That white, an' 'er cried that much, I 'd like to begin

Scraightin' mysen as well. 'Er undid 'er black
Jacket at th' bosom, an' took out
Over a double 'andful o' violets, a' in a pack
An' white an' blue in a ravel, like a clout.

An' warm, for th' smell come waftin' to me. 'Er put
    'er face
Right in 'em, an' scraighted a bit again,
Then after a bit 'er dropped 'em down that place,
An' I come away, acause o' th' teemin' rain.

But I thowt ter mysen, as that wor th' only bit
O' warmth as 'e got down theer; th' rest wor stone cold.
From that bit of a wench's bosom; 'e 'd be glad of it,
Gladder nor of thy lilies, if tha maun be told.

BABY RUNNING BAREFOOT

When the white feet of the baby beat across the grass
The little white feet nod like white flowers in a wind,
They poise and run like puffs of wind that pass
Over water where the weeds are thinned.

And the sight of their white playing in the grass
Is winsome as a robin's song, so fluttering;
Or like two butterflies that settle on a glass
Cup for a moment, soft little wing-beats uttering.

And I wish that the baby would tack across here to me
Like a wind-shadow running on a pond, so she could stand
With two little bare white feet upon my knee
And I could feel her feet in either hand,

Cool as syringa buds in morning hours,
Or firm and silken as young peony flowers.

TEASE

I will give you all my keys,
  You shall be my châtelaine,
You shall enter as you please,
  As you please shall go again.

When I hear you jingling through
  All the chambers of my soul,
How I sit and laugh at you
  In your close housekeeping role!

Jealous of the smallest cover,
  Angry at the simplest door;
Well, you anxious, inquisitive lover,
  Are you pleased with what's in store?

You have fingered all my treasures;
  Have you not, most curiously,
Handled all my tools and measures
  And masculine machinery?

Over every single beauty
  You have had your little rapture;
You have slain, as was your duty,
  Every sin-mouse you could capture.

Still you are not satisfied!
  Still you tremble faint reproach!
Challenge me I keep aside
  Secrets that you may not broach.

Maybe yes, and maybe no;
  Maybe there *are* secret places,
Altars barbarous below,
  Elsewhere halls of high disgraces.

Maybe yes, and maybe no,
  You may have it as you please;
Since you are so keen to know
  Everything, Miss Ill-at-ease!

AFTER THE OPERA

Down the stone stairs
Girls with their large eyes wide with tragedy
Lift looks of shocked and momentous emotion up at me.
And I smile.

Ladies
Stepping like birds with their bright and pointed feet
Peer anxiously forth, as if for a boat to carry them out
    of the wreckage;
And among the wreck of the theatre crowd
I stand and smile.
They take tragedy so becomingly;
Which pleases me.

But when I meet the weary eyes
The reddened, aching eyes of the barman with thin
    arms
I am glad to go back to where I came from.

SORROW

Why does the thin grey strand
Floating up from the forgotten
Cigarette between my fingers,
Why does it trouble me?

Ah, you will understand;
When I carried my mother downstairs,
A few times only, at the beginning
Of her soft-foot malady,

I should find, for a reprimand
To my gaiety, a few long grey hairs
On the breast of my coat; and one by one
I watched them float up the dark chimney.

ON THAT DAY

On that day
I shall put roses on roses, and cover your grave
With multitude of white roses: and, since you were
        brave,
    One bright red ray.

So people, passing under
The ash-trees of the valley-road, will raise
Their eyes and look at the grave on the hill, in wonder,
      Wondering mount, and put the flowers asunder:

To see whose praise
Is blazoned here so white and so bloodily red.
Then they will say: ''Tis long since she is dead,
      Who has remembered her after many days?'

And standing there
They will consider how you went your ways
Unnoticed among them, a still queen lost in the maze
      Of this earthly affair.

A queen, they 'll say,
Has slept unnoticed on a forgotten hill.
Sleeps on unknown, unnoticed there, until
      Dawns my insurgent day.

A DOE AT EVENING

As I went through the marshes
a doe sprang out of the corn
and flashed up the hill-side
leaving her fawn.

On the sky-line
she moved round to watch,
she pricked a fine black blotch
on the sky.

I looked at her
and felt her watching;
I became a strange being.
Still, I had my right to be there with her.

Her nimble shadow trotting
along the sky-line, she
put back her fine, level-balanced head.
And I knew her.

Ah yes, being male, is not my head hard-balanced,
  antlered?
Are not my haunches light?
Has she not fled on the same wind with me?
Does not my fear cover her fear?

Irschenhausen.

SONG OF A MAN WHO HAS COME
THROUGH

Not I, not I, but the wind that blows through me!
A fine wind is blowing the new direction of Time.
If only I let it bear me, carry me, if only it carry me!
If only I am sensitive, subtle, oh, delicate, a winged
  gift!
If only, most lovely of all, I yield myself and am
  borrowed
By the fine, fine wind that takes its course through the
  chaos of the world
Like a fine, an exquisite chisel, a wedge-blade inserted;
If only I am keen and hard like the sheer tip of a wedge
Driven by invisible blows,
The rock will split, we shall come at the wonder, we
  shall find the Hesperides.

Oh, for the wonder that bubbles into my soul,
I would be a good fountain, a good well-head,
Would blur no whisper, spoil no expression.

What is the knocking?
What is the knocking at the door in the night?
It is somebody wants to do us harm.

No, no, it is the three strange angels.
Admit them, admit them.

PEACH

WOULD you like to throw a stone at me?
Here, take all that's left of my peach.

Blood-red, deep;
Heaven knows how it came to pass.
Somebody's pound of flesh rendered up.

Wrinkled with secrets
And hard with the intention to keep them.

Why, from silvery peach-bloom,
From that shallow-silvery wine-glass on a short stem
This rolling, dropping, heavy globule?

I am thinking, of course, of the peach before I ate it.

Why so velvety, why so voluptuous heavy?
Why hanging with such inordinate weight?
Why so indented?

Why the groove?
Why the lovely, bivalve roundnesses?
Why the ripple down the sphere?
Why the suggestion of incision?

Why was not my peach round and finished like a billiard
    ball?
It would have been if man had made it.
Though I've eaten it now.

But it wasn't round and finished like a billiard ball.
And because I say so, you would like to throw some-
      thing at me.

Here, you can have my peach stone.

San Gervasio.

GRAPES

So many fruits come from roses,
From the rose of all roses,
From the unfolded rose,
Rose of all the world.

Admit that apples and strawberries and peaches and
      pears and blackberries
Are all Rosaceae,
Issue of the explicit rose,
The open-countenanced, skyward-smiling rose.

What then of the vine?
Oh, what of the tendrilled vine?

Ours is the universe of the unfolded rose,
The explicit,
The candid revelation.

But long ago, oh, long ago,
Before the rose began to simper supreme,
Before the rose of all roses, rose of all the world, was
      even in bud,
Before the glaciers were gathered up in a bunch out of
      the unsettled seas and winds,
Or else before they had been let down again, in Noah's
      flood,
There was another world, a dusky, flowerless, tendrilled
      world
And creatures webbed and marshy,
And on the margin, men soft-footed and pristine,

Still, and sensitive, and active,
Audile, tactile sensitiveness as of a tendril which
    orientates and reaches out,
Reaching out and grasping by an instinct more deli-
    cate than the moon's as she feels for the tides.

Of which world, the vine was the invisible rose,
Before petals spread, before colour made its disturbance,
    before eyes saw too much.

In a green, muddy, web-foot, unutterly songless world
The vine was rose of all roses.

There were no poppies or carnations,
Hardly a greenish lily, watery faint.
Green, dim, invisible flourishing of vines
Royally gesticulate.

Look now even now, how it keeps its power of invisi-
    bility!
Look how black, how blue-black, how globed in Egyptian
    darkness
Dropping among his leaves, hangs the dark grape!
See him there, the swart, so palpably invisible:
Whom shall we ask about him?

The negro might know a little.
When the vine was rose, Gods were dark-skinned.
Bacchus is a dream's dream.
Once God was all negroid, as now he is fair.
But it 's so long ago, the ancient Bushman has forgotten
    more utterly than we, who have never known.

For we are on the brink of re-remembrance.
Which, I suppose, is why America has gone dry.
Our pale day is sinking into twilight,
And if we sip the wine, we find dreams coming upon us
Out of the imminent night.

Nay, we find ourselves crossing the fern-scented frontiers
Of the world before the floods, where man was dark
    and evasive
And the tiny vine-flower rose of all roses, perfumed,
And all in naked communion communicating as now
    our clothed vision can never communicate.
Vistas, down dark avenues,
As we sip the wine.

The grape is swart, the avenues dusky and tendrilled,
    subtly prehensile,
But we, as we start awake, clutch at our vistas demo-
    cratic, boulevards, tram-cars, policemen.
Give us our own back,
Let us go to the soda-fountain, to get sober.
Soberness, sobriety.
It is like the agonized perverseness of a child heavy with
    sleep, yet fighting, fighting to keep awake;
Soberness, sobriety, with heavy eyes propped open.

Dusky are the avenues of wine,
And we must cross the frontiers, though we will not,
Of the lost, fern-scented world:
Take the fern-seed on our lips,
Close the eyes, and go
Down the tendrilled avenues of wine and the other-
    world.

San Gervasio.

SNAKE

A SNAKE came to my water-trough
On a hot, hot day, and I in pyjamas for the heat,
To drink there.

In the deep, strange-scented shade of the great dark
    carob-tree
I came down the steps with my pitcher
And must wait, must stand and wait, for there he was
    at the trough before me.

He reached down from a fissure in the earth-wall in
    the gloom
And trailed his yellow-brown slackness soft-bellied down,
    over the edge of the stone trough
And rested his throat upon the stone bottom,
And where the water had dripped from the tap, in a
    small clearness,
He sipped with his straight mouth,
Softly drank through his straight gums, into his slack
    long body,
Silently.

Someone was before me at my water-trough,
And I, like a second comer, waiting.

He lifted his head from his drinking, as cattle do,
And looked at me vaguely, as drinking cattle do,
And flickered his two-forked tongue from his lips, and
    mused a moment,
And stooped and drank a little more,
Being earth-brown, earth-golden from the burning bowels
    of the earth
On the day of Sicilian July, with Etna smoking.

The voice of my education said to me
He must be killed,
For in Sicily the black, black snakes are innocent, the
    gold are venomous.

And voices in me said, If you were a man
You would take a stick and break him now, and finish
    him off.

But must I confess how I liked him,
How glad I was he had come like a guest in quiet, to
    drink at my water-trough
And depart peaceful, pacified, and thankless,
Into the burning bowels of this earth?

Was it cowardice, that I dared not kill him?
Was it perversity, that I longed to talk to him?
Was it humility, to feel so honoured?
I felt so honoured.

And yet those voices:
If you were not afraid, you would kill him!

And truly I was afraid, I was most afraid,
But even so, honoured still more
That he should seek my hospitality
From out the dark door of the secret earth.

He drank enough
And lifted his head, dreamily, as one who has drunken,
And flickered his tongue like a forked night on the air, so black,
Seeming to lick his lips,
And looked around like a god, unseeing, into the air,
And slowly turned his head,
And slowly, very slowly, as if thrice adream,
Proceeded to draw his slow length curving round
And climb again the broken bank of my wall-face.

And as he put his head into that dreadful hole,
And as he slowly drew up, snake-easing his shoulders, and entered farther,
A sort of horror, a sort of protest against his withdrawing into that horrid black hole,
Deliberately going into the blackness, and slowly drawing himself after,
Overcame me now his back was turned.

I looked round, I put down my pitcher,
I picked up a clumsy log
And threw it at the water-trough with a clatter.

I think it did not hit him,
But suddenly that part of him that was left behind
convulsed in undignified haste,

Writhed like lightning, and was gone
Into the black hole, the earth-lipped fissure in the wall-
    front,
At which, in the intense still noon, I stared with fasci-
    nation.

And immediately I regretted it.
I thought how paltry, how vulgar, what a mean act!
I despised myself and the voices of my accursed human
    education.
And I thought of the albatross,
And I wished he would come back, my snake.

For he seemed to me again like a king,
Like a king in exile, uncrowned in the underworld,
Now due to be crowned again.

And so, I missed my chance with one of the lords
Of life.
And I have something to expiate;
A pettiness.

Taormina.

KANGAROO

In the northern hemisphere
Life seems to leap at the air, or skim under the wind
Like stags on rocky ground, or pawing horses, or springy
    scut-tailed rabbits.

Or else rush horizontal to charge at the sky's horizon,
Like bulls or bisons or wild pigs.

Or slip like water slippery towards its ends,
As foxes, stoats, and wolves, and prairie dogs.

Only mice, and moles, and rats, and badgers, and
    beavers, and perhaps bears
Seem belly-plumbed to the earth's mid-navel.
Or frogs that when they leap come flop, and flop to the
    centre of the earth.

But the yellow antipodal Kangaroo, when she sits up,
Who can unseat her, like a liquid drop that is heavy,
    and just touches earth?

The downward drip,
The down-urge.
So much denser than cold-blooded frogs.
Delicate mother Kangaroo
Sitting up there rabbit-wise, but huge, plump-weighted,
And lifting her beautiful slender face, oh! so much more
    gently and finely lined that a rabbit's, or than a
    hare's,
Lifting her face to nibble at a round white peppermint
    drop which she loves, sensitive mother Kangaroo.

Her sensitive, long, pure-bred face.
Her full antipodal eyes, so dark,
So big and quiet and remote, having watched so many
    empty dawns in silent Australia.

Her little loose hands, and drooping Victorian shoulders,
And then her great weight below the waist, her vast
    pale belly
With a thin young yellow little paw hanging out, and
    straggle of a long thin ear, like ribbon,
Like a funny trimming to the middle of her belly, thin
    little dangle of an immature paw, and one thin ear.

Her belly, her big haunches
And, in addition, the great muscular python-stretch of
    her tail.

There, she shan't have any more peppermint drops.
So she wistfully, sensitively sniffs the air, and then turns,
    goes off in slow sad leaps

On the long flat skis of her legs,
Steered and propelled by that steel-strong snake of a
    tail.
Stops again, half turns, inquisitive to look back.

While something stirs quickly in her belly, and a lean
   little face comes out, as from a window,
Peaked and a bit dismayed,
Only to disappear again quickly away from the sight of
   the world, to snuggle down in the warmth,
Leaving the trail of a different paw hanging out.

Still she watches with eternal, cocked wistfulness!
How full her eyes are, like the full, fathomless, shining
   eyes of an Australian black-boy
Who has been lost so many centuries on the margins of
   existence!
She watches with insatiable wistfulness.
Untold centuries of watching for something to come,
For a new signal from life, in that silent lost land of the
   South.

Where nothing bites but insects and snakes and the sun,
   small life.
Where no bull roared, no cow ever lowed, no stag cried,
   no leopard screeched, no lion coughed, no dog
   barked,
But all was silent save for parrots occasionally, in the
   haunted blue bush.

Wistfully watching, with wonderful liquid eyes.
And all her weight, all her blood, dripping sack-wise
   down towards the earth's centre,
And the live little-one taking in its paw at the door of
   . her belly.

Leap then, and come down on the line that draws to
   the earth's deep, heavy centre.

                                        Sydney.

TURKEY-COCK

You ruffled black blossom,
You glossy dark wind.

Your sort of gorgeousness,
Dark and lustrous
And skinny repulsive
And poppy-glossy,
Is the gorgeousness that evokes my most puzzled
    admiration.

Your aboriginality,
Deep, unexplained,
Like a Red Indian darkly unfinished and aloof,
Seems like the black and glossy seeds of countless
    centuries.

Your wattles are the colour of steel-slag which has been
    red-hot
And is going cold,
Cooling to a powdery, pale-oxydized sky-blue.

Why do you have wattles, and a naked, wattled head?
Why do you arch your naked-set eye with a more-than-
    comprehensible arrogance?

The vulture is bald, so is the condor, obscenely,
But only you have thrown this amazing mantilla of
    oxydized sky-blue
And hot red over you.
This queer dross shawl of blue and vermilion,
Whereas the peacock has a diadem.

I wonder why.
Perhaps it is a sort of uncanny decoration, a veil of
    loose skin.
Perhaps it is your assertion, in all this ostentation, of
    raw contradictoriness.

Your wattles drip down like a shawl to your breast
And the point of your mantilla drops across your nose,
   unpleasantly.

Or perhaps it is something unfinished,
A bit of slag still adhering, after your firing in the
   furnace of creation.

Or perhaps there is something in your wattles of a
   bull's dewlap
Which slips down like a pendulum to balance the
   throbbing mass of a generous breast,

The over-drip of a great passion hanging in the balance.
Only yours would be a raw, unsmelted passion, that will
   not quite fuse from the dross.

You contract yourself,
You arch yourself as an archer's bow
Which quivers indrawn as you clench your spine
Until your veiled head almost touches backward
To the root-rising of your erected tail.
And one intense and backward-curving frisson
Seizes you as you clench yourself together
Like some fierce magnet bringing its poles together.

Burning, pale positive pole of your wattled head!
And from the darkness of that opposite one
The upstart of your round-barred, sun-round tail!

Whilst between the two, along the tense arch of your
   back
Blows the magnetic current in fierce blasts,
Ruffling black, shining feathers like lifted mail,
Shuddering storm wind, or a water rushing through.

Your brittle, super-sensual arrogance
Tosses the crape of red across your brow and down
   your breast
As you draw yourself upon yourself in insistence.

It is a declaration of such tension in will
As time has not dared to avouch, nor eternity been
    able to unbend
Do what it may.
A raw American will, that has never been tempered by
    life;
You brittle, will-tense bird with a foolish eye.

The peacock lifts his rods of bronze
And struts blue-brilliant out of the far East.
But watch a turkey prancing low on earth
Drumming his vaulted wings, as savages drum
Their rhythms on long-drawn, hollow, sinister drums.
The ponderous, sombre sound of the great drum of
    Huichilobos
In pyramid Mexico, during sacrifice.

Drum, and the turkey onrush
Sudden, demonic dauntlessness, full abreast,
All the bronze gloss of all his myriad petals
Each one apart and instant.

Delicate frail crescent of the gentle outline of white
At each feather-tip
So delicate:
Yet the bronze wind-bell suddenly clashing
And the eye overweening into madness.

Turkey-cock, turkey-cock,
Are you the bird of the next dawn?

Has the peacock had his day, does he call in vain,
    screecher, for the sun to rise?
The eagle, the dove, and the barnyard rooster, do they
    call in vain, trying to wake the morrow?
And do you await us, wattled father, Westward?
Will your yell do it?

Take up the trail of the vanished American
Where it disappeared at the foot of the crucifix.

Take up the primordial Indian obstinacy,
The more than human, dense insistence of will,
And disdain, and blankness, and onrush, and prise open
    the new day with them?

The East a dead letter, and Europe moribund. . . .
    Is that so?
And those sombre, dead, feather-lustrous Aztecs,
    Amerindians,
In all the sinister splendour of their red blood-sacrifices,
Do they stand under the dawn, half-godly, half-demon,
    awaiting the cry of the turkey-cock?

Or must you go through the fire once more, till you 're
    smelted pure,
Slag-wattled turkey-cock,
Dross-jabot? *Fiesole.*

TO LET GO OR TO HOLD ON——?

SHALL we let go,
and allow the soul to find its level
downwards, ebbing downwards, ebbing downwards to
    the flood?
till the head floats tilted like a bottle forward tilted
on the sea, with no message in it; and the body is
    submerged
heavy and swaying like a whale recovering
from wounds, below the deep black wave?
like a whale recovering its velocity and strength
under the cold black wave.

Or else, or else
shall a man brace himself up
and lift his face and set his breast
and go forth to change the world?
gather his will and his energy together
and fling himself in effort after effort
upon the world, to bring a change to pass?

Tell me first, O tell me,
will the dark flood of our day's annihilation
swim deeper, deeper, till it leaves no peak emerging?
Shall we be lost, all of us,
and gone like weed, like weed, like eggs of fishes,
like sperm of whales, like germs of the great dead past
into which the creative future shall blow strange, un-
    known forms?

Are we nothing, already, but the lapsing of a great
    dead past?
Is the best that we are but sperm, loose sperm, like the
    sperm of fishes
that drifts upon time and chaos, till some unknown
    future takes it up
and is fecund with a new Day of new creatures? different
    from us.

Or is our shattered Argosy, our leaking ark,
at this moment scraping tardy Ararat?
Have we got to get down and clear away the debris
of a swamped civilization, and start a new world of man
that will blossom forth the whole of human nature?

Must we hold on, hold on
and go ahead with what is human nature
and make a new job of the human world?

Or can we let it go?
O can we let it go,
and leave it to some nature that is more than human
to use the sperm of what 's worth while in us
and thus eliminate us?
Is the time come for humans
now to begin to disappear,
leaving it to the vast revolutions of creative chaos
to bring forth creatures that are an improvement on
    humans,
as the horse was an improvement on the ichthyosaurus?

Must we hold on?
Or can we now let go?

Or is it even possible we must do both?

WE ARE TRANSMITTERS——

As we live, we are transmitters of life.
And when we fail to transmit life, life fails to flow
    through us.

That is part of the mystery of sex, it is a flow onwards.
Sexless people transmit nothing.

And if, as we work, we can transmit life into our work,
life, still more life, rushes into us to compensate, to be
    ready
and we ripple with life through the days.

Even if it is a woman making an apple dumpling, or a
    man a stool,
if life goes into the pudding, good is the pudding,
good is the stool,
content is the woman, with fresh life rippling into her,
content is the man.

Give, and it shall be given unto you
is still the truth about life.
But giving life is not so easy.
It doesn't mean handing it out to some mean fool, or
    letting the living dead eat you up.
It means kindling the life-quality where it was not,
even if it's only in the whiteness of a washed pocket-
    handkerchief.

DON'TS

FIGHT your little fight, my boy,
fight and be a man.
Don't be a good little, good little boy
being as good as you can
and agreeing with all the mealy-mouthed, mealy-
      mouthed
truths that the sly trot out
to protect themselves and their greedy-mouthed, greedy-
      mouthed
cowardice, every old lout.

Don't live up to the dear little girl who costs
you your manhood, and makes you pay.
Nor the dear old mater who so proudly boasts
that you 'll make your way.

Don't earn golden opinions, opinions golden,
or at least worth Treasury notes,
from all sorts of men; don't be beholden
to the herd inside the pen.

Don't long to have dear little, dear little boys
whom you 'll have to educate
to earn their living; nor yet girls, sweet joys
who will find it so hard to mate.

Nor a dear little home, with its cost, its cost
that you have to pay,
earning your living while your life is lost
and dull death comes in a day.

Don't be sucked in by the su-superior,
don't swallow the culture bait,
don't drink, don't drink and get beerier and beerier,
do learn to discriminate.

    * M 958

Do hold yourself together, and fight
with a hit-hit here and a hit-hit there,
and a comfortable feeling at night
that you 've let in a little air.

A little fresh air in the money sty,
knocked a little hole in the holy prison,
done your own little bit, made your own little try
that the risen Christ should *be* risen.

FIDELITY

FIDELITY and love are two different things, like a flower
      and a gem.
And love, like a flower, will fade, will change into some-
      thing else
or it would not be flowery.

O flowers they fade because they are moving swiftly; a
      little torrent of life
leaps up to the summit of the stem, gleams, turns over
      round the bend
of the parabola of curved flight,
sinks, and is gone, like a comet curving into the invisible.

O flowers they are all the time travelling
like comets, and they come into our ken
for a day, for two days, and withdraw, slowly vanish
      again.

And we, we must take them on the wing, and let them go.
Embalmed flowers are not flowers, immortelles are not
      flowers;
flowers are just a motion, a swift motion, a coloured
      gesture;
that is their loveliness. And that is love.

But a gem is different. It lasts so much longer than
    we do,
so much much much longer
that it seems to last for ever.
Yet we know it is flowing away
as flowers are, and we are, only slower.
The wonderful slow flowing of the sapphire!
All flows, and every flow is related to every other flow.
Flowers and sapphires and us, diversely streaming.

In the old days, when sapphires were breathed upon
    and brought forth
during the wild orgasms of chaos,
time was much slower, when the rocks came forth
It took aeons to make a sapphire, aeons for it to pass
    away.

And a flower it takes a summer.

And man and woman are like the earth, that brings
    forth flowers
in summer, and love, but underneath is rock.
Older than flowers, older than ferns, older than fora-
    miniferae
older than plasm altogether is the soul of a man under-
    neath.

And when, throughout all the wild orgasms of love,
slowly a gem forms, in the ancient, once-more-molten
    rocks
of two human hearts, two ancient rocks, a man's heart
    and a woman's,
that is the crystal of peace, the slow hard jewel of trust,
the sapphire of fidelity.
The gem of mutual peace emerging from the wild chaos
    of love.

TO WOMEN, AS FAR AS I'M CONCERNED

THE feelings I don't have I don't have.
The feelings I don't have, I won't say I have.
The feelings you say you have, you don't have.
The feelings you would like us both to have, we neither
    of us have.
The feelings people ought to have, they never have.
If people say they 've got feelings, you may be pretty
    sure they haven't got them.

So if you want either of us to feel anything at all
you 'd better abandon all idea of feelings altogether.

OLD PEOPLE

NOWADAYS everybody wants to be young,
so much so, that even the young are old with the effort
    of being young.
As for those over fifty, either they rush forward in
    self-assertion
fearful to behold,
or they bear everybody a grim and grisly grudge
because of their own fifty or sixty or seventy or eighty
    summers.
As if it 's my fault that the old girl is seventy-seven!

BEAUTIFUL OLD AGE

IT ought to be lovely to be old,
to be full of the peace that comes of experience
and wrinkled ripe fulfilment.

The wrinkled smile of completeness that follows a life
lived undaunted and unsoured with accepted lies.
If people lived without accepting lies
they would ripen like apples, and be scented like pippins
in their old age.

Soothing, old people should be, like apples
when one is tired of love.
Fragrant like yellowing leaves, and dim with the soft
stillness and satisfaction of autumn.

And a girl should say:
It must be wonderful to live and grow old.
Look at my mother, how rich and still she is!—

And a young man should think: By Jove,
my father has faced all weathers, but it 's been a life!—

DESIRE IS DEAD

Desire may be dead
and still a man can be
a meeting place for sun and rain,
wonder outwaiting pain
as in a wintry tree.

MAN 'S IMAGE

What a pity, when a man looks at himself in a glass
he doesn't bark at himself, like a dog does,
or fluff up in indignant fury, like a cat!

What a pity he sees himself so wonderful,
a little lower than the angels!
and so interesting!

ULTIMATE REALITY

A young man said to me:
I am interested in the problem of reality.

I said: Really!
Then I saw him turn to glance, surreptitiously,
in the big mirror, at his own fascinating shadow.

LATTER-DAY SINNERS

THE worst of the younger generation, those Latter-Day
    sinners,
is that they calmly assert: We only thrill to perversity,
    murder, suicide, rape—
bragging a little, really,
and at the same time, expect to go on calmly eating
    good dinners for the next fifty years.

They say: *Après moi le déluge !* and calmly expect
that the deluge will never be turned on them, only
    after them.

Post me, nihil !—But perhaps, my dears,
nihil will come along and hit you on the head.

Why should the deluge wait while these young gentry
    go on eating
good dinners for fifty more long years?
Why should our Latter-Day sinners expect such a long
    smooth run
for their very paltry little bit of money?

If you are expecting a Second Advent in the shape of a
    deluge
you mustn't expect it also to wait for your convenience.

IT 'S NO GOOD!

IT 's no good, the women are in eruption,
and those that have been good so far
now begin to steam ominously,
and if they 're over forty-five, hurl great stones into
    the air
which are very like to hit you on the head as you sit
on the very slopes of the matrimonial mountain
where you 've sat peacefully all these years.

Vengeance is mine, saith the Lord,
but the women are my favourite vessels of wrath.

SHIPS IN BOTTLES

O SHIP in a bottle
with masts erect and spars all set and sails spread,
how you remind me of my London friends,
O ships in bottles!

Little fleets
that put to sea on certain evenings,
frigates, barks and pinnaces, yawls
all beautifully rigged and bottled up
that put to sea and boldly sink Armadas
in a pub parlour, in literary London, on certain evenings.

O small flotilla of sorry souls
sail on, over perilous seas of thought,
cast your little anchors in ports of eternity,
then weigh, and out to the infinities,
skirting the poles of being and of not-being.

Ah, in that parlour of the London pub
what dangers, ah what dangers!
Caught between great icebergs of doubt
they are all but crushed,
little ships.
Nipped upon the frozen floods of philosophic despair
they lie high and dry,
high and dry.
Reeling in the black end of all beliefs
they sink.

Yet there they are, there they are,
little ships
safe inside their bottles!

Whelmed in profundities of profound conversation,
lost between great waves of ultimate ideas
they are—why there they are,
safe inside their bottles!
Safer than in the arms of Jesus!
Oh safer than anything else is a well-corked, glassy ego,
and sounder than all insurance is a shiny mental conceit!

Sail, little ships in your glass bottles
safe from every contact,
safe from all experience,
safe, above all, from life!

And let the nodding tempests of verbosity
weekly or twice-weekly whistle round your bottles.
Spread your small sails immune, little ships!
The storm is words, the bottles never break.

THOUGHT

THOUGHT, I love thought.
But not the jaggling and twisting of already existent
    ideas.
I despise that self-important game.
Thought is the welling up of unknown life into con-
    sciousness.
Thought is the testing of statements on the touch-
    stone of the conscience.
Thought is gazing on to the face of life, and reading
    what can be read.
Thought is pondering over experience, and coming to
    conclusion.
Thought is not a trick, or an exercise, or a set of dodges.
Thought is a man in his wholeness wholly attending.

MYSTIC

THEY call all experience of the senses *mystic*, when the
    experience is considered.
So an apple becomes *mystic* when I taste in it
the summer and the snows, the wild welter of earth
and the insistence of the sun.
All of which things I can surely taste in a good apple.
Though some apples taste preponderantly of water, wet
    and sour,
and some of too much sun, brackish sweet
like lagoon-water, that has been too much sunned.

If I say I taste these things in an apple, I am called
    mystic, which means a liar.
The only way to eat an apple is to hog it down like a pig
and taste nothing,
that is *real*.

But if I eat an apple, I like to eat it with all my senses
    awake.
Hogging it down like a pig I call the feeding of corpses.

ABYSMAL IMMORTALITY

IT is not easy to fall out of the hands of the living God.
They are so large, and they cradle so much of a man.
It is a long time before a man can get himself away.
Even through the greatest blasphemies, the hands of
    the living God still continue to cradle him.

And still through knowledge and will, he can break
    away.
man can break away, and fall from the hands of God
into himself alone, down the godless plunge of the abyss,
a god-lost creature turning upon himself
in the long, long fall, revolving upon himself
in the endless writhe of the last, the last self-knowledge
which he can never reach till he touch the bottom of the
    abyss
which he can never touch, for the abyss is bottomless.

And there is nothing else, throughout time and eternity,
but the abyss, which is bottomless,
and the fall to extinction, which can never come,
for the abyss is bottomless,
and the turning down plunge of writhing of self-know-
    ledge, self-analysis
which goes farther and farther, and yet never finds
    an end
for there is no end,
it is the abyss of the immortality
of those that have fallen from God.

SHADOWS

AND if to-night my soul may find her peace
in sleep, and sink in good oblivion,
and in the morning wake like a new-opened flower
then I have been dipped again in God, and new-created.

And if, as weeks go round, in the dark of the moon
my spirit darkens and goes out, and soft strange gloom
pervades my movements and my thoughts and words,
then I shall know that I am walking still
with God, we are close together now the moon's in
shadow.

And if, as autumn deepens and darkens,
I feel the pain of falling leaves, and stems that break
in storms
and trouble and dissolution and distress
and then the softness of deep shadows folding, folding
around my soul and spirit, around my lips
so sweet, like a swoon, or more like the drowse of a
low, sad song
singing darker than the nightingale, on, on to the solstice
and the silence of short days, the silence of the year,
the shadow,
then I shall know that my life is moving still
with the dark earth, and drenched
with the deep oblivion of earth's lapse and renewal.

And if, in the changing phases of man's life,
I fall in sickness and in misery,
my wrists seem broken and my heart seems dead
and strength is gone, and my life
is only the leavings of a life:

and still, among it all, snatches of lovely oblivion, and
snatches of renewal,
odd, wintry flowers upon the withered stem, yet new,
strange flowers
such as my life has not brought forth before, new
blossoms of me.

Then I must know that still
I am in the hands of the unknown God,
he is breaking me down to his own oblivion
to send me forth on a new morning, a new man.

THE SHIP OF DEATH

I

Now it is autumn and the falling fruit
and the long journey towards oblivion.
The apples falling like great drops of dew
to bruise themselves an exit from themselves.

And it is time to go, to bid farewell
to one's own self, and find an exit
from the fallen self.

II

Have you built your ship of death, O have you?
O build your ship of death, for you will need it.

The grim frost is at hand, when the apples will fall
thick, almost thundrous, on the hardened earth.

And death is on the air like a smell of ashes!
Ah! can't you smell it?
And in the bruised body, the frightened soul
finds itself shrinking, wincing from the cold
that blows upon it through the orifices.

III

And can a man his own quietus make
with a bare bodkin?

With daggers, bodkins, bullets, man can make
a bruise or break of exit for his life;
but is that a quietus, O tell me, is it quietus?

Surely not so! for how could murder, even self-murder
ever a quietus make?

IV

O let us talk of quiet that we know,
that we can know, the deep and lovely quiet
of a strong heart at peace!

How can we this, our own quietus, make?

V

Build then the ship of death, for you must take
the longest journey, to oblivion.

And die the death, the long and painful death
that lies between the old self and the new.

Already our bodies are fallen, bruised, badly bruised,
already our souls are oozing through the exit
of the cruel bruise.

Already the dark and endless ocean of the end
is washing in through the breaches of our wounds,
already the flood is upon us.

Oh build your ship of death, your little ark,
and furnish it with food, with little cakes, and wine
for the dark flight down oblivion.

VI

Piecemeal the body dies, and the timid soul
has her footing washed away, as the dark flood rises.

We are dying, we are dying, we are all of us dying
and nothing will stay the death-flood rising within us
and soon it will rise on the world, on the outside world.

We are dying, we are dying, piecemeal our bodies are
    dying
and our strength leaves us,
and our soul cowers naked in the dark rain over the
    flood,
cowering in the last branches of the tree of our life.

VII

We are dying, we are dying, so all we can do
is now to be willing to die, and to build the ship
of death to carry the soul on the longest journey.

A little ship, with oars and food
and little dishes, and all accoutrements
fitting and ready for the departing soul.

Now launch the small ship, now as the body dies
and life departs, launch out, the fragile soul
in the fragile ship of courage, the ark of faith
with its store of food and little cooking pans
and change of clothes,
upon the flood's black waste,
upon the waters of the end,
upon the sea of death, where still we sail
darkly, for we cannot steer, and have no port.

There is no port, there is nowhere to go,
only the deepening blackness darkening still
blacker upon the soundless, ungurgling flood,
darkness at one with darkness, up and down
and sideways utterly dark, so there is no direction any
    more
and the little ship is there; yet she is gone.
She is not seen, for there is nothing to see her by.
She is gone! gone! and yet
somewhere she is there.
Nowhere!

VIII

And everything is gone, the body is gone
completely under, gone, entirely gone.
The upper darkness is heavy as the lower,
between them the little ship
is gone.

It is the end, it is oblivion.

IX

And yet out of eternity a thread
separates itself on the blackness,
a horizontal thread
that fumes a little with pallor upon the dark.

Is it illusion? or does the pallor fume
A little higher?
Ah wait, wait, for there 's the dawn,
the cruel dawn of coming back to life
out of oblivion.

Wait, wait, the little ship
drifting, beneath the deathly ashy grey
of a flood-dawn.

Wait, wait! even so, a flush of yellow
and strangely, O chilled wan soul, a flush of rose.

A flush of rose, and the whole thing starts again.

X

The flood subsides, and the body, like a worn sea-shell,
emerges strange and lovely.
And the little ship wings home, faltering and lapsing
on the pink flood,
and the frail soul steps out, into the house again
filling the heart with peace.

Swings the heart renewed with peace
even of oblivion.

Oh build your ship of death.   Oh build it!
for you will need it.
For the voyage of oblivion awaits you.

LETTERS

NOTE

An asterisk at the beginning of a paragraph indicates that a *preceding* paragraph or sentence has been omitted by the editor of the present edition. Similarly, an asterisk at the end of a paragraph indicates that matter *following* has been omitted.

To Edward Garnett.   *17th Dec.* 1911.

DEAR GARNETT,

I got the cheque yesterday, and accept it gladly from you. But a little later, when I have some money, you must let me pay it back to you, because that seems to me honester.

I am very well. Yesterday I sat up to tea for an hour. It is a weird, not delightful experience, which makes me feel like the seated statues of kings in Egypt. My chest gets rapidly well, but my brain is too active. To keep myself at all in order, I ought to be up and doing. By nature I am ceaselessly active. Now I sleep badly, because I don't do enough—and I mustn't work, because then away goes my strength. But I feel my life burn like a free flame floating on oil—wavering and leaping and snapping. I shall be glad to get it confined and conducted again.

The doctor says I mustn't go to school again or I shall be consumptive. But he doesn't know. I shan't send in my notice, but shall ask for long leave of absence. Then I can go back if I get broke. The headmaster grieves loudly over my prolonged absence. He knows he would scarcely get another man to do for him as I have done.

I shall look for you on Wednesday. Don't bring back that novel MSS. unless you have read all you want to read. I don't want it a bit. It is a work too chargé, too emotional. It 's a sponge dipped too full of vinegar, or wine, or whatever—it wants squeezing out. I shrink from it rather. I wonder whether Jefferies used to wince away from the *Story of my Heart*.

This is too long a letter to send to a busy man: excuse me.

Yours sincerely,

D. H. LAWRENCE.

16 *Colworth Rd.*,
Addiscombe, Croydon.

To Edward Garnett. 30*th Dec.* 1911.

DEAR GARNETT,

Have I kept the *Downland* too long?—I am sorry. For a day or two I have intended writing, and returning it, but one is so dilatory convalescent.

I am getting on very well. Yesterday I went out for the first time, a little way down the road. I could walk like a grenadier guard, but for my left leg, which slumbers on, when all the rest of me is awake. The doctor says it is neuritis. However, it gets much better.

☆ . . . My girl is here. She's big, and swarthy, and passionate as a gipsy—but good, awfully good, churchy. She rubs her cheek against me, just like a cat, and says: 'Are you happy?' It makes me laugh. But I am not particularly happy, being only half here, yet awhile. She never understands that—so I have to pitch all my wits against her. It's very weird.

The Americans are just as stupid as we expected. Their reason, however, is really comical. It amused me —that's something unexpected. Keep the MS. as long as you like.

I am to go to Bournemouth—Lord, how sick I am of this ordering and countermanding—I loathe to be an invalid. It is nearly unendurable to have to wait for one's strength to come back—like Penelope. I hate my legs, miserable defaulters—I detest them. I hate to be waited on, and to be treated gently. If ever I'm ill again I shall die of mortification. I am to go to Bournemouth some time next week—probably Friday.

I think I'll send you this story. My sense of beauty and of interest comes back very strong. I wrote this story last week, in bed—before I could sit up much. You'll find it, perhaps, thin—maladif. I can't judge it at all—one reason why I send it.

There's no news. My sister sends her greetings.

Yours sincerely,
D. H. LAWRENCE.

PS.—For a title to that MS. called at present *The Saga*, will *Trespassers in Cythera* or *The Trespasser* or something like that, do? Or for *Cythera* what can one put—what are the Isles of the Happy——? Evin, Evna?—Help me out.

I shall begin re-writing the first part to-day.

D. H. L.

20 Dulverton Rd,
Leicester.

To Edward Garnett.   *29th April* 1912.

DEAR GARNETT,

I believe Mrs W—— after all left those first chapters of my Heinemann novel *Paul Morel* in your book-room: I am sure they are there. And I left my scrubby gloves. Send me them on to Eastwood, will you. I am going home to-day. Probably I shall go to Germany on Friday. I am so anxious to know what W—— will say. She is going to tell him to-day.

Tell me what you think of Mrs W——. I am afraid of you suddenly donning the cassock of a monk, and speaking out of the hood. Don't sound wise, and old, and—'When you 've lived as long as I have'—sort of thing. It 's insulting.

Tell me when Duckworth will publish the novel.

To-day isn't like yesterday. I hate this house—full of old books, gloomy as hell, and silent with books. I hate the glum silence of ranks of shut books. I imagine your apple-blossom. It seems so sociable and lovable in comparison.

Vale !
D. H. LAWRENCE.

bei Herr Karl Krenkow,
Waldbröl, Rheinprovinz.

To Edward Garnett.

DEAR GARNETT,

I suppose I shall have to keep on amusing you, though I myself am anything but amused. I tell you, making history is no joke. But I won't die in the attempt, if I can help it.

Now that title—the readers at Duckworth's ought to have altered it, for *I* did not know that *A Game of Forfeits* was finally settled upon. As for *Author of the White Peacock*—now would you expect me to think of it? I wonder you can be so heartless. I've not signed any agreement with Messrs Duckworth—I suppose it doesn't matter. And supposing I actually haven't a penny in the world—at present I've about four quid— would your chief give me a sub—£10? But for the Lord's sake, don't ask him yet—I'd rather anything. Always, somewhere, I shall find *some* woman who'll give me bed and board. Thank God for the women.

F.—that is Mrs W——— her name is Frieda—'The Peaceful'—let me call her F.—she has gone to Munich —hundreds of miles away—and I am eating my heart out, and revising my immortal Heinemann novel, *Paul Morel*, in this tiny village stuck up in the Rhineland. If you wouldn't make it a laughing matter—I'd open my poor heart to you—a rare museum. But you are too *narquois*! I left F. in Trier—200 miles from here —a week ago. Oh, there has been *such* a to-do.

To live, one must hurt people so. One has to make up one's mind, it must be so. Of course my people at home wonder what I'm up to—I shall tell them all later, but nothing now—and they too are hurt. And F. is making herself ill. Now she's gone to München, to her sister. The Richthofens are an astonishing family —three girls—women—the eldest a Doctor of Social Economics—a Professor too—then Frieda—then the youngest—28—very beautiful, rather splendid in her deliberate worldliness. They are a rare family—father a fierce old aristocrat—mother utterly non-moral, very kind. You should know them.

I am going to Munich directly—perhaps Saturday. The soles of my feet burn as I wait. Here, the slow oxen go down the main street, drawing the wagons, under my window—the country is all still, and oxen plough and harrow. In the Gasthaus, the Lutheran

choir practises in one room, we drink in the next. My
cousin —— is newly married—and wishes she weren't.
She's getting in love with me. Why is it women *will*
fall in love with me? And I haven't an eye for a girl,
damn it. I just remain in a state of suspense, till I can
go to Munich.

Frieda sort of clings to the idea of you, as the only
man in England who would be a refuge. She wanted
to write to you—so I send you her letter. Don't be
wise and cryptic. After all, Frieda isn't in any book,
and I'm not, and life hurts—and sometimes rejoices
one. But—you see—in life one's own flesh and blood
goes through the mill—and F.'s eyes are tired now.
I hope I can go to Munich on Saturday—it is 15 hours'
journey from this God-forsaken little hole. But people
are wonderfully good to me. The Rhineland is nice—
we were at Bonn and on the Drachenfels on Sunday—
so magical. But it will always be to me a land of exile
—and slow, slow cattle drawing the wagons. Those
slow, buff oxen, with their immense heads that seem
always asleep, nearly drive me mad as they step tinkling
down the street. After them, I could hug the dog in
the milk-cart, that lifts his paw quickly and daintily
over the shaft, and sits down panting.

Is it Tuesday?—I never know how the days go. Miss
Whale is quite right when she says I'm good—I *am*
good. Give her my love. Only the women have eyes
for goodness—and *they* wear green moral spectacles,
most of 'em.

Vale!
D. H. LAWRENCE.

bei Professor Alf. Weber,
Icking,
bei München.

To Mrs S. A. Hopkin.   *2nd June* 1912.

DEAR MRS HOPKIN,

Although I haven't heard from you, I'll get a letter
off to you, because to people I like, I always want to

tell my good news. When I came to Germany I came with Mrs W—— went to Metz with her. Her husband knows all about it—but I don't think he will give her a divorce—only a separation. I wish he'd divorce her, so we could be married. But that's as it is. . . .

Now Frieda and I are living alone in Professor Weber's flat. It is the top story of this villa—quite small—four rooms beside kitchen. But there's a balcony, where we sit out, and have meals, and I write. Down below, is the road where the bullock wagons go slowly. Across the road the peasant women work in the wheat. Then the pale, milk-green river runs between the woods and the plain—then beyond, the mountains, range beyond range, and their tops glittering with snow.

I've just had to run into the kitchen—a jolly little place—wondering what Frieda was up to. She'd only banged her head on the cupboard. So we stood and looked out. Over the hills was a great lid of black cloud, and the mountains nearest went up and down in a solid blue-black. Through, was a wonderful gold space, with a tangle of pale, wonderful mountains, peaks pale gold with snow, and farther and farther away—such a silent, glowing confusion, brilliant with snow. Now the thunder is going at it, and the rain is here.

I love Frieda so much, I don't like to talk about it. I never knew what love was before. She wanted me to write to you. I want you and her to be friends always. Sometime perhaps she—perhaps we—shall need you. Then you'll be good to us, won't you?

The world is wonderful and beautiful and good beyond one's wildest imagination. Never, never, never could one conceive what love is, beforehand, never. Life *can* be great—quite godlike. It *can* be so. God be thanked I have proved it.

You might write to us here. Our week of honeymoon is over. Lord, it was lovely. But this—do I like this better?—I like it so much. Don't tell anybody. This is only for the good to know. Write to us.

D. H. LAWRENCE.

Icking,
bei München, Isarthal.

To Edward Garnett.   *3rd July* 1912.

DEAR GARNETT,

Your news of the *Trespasser* is rather cheering. Everything else is pretty bad. There are storms of letters from England, imploring her to renounce for ever all her ideas of love, to go back and give her life to her husband and her children. —— would have her back, on those conditions. The children are miserable, missing her so much. She lies on the floor in misery—and then is fearfully angry with me because I won't say 'stay for my sake.' I say 'decide what you want most, to live with me and share my rotten chances, or go back to security, and your children—decide for yourself—choose for *yourself*.' And then she almost hates me, because I won't say 'I love you—stay with me whatever happens.' I *do* love her. If she left me, I do not think I should be alive six months hence. And she won't leave me, I think. God, how I love her—and the agony of it. She is a woman who also makes a man suffer, by being blind to him when her anger or resentment is roused. She is staying in Wolfratshausen with her sister's children for the four nights—her sister is away, and the nurse has just left. The letters to-day have nearly sent us both crazy. I didn't know life was so hard. But really, for me, it's been a devilish time ever since I was born. But for the fact that when one's got a job on, one ought to go through with it, I'd prefer to be dead any minute. I can't bear it when F. is away. I could bang my head against the wall, for relief. It's a bit too much.

My dear Garnett, at this eleventh hour I love you and understand you a bit. Don't sympathise with me, don't.

Yours sincerely,
D. H. LAWRENCE.

Icking,
bei München, Isarthal.
To Edward Garnett.   *25th July* 1912.

☆ There is talk of getting me some lecturing in München for the winter. I dread it a bit. Here, in this tiny savage little place, F. and I have got awfully wild. I loathe the idea of England, and its enervation and misty miserable modernness. I *don't* want to go back to town and civilisation. I want to rough it and scramble through free, free. I *don't* want to be tied down. And I can live on a tiny bit. I shan't let F. leave me, if I can help it. I feel I 've got a mate and I 'll fight tooth and claw to keep her. She says I 'm reverting, but I 'm not—I 'm only coming out wholesome and myself. Say I 'm right, and I ought to be always common. I *loathe Paul Morel.* F. sends love.

D. H. LAWRENCE.

Mayrhofen 138, *in Zillertal,*
Tirol, Austria.
To Mrs S. A. Hopkin.   *19th Aug.* 1912.

You know that it is not forgetfulness makes us not write to you. You know you are one of the very, very few who will take us into your heart, together. So, if the months go by without your hearing, I know you will understand—I know you will be sticking by us, and we shall be depending on you. I wanted my sister to come and talk with you, but she wouldn't; you see, it is harder for her, she is young, and doesn't understand quite. And she is going to marry Eddie Clarke in the spring, is going to become a hard, respectable married woman—I think the thought of me is very bitter to her —and she won't speak of me to anybody. Only she, of all my people, knows. And I told Jessie to leave her a chance of ridding herself of my influence: nobody else. Mrs —— writes me—I told her I was with another woman—but no details. I am sorry for her, she is so ill. Things have been hard, and worth it. There has been some sickening misery. . . . F. is to see the children, and stay with them, next Easter. It has been rather ghastly, that part of the affair. If only one didn't hurt so many people.

For ourselves, Frieda and I have struggled through some bad times into a wonderful naked intimacy, all kindled with warmth, that I know at last is love. I think I ought not to blame women, as I have done, but myself, for taking my love to the wrong woman, before now. Let every man find, keep on trying till he finds, the woman who can take him and whose love he can take, then who will grumble about men or about women? But the thing must be two-sided. At any rate, and whatever happens, I do love, and I am loved. I have given and I have taken—and that is eternal. Oh, if only people could marry properly; I believe in marriage. ☆

Yours,
D. H. LAWRENCE.

Villa Igéa,
Villa di Gargnano,
Lago di Garda (Brescia).

To Ernest Collings.   17th Jan. 1913.

☆ My great religion is a belief in the blood, the flesh, as being wiser than the intellect. We can go wrong in our minds. But what our blood feels and believes and says, is always true. The intellect is only a bit and a bridle. What do I care about knowledge? All I want is to answer to my blood, direct, without fribbling intervention of mind, or moral, or what-not. I conceive a man's body as a kind of flame, like a candle flame, forever upright and yet flowing: and the intellect is just the light that is shed on to the things around. And I am not so much concerned with the things around—which is really mind—but with the mystery of the flame forever flowing, coming God knows how from out of practically nowhere, and being *itself*, whatever there is around it, that it lights up. We have got so ridiculously

mindful, that we never know that we ourselves are anything—we think there are only the objects we shine
upon. And there the poor flame goes on burning
ignored, to produce this light. And instead of chasing
the mystery in the fugitive, half-lighted things outside
us, we ought to look at ourselves, and say 'My God,
I am myself!' That is why I like to live in Italy. The
people are so unconscious. They only feel and want:
they don't know. We know too much. No, we only
think we know such a lot. A flame isn't a flame because
it lights up two, or twenty objects on a table. It's a
flame because it is itself. And we have forgotten ourselves. We are Hamlet without the Prince of Denmark.
We cannot *be*. 'To be or not to be'—it is the question
with us now, by Jove. And nearly every Englishman
says 'Not to be.' So he goes in for Humanitarianism
and suchlike forms of not-being. The real way of living
is to answer to one's wants. Not 'I want to light up
with my intelligence as many things as possible' but
'For the living of my full flame—I want that liberty,
I want that woman, I want that pound of peaches,
I want to go to sleep, I want to go to the pub and have
a good time, I want to look a beastly swell to-day,
I want to kiss that girl, I want to insult that man.'
Instead of that, all these wants, which are there whether-
or-not, are utterly ignored, and we talk about some sort
of ideas. I'm like Carlyle, who, they say, wrote 50
volumes on the value of silence. ☆

> *Villa Igéa,*
> *Villa di Gargnano,*
> *Lago di Garda* (*Brescia*),

To Edward Garnett.   1*st Feb.* 1913.

☆ About coming to England—Frieda is determined to
come at Easter, but we have as yet heard nothing,
neither of the divorce, nor of the children, whether she
is to have them or not. We shall come to the Cearne.
It is the only place in England open to the pair of us.

Perhaps you will have us for a week or two, till we can find another place.

☆ I have done 100 pages of a novel. I think you will hate it, but I think, when it is re-written, it might find a good public amongst the Meredithy public. It is quite different in manner from my other stuff—far less visualised. It is what I *can* write just now, and write with pleasure, so write it I must, however you may grumble. And it is good, too. I think, do you know, I have inside me a sort of answer to the *want* of to-day: to the real, deep want of the English people, not to just what they fancy they want. And gradually, I shall get my hold on them. And this novel is perhaps not such good art, but it is what they want, need, more or less. But I needn't talk about it, when only 106 pages are written. ☆

28 *Percy Avenue,*
Kingsgate, Broadstairs.

To J. M. Murry.   [*About* 15*th July* 1913.]

DEAR MURRY,

Oh, but why didn't you come and let us lend you a pound. I think that when times have been so rough, you *shouldn't* bring about a disappointment on yourselves, just for the money. That seems to me wrong. We could just as well lend you five pounds as have it in the bank—if you want it. I consider now that your not coming on Sunday was a piece of obtuseness on your part. You are one of the people who *should* have a sense of proportionate values; you ought to know when it 's worth while to let yourself borrow money, and when it isn't. Because you *must* save your soul and Mrs Murry's soul from any further hurts, for the present, or any disappointments, or any dreary stretches of misery.

When Marsh said on Sunday, because we couldn't understand why you hadn't come: 'I suppose they hadn't the money for the railway tickets,' I thought it was stupid, because you seemed so rich, because you can earn so much more than I can. I had no idea.

So now I think you 'd better come down for the week-end. Come on Saturday and stay till Monday morning. We can put you up. Don't on any account bring chickens or any such like rubbish. We can get them down here. Though perhaps they are cheaper in town. Bring one if you like.

Come for the week-end, and bathe. We 've got a tent in a little bay on the foreshore, and great waves come and pitch one high up, so I feel like Horace, about to smite my cranium on the sky. I can only swim a little bit and am a clown in the water, but it 's jolly. So you come, and bathe on Saturday. It 'll be high tide then about 5.0. And bathe on Sunday, and bathe on Monday morning. Then you 'll feel much jollier.

I am not poor, you know. But I didn't know you were really stony. Only I have to watch it, because Frieda doesn't care.

Harold Hobson *might* be here—but you 'd like him.

Regards to you both,

D. H. LAWRENCE.

Irschenhausen,
(Post) *Ebenhausen, bei München,*
Oberbayern.

To S. A. Hopkin.   11*th Aug.* 1913.

☆ It is Frieda's birthday to-day. Her little niece came crowned with flowers, her little nephews in white, carrying a basket of peaches, and of apricots, and sweets in boxes, and perfumes and big bunches of flowers, and other presents, walking in procession up the path through the meadow. Frieda stood on the verandah, dressed in Bavarian peasant's dress, and received them. Then Peter, aged seven, recited some birthday verses, and Frieda blew on a mouth organ. I wanted to laugh, and to hide my head. We 've had quite a feast.

We both send our love to you. Again thank you for having me at Devonshire Drive. I kiss my hand to that haughty Enid.   Yours,

D. H. LAWRENCE.

Irschenhausen,
(Post) Ebenhausen,
Oberbayern.

To Edward Marsh.   18*th Aug.* 1913.

DEAR MARSH,

I was glad to get your letter. Here it does nothing
but rain. It is enough to make one's verse as sloppy
as Lamartine.

I think you will find my verse smoother—not because
I consciously attend to rhythms, but because I am no
longer so criss-crossy in myself. I think, don't you
know, that my rhythms fit my mood pretty well, in
the verse. And if the mood is out of joint, the rhythm
often is. I have always tried to get an emotion out in
its own course, without altering it. It needs the finest
instinct imaginable, much finer than the skill of the
craftsmen. That Japanese Yone Noguchi tried it. He
doesn't quite bring it off. Often I don't—sometimes
I do. Sometimes Whitman is perfect. Remember
skilled verse is dead in fifty years—I am thinking of
your admiration of Flecker. ☆

Yours,
D. H. LAWRENCE.

Fiascherino, Lerici,
Golfo della Spezia, Italy

To Edward Marsh.   14*th Oct.* 1913.

☆ We've been on the move since God knows when.
That is why I haven't written. When we left Bavaria,
I walked across Switzerland to Italy. Switzerland is
rather banal. Then we have prospected here and there
to find a spot for the winter. Now we are settled in
Fiascherino. It is an hour's walk from San Terenzo,
Shelley's place. We've got a little pink cottage among
vines and olives. I also just caught a flea, and am in a
rage because it leapt from my fingers out again into the
infinite. What a glorious flying jump a flea can take!
The full moon shines on the sea, which moves about all

glittering among black rocks. I go down and bathe and enjoy myself. You never saw such clear, buoyant water. Also I don't swim more than a dozen yards, so am always trying to follow the starry Shelley and set amid the waves. I don't work much, and don't want to work. If I'd got the smallest income I should be delighted to loaf for ever. But now I watch the servant, Felice, and my heart goes down plump. She is delighted to serve such grand and glorious people as we are. She is sixty, very wrinkled, but full of gusto. She strides up to the little arbour they call the Belvedere—it is impossible to think it only means Bellevue—bearing the soup-tureen as if she were the Queen of Sheba taking spice to Solomon: barefoot, she comes, with her petticoats kilted up, and a gleam of triumph in her eye. Think if I couldn't afford to pay her wages. I would take my last bathe. Don't mind my lapsing into pounds shillings and pence. If I die rich, I shall order my tombstone to be a big gold sovereign, with me for king —Fidei Defensor, etc., round the rim. I caught the flea, by the way. One can be so keen on the chase. Figs are falling with ripeness in the garden. I am trying drying some—you dip them in boiling water. But I am in such a rage that the bright and shiny flies hover so thick about them when they are spread out, that they can't really get enough sun to dry them: always clouded with shadow.

How did you like your walk in Spain? I try to think of you, but can't quite see you. I suppose it would be rather fine. How did you like Lascelles Abercrombie? You will introduce me to him when there is an opportunity, will you not? Davies says he 'll come here in the spring. I can see his one eating, gnawing anxiety is to write. God help us, when a poet must hunt his muse like Tartarin de Tarascon the one remaining hare. We take ourselves too seriously, *nous autres poètes.* ☆

D. H. LAWRENCE.

Fiascherino, Lerici,
Golfo della Spezia, Italy.

To Edward Marsh.   *28th Oct.* 1913.

☆ Poor Davies—he makes me so furious, and so sorry. He's really like a linnet that's got just a wee little sweet song, but it only sings when it's wild. And he's made himself a tame bird—poor little devil. He makes me furious. 'I shall be all right now the winter is coming,' he writes, 'now I can sit by the fire and work.' As if he could sing when he's been straining his heart to make a sound of music, for months. It isn't as if he were a passionate writer, writing his *agon.* Oh, my God, he's like teaching a bull-finch to talk. I think one ought to be downright cruel to him, and drive him back: say to him, Davies, your work is getting like Birmingham tin-ware; Davies, you drop your h's, and everybody is tempering the wind to you, because you are a shorn lamb; Davies, your accent is intolerable in a carpeted room; Davies, you hang on like the mud on a lady's silk petticoat. Then he might leave his Seven-oaks room, where he is rigged up as a rural poet, proud of the gilt mirror and his romantic past: and he might grow his wings again, and chirrup a little sadder song.

And now I've got to quarrel with you about the Ralph Hodgson poem: because I think it is banal in utterance. The feeling is there, right enough—but not in itself, only represented. It's like 'I asked for bread, and he gave me a penny.' Only here and there is the least touch of personality in the poem: it is the currency of poetry, not poetry itself. Every single line of it is poetic currency—and a good deal of emotion handling it about. But it isn't really poetry. I hope to God you won't hate me and think me carping, for this. But look: The ruby's and the rainbow's song,
The nightingale's—all three.

There's the emotion in the rhythm, but it's loose emotion, inarticulate, common—the words are mere currency. It is exactly like a man who feels very strongly for a beggar, and gives him a sovereign. The feeling is

at either end, for the moment, but the sovereign is a
dead bit of metal. And this poem is the sovereign.
'Oh, I do want to give you this emotion,' cries Hodgson,
'I do.' And so he takes out his poetic purse, and gives
you a handful of cash, and feels very strongly, even a
bit sentimentally over it.

> ——the sky was lit,
> The sky was stars all over it,
> I stood, I knew not why.

No one should say, 'I knew not why' any more. It is
as meaningless as 'yours truly' at the end of a letter. ☆

A rivederla,

D. H. LAWRENCE.

Lerici, per Fiascherino,
Golfo della Spezia, Italy.

To J. M. Murry.   *Thursday* [1913].

DEAR MURRY,

I'm going to answer your letter immediately, and frankly.

When you say you won't take Katherine's money, it
means you don't trust her love for you. When you say
she needs little luxuries, and you couldn't bear to deprive
her of them, it means you don't respect either yourself
or her sufficiently to do it.

It looks to me as if you two, far from growing nearer,
are snapping the bonds that hold you together, one
after another. I suppose you must both of you consult
your own hearts, honestly. She must see if she really
wants you, wants to keep you and to have no other man
all her life. It means forfeiting something. But the
only principle I can see in this life, is that one *must*
forfeit the less for the greater. Only one must be
thoroughly honest about it.

She must say, 'Could I live in a little place in Italy,
with Jack, and be lonely, have rather a bare life, but
be happy?' If she could, then take her money. If she
doesn't want to, don't try. But don't beat about the
bush. In the way you go on, you are inevitably coming
apart. She is perhaps beginning to be unsatisfied with

you. And you can't make her more satisfied by being unselfish. You must say, 'How can I make myself most healthy, strong, and satisfactory to myself and to her?' If by being lazy for six months, then be lazy, and take her money. It doesn't matter if she misses her luxuries: she won't die of it. What luxuries do you mean?

If she doesn't want to stake her whole life and being on you, then go to your University abroad for a while, alone. I warn you, it'll be hellish barren.

Or else you can gradually come apart in London, and then flounder till you get your feet again, severally, but be clear about it. It lies between you and Katherine, nowhere else.

Of course you can't dream of living long without work. Couldn't you get the *Westminster* to give you *two* columns a week, abroad? You must *try*. You must stick to criticism. You ought also to plan a book, either on some literary point, or some man. I should like to write a book on English heroines. You ought to do something of that sort, but not so cheap. Don't try a novel—try essays—like Walter Pater or somebody of that style. But you *can* do something *good* in that line; something concerning *literature* rather than life. And you must rest, and you and Katherine must heal, and come together, before you do *any serious* work of any sort. It's the split in the love that drains you. You see, while she doesn't really love you, and is not satisfied, *you* show to frightful disadvantage. But it would be a pity not to let your mind flower—it might, under decent circumstances, produce beautiful delicate things, in perception and appreciation. And *she* has a right to provide the conditions. But not if you don't trust yourself nor her nor anybody, but go on slopping, and pandering to her smaller side. If you work yourself sterile to get her chocolates, she will most justly detest you—she is *perfectly* right. She doesn't want you to sacrifice yourself to her, you fool. Be more natural, and positive, and stick to your own guts. You spread them on a tray for her to throw to the cats.

If you want things to come right—if you are ill and

exhausted, then take her money to the last penny, and let her do her own housework. Then she 'll know you love her. You can't blame her if she 's not satisfied with you. If I haven't had enough dinner, you can't blame *me*. But, you fool, you squander yourself, not for *her*, but to provide her with petty luxuries she doesn't really want. You insult her. A woman unsatisfied must have luxuries. But a woman who loves a man would sleep on a board.

It strikes me you 've got off your lines somewhere, you 've not been man enough: you 've felt it rested with your honour to give her a place to be proud of. It rested with your honour to give her a man to be satisfied with—and satisfaction is never accomplished even physically unless the man is strongly and surely himself, and doesn't depend on anything but his own *being* to make a woman love him. You 've tried to satisfy Katherine with what you could earn for her, give her: and she will only be satisfied with what you *are*.

And you don't know what you are. You 've never come to it. You 've always been dodging round, getting Rhythms and flats and doing criticisms for money. You are a fool to work so hard for Katherine—she hates you for it—and quite right. You want to be strong in the possession of your own soul. Perhaps you will only come to that when this affair of you and her has gone crash. I should be sorry to think that—I don't believe it. You must save yourself, and your self-respect, by making it complete between Katherine and you—if you devour her money till she walks in rags, if you are both outcast. Make her certain—don't pander to her—stick to *yourself*—do what you *want* to do—don't *consider* her —she hates and loathes being considered. You insult her in saying you wouldn't take her money.

The University idea is a bad one. It would further disintegrate you.

If you are disintegrated, then get integrated again. Don't be a coward. If you are disintegrated your first duty is to yourself, and you may use Katherine—her money and everything—to get right again. You 're not well, man. Then have the courage to get well. If you are strong again, and a bit complete, *she* 'll be satisfied with you. She 'll love you hard enough. But don't you see, at this rate, you distrain on her day by day and month by month. I 've done it myself.

Take your rest—do *nothing* if you like for a while— though I 'd do a *bit*. Get better, first and foremost— use anybody's money, to do so. Get better—and do things you like. Get yourself into condition. It drains and wearies Katherine to have you like this. What a fool you are, what a fool. Don't bother about her— what she wants or feels. Say, 'I am a man at the end of the tether, therefore I become a man blind to everything but my own need.' But keep a heart for the long run.

Look. We pay 60 lire a month for this house: 25 lire for the servant; and food is *very* cheap. You could live on 185 lire a month in plenty — and be greeted as 'Signoria' when you went out together—it is the same as 'Guten Tag, Herrschaften'; that would be luxury enough for Katherine.

Get up, lad, and be a man for yourself. It 's the man who dares to take, who is independent, not he who gives.

I think Oxford did you harm.

It is beautiful, wonderful, here.

A ten-pound note is 253 lire. We would get you, I believe, a jolly nice apartment in a big garden, in a house alone, for 80 lire a month. Don't waste yourself —don't be silly and floppy. You know what you *could* do—you *could* write—then prepare yourself: and first make Katherine at rest in her love for you. Say, 'This I will certainly do'—it would be a relief for her to hear you. Don't be a child—don't keep that rather childish charm. Throw everything away, and say, 'Now I act for my own good, at last.'

We are getting gradually nearer again, Frieda and I. It is very beautiful here.

We are awfully sorry Katherine is so seedy. She ought to write to us. Our love to her and you.

D. H. LAWRENCE.

Lerici, per Fiascherino,
Golfo della Spezia, Italy.

22nd April 1914.

To Edward Garnett.

☆ You know how willing I am to hear what you have to say, and to take your advice and to act on it when I have taken it. But it is no good unless you will have patience and understand what I *want* to do. I am not after all a child working erratically. All the time, underneath, there is something deep evolving itself out in me. And it is *hard* to express a new thing, in sincerity. And you should understand, and help me to the new thing, not get angry and say it is *common*, and send me back to the tone of the old *Sisters*. In the *Sisters* was the germ of this novel: woman becoming individual, self-responsible, taking her own initiative. But the first *Sisters* was flippant and often vulgar and jeering. I had to get out of that attitude, and make my subject really worthy. You see—you tell me I am half a Frenchman and one-eighth a Cockney. But that isn't it. I have very often the vulgarity and disagreeableness of the common people, as you say Cockney, and I may be a Frenchman. But primarily I am a passionately religious man, and my novels must be written from the depth of my religious experience. That I must keep to, because I can only work like that. And my Cockneyism and commonness are only when the deep feeling doesn't find its way out, and a sort of jeer comes instead, and sentimentality, and purplism. But you should see the religious, earnest, suffering man in me first, and then the flippant or common things after. Mrs Garnett says I have no true nobility—with all my cleverness and charm. But that is not true. It is there, in spite of all the littlenesses and commonnesses.

And that is why I didn't like the second letter you wrote me about the failed novel, where you rubbed it in: because you seemed to insult my real *being*. You had a right to go for my work, but in doing that, you must not make *me* cheap in your own eyes. You can be angry with a person without holding him cheap, and making him feel cheap. You believe too much in the Frenchman and the Cockney. Those are the things to criticise in me, not to rest your belief on. ☆

Lerici, per Fiascherino,
Golfo della Spezia, Italy.
5th *June* 1914.

To Edward Garnett.

☆ I don't agree with you about the *Wedding Ring*. You will find that in a while you will like the book as a whole. I don't think the psychology is wrong: it is only that I have a different attitude to my characters, and that necessitates a different attitude in you, which you are not prepared to give. As for its being my *cleverness* which would pull the thing through—that sounds odd to me, for I don't think I am so very clever, in that way. I think the book is a bit futuristic—quite unconsciously so. But when I read Marinetti—'the profound intuitions of life added one to the other, word by word, according to their illogical conception, will give us the general lines of an intuitive physiology of matter'—I see something of what I am after. I translate him clumsily, and his Italian is obfuscated—and I don't care about physiology of matter—but somehow —that which is physic—non-human, in humanity, is more interesting to me than the old-fashioned human element—which causes one to conceive a character in a certain moral scheme and make him consistent. The certain moral scheme is what I object to. In Turgenev, and in Tolstoi, and in Dostoievsky, the moral scheme into which all the characters fit—and it is nearly the same scheme—is, whatever the extraordinariness of the characters themselves, dull, old, dead. When Marinetti writes: 'It is the solidity of a blade of steel that is interesting by itself, that is, the incomprehending and inhuman alliance of its molecules in resistance to, let us say, a bullet. The heat of a piece of wood or iron is in fact more passionate, for us, than the laughter or tears of a woman'—then I know what he means. He is stupid, as an artist, for contrasting the heat of the iron and the laugh of the woman. Because what is interesting in the laugh of the woman is the same as the binding of the molecules of steel or their action in heat: it is the inhuman will, call it physiology, or like Marinetti—physiology of matter, that fascinates me. I don't so much care about what the woman *feels*—in the ordinary usage of the word. That presumes an *ego* to feel with. I only care about what the woman *is*—what she IS—inhumanly, physiologically, materially—according to the use of the word: but for me, what she *is* as a phenomenon (or as representing some greater, inhuman will), instead of what she feels according to the human conception. That is where the futurists are stupid. Instead of looking for the new human phenomenon, they will only look for the phenomena of the science of physics to be found in human beings. They are crassly stupid. But if any one would give them eyes, they would pull the right apples off the tree, for their stomachs are true in appetite. You mustn't look in my novel for the old stable *ego* of the character. There is another *ego*, according to whose action the individual is unrecognisable, and passes through, as it were, allotropic states which it needs a deeper sense than any we 've been used to exercise, to discover are states of the same single radically unchanged element. (Like as diamond and coal are the same pure single element of carbon. The ordinary novel would trace the history of the diamond—but I say, 'Diamond, what! This is carbon.' And my diamond might be coal or soot, and my theme is carbon.) You must not say my novel is shaky—it is not perfect, because I am not expert in what I want to do. But it is the real thing, say what you like. And I shall get my reception, if not now, then before long. Again I say, don't look for the development of the novel to follow the lines of certain characters: the characters fall into the form of some other rhythmic form, as when one draws a fiddle-bow across a fine tray delicately sanded, the sand takes lines unknown. ☆ *Au revoir*,

D. H. LAWRENCE.

Greatham, Pulborough, Sussex.
Monday, 19*th April* '15.

To Lady Ottoline Morrell.

MY DEAR LADY OTTOLINE,

To-day you will be going to Buxton, through this magnificent sunshine. I almost wish it were my turn to rise up and depart. My soul is restless and not to be appeased. One walks away to another place, and life begins anew. But it is a midge's life.

We have had MacQueen and David Garnett and Francis Birrell here for the week-end. When Birrell comes—tired and a bit lost and wondering—I love him. But, my God, to hear him talk sends me mad. To hear these young people talking really fills me with black fury: they talk endlessly, but endlessly—and never, never a good or real thing said. Their attitude is so irreverent and blatant. They are cased each in a hard little shell of his own, and out of this they talk words. There is never for one second any outgoing of feeling, and no reverence, not a crumb or grain of reverence. I cannot stand it. I *will not* have people like this— I had rather be alone. They made me dream in the night of a beetle that bites like a scorpion. But I killed it—a very large beetle. I scotched it and it ran off— but I came upon it again and killed it. It is this horror of little swarming selves that I can't stand.

D. H. LAWRENCE.

Greatham, Pulborough, Sussex.
14*th May* 1915.

To Lady Ottoline Morrell.

We went to Worthing yesterday on the motor-bus; very beautiful, even I loved Worthing: and snch light, such quantities of light beating and throbbing all around. I felt like Persephone come up from hell. But to-day I would rather say, like Eurydice, *jamque vale!*

☆ Yesterday, at Worthing, there were many soldiers. Can I ever tell you how ugly they were. 'To insects— sensual lust.' I like sensual lust—but insectwise, no—

it is obscene. I like men to be beasts—but insects—one insect mounted on another—oh, God! The soldiers at Worthing are like that—they remind me of lice or bugs: 'to insects—sensual lust.' They will murder their officers one day. They are teeming insects. What massive creeping hell is let loose nowadays.

It isn't my disordered imagination. There is a wag-tail sitting on the gate-post. I see how sweet and swift heaven is. But hell is slow and creeping and viscous and insect-teeming: as is this Europe now, this England.

Vale !
                        D. H. LAWRENCE.

Greatham, Pulborough, Sussex.
                    14*th May* 1915.

To Lady Cynthia Asquith.

MY DEAR LADY CYNTHIA,

When we talked in Brighton, lying on the cliff, I did not take much notice of what I said, because my sub-consciousness was occupied with the idea of how pleasant it would be to walk over the edge of the cliff. There seemed another, brighter sort of world away below, and this world on top is all torture and a flounder of stupidity. But I will write to you. . . .

For yourself, you must learn to believe in God. Believe me, in the end, we will unite in our knowledge of God. Believe me, this England, we very English people, will at length join together and say, 'We will not do these things, because in our knowledge of God we know them wrong.' We shall put away our great-ness and our living for material things only, because we shall agree we don't want these things. We know they are inferior, base, we shall have courage to put them away. We shall unite in our knowledge of God—not perhaps in our expression of God—but in our *knowledge* of God: and we shall agree that we don't want to live only to write and make riches, that England does not care only to have the greatest Empire or the greatest

commerce, but that she does care supremely for the pure
truth of God, which she will try to fulfil.

This isn't ranting, it is pure reasoning from the knowledge of God and the truth. It is not our wickedness
that kills us, but our unbelief. You learn to believe in
your very self, that we in England shall unite in our
knowledge of God to live according to the best of our
knowledge, Prime Ministers and Capitalists and artisans
all working in pure effort towards God—here, to-morrow,
in this England—and you will save your own soul and
the soul of your son. *Then* there will be love enough.

You see, this change must come to pass. But nobody
will believe it, however obvious it is. So it almost
sends me mad, I am almost a lunatic.

Please write to me and ask me anything you like—
but please do believe that the thing *shall* be.

D. H. LAWRENCE.

1 Byron Villas,
Vale of Health,
Hampstead, N.W.

5<i>th September</i>, 1915.</div>

To Lady Cynthia Asquith.

MY DEAR LADY CYNTHIA,

I think you did not like my last letter. But I don't
know that I am any the better for your rebuke. My
soul is still fizzling savagely.

We are thinking—Murry and Mrs Murry and I,
primarily, of issuing a little paper, fortnightly, to private
subscribers—2/6 for three months (6 copies) including
postage. Perhaps Bertie Russell and Gilbert Cannan
will come in. I don't know.

We have a little Jew in the East End, who is engaged
on the Jewish Encyclopaedia. He will print us 250
copies, of 28 pages, of 36 lines, for £5; or 36 pages for £6.
It will be about the same size as the *Mercure de France*,
but 28 or 36 pages thick. If it is 28 pages thick, that
costs £30 for three months: 250 half-crowns is just
£31 . 5 . 0. So we must get 250 subscribers. You must

subscribe and find one or two people who care about the real living truth of things: for God's sake, not people who only trifle and don't care.

I am going to do the preaching—sort of philosophy— the beliefs by which one can reconstruct the world: Murry will do his ideas on freedom for the individual soul, Katherine Mansfield will do her little satirical sketches. Then there is perhaps Bertie Russell and Cannan.

I hope you are interested. As for Lectures, I have quarrelled in my soul with Bertie Russell—I don't think he will give his. I shall do nothing at all in that line. The sight of the people of London strikes me into a dumb fury. The persistent nothingness of the war makes me feel like a paralytic convulsed with rage. Meanwhile I am writing a book of sketches, or preparing a book of sketches, about the nations, Italian, German and English, full of philosophising and struggling to show things real. My head feels like a hammer that keeps hammering on a nail. The only thing I know is, that the hammer is tougher than the nail, in the long run. It is not I who will break.

The novel comes out on the 30th of this month. I will send you a copy. Presently you will be bored with my I, I, and my, my.

Tell us how you are, and what you are doing. Mind you help with our paper. I think it is to be called *The Signature*. Frieda sends her love. She hates me for the present. But I shall not go to the war.

D. H. LAWRENCE.

Hampstead.

To Lady Cynthia Asquith.   *2nd November* 1915.

MY DEAR LADY CYNTHIA,

I will answer you straight away about the 'downing tools.' First of all I want to send you the poem, which might help to convince you. You say that the war does not prevent personal life from going on, that the individual can still love and be complete. It isn't true.

The one quality of love is that it universalises the individual. If I love, then I am extended over all people, but particularly over my own nation. It is an extending in concentric waves over all people. This is the process of love. And if I love, I, the individual, then necessarily the love extends from me to my nearest neighbour, and outwards, till it loses itself in vast distance. This *is* love, there is no love but this. So that if I love, the love must beat upon my neighbours, till they too live in the spirit of the love, and so on, further and further. And how can this be, in war, when the spirit is against love?

The spirit of war is, that I am a unit, a single entity that has no *intrinsic* reference to the rest: the reference is extrinsic, a question of living, not of *being*. In war, in my being I am a detached entity, and every one of my actions is an act of further detaching my own single entity from all the rest.

If I love, then, I am in direct opposition to the principle of war. If war prevails, I do not love. If love prevails there is no war. War is a great and necessary disintegrating autumnal process. Love is the great creative process, like spring, the making of an integral unity out of many disintegrated factors. We have had enough of the disintegrating process. If it goes on any further, we shall so thoroughly have destroyed the unifying force from among us, we shall have become each one of us so completely a separate entity, that the whole will be an amorphous heap, like sand, sterile, hopeless, useless, like a dead tree. This is true, and it is so great a danger, that one almost goes mad facing it.

That is why I almost went away out of the country: I may still have to go: because in myself I can never agree to the complete disintegration, never stand witness to it, never.

Then the Prussian rule. The Prussian rule would be an external evil. The disintegrating process of the war has become an internal evil, so vast as to be almost unthinkable, so nearly overwhelming us, that we stand on the very brink of oblivion. Better *anything* than the utter disintegration. And it is *England* who is the determining factor for Europe: if England goes, then Europe goes: for we are at this time the vital core of the whole organism. Let the leaves perish, but let the tree stand, living and bare. For the tree, the living organism of the soul of Europe is good, only the external forms and growths are bad. Let all the leaves fall, and many branches. But the quick of the tree must not perish. There are unrevealed buds which can come forward into another epoch of civilisation, if only we can shed this dead form and be strong in the spirit of love and creation.

Besides, Germany, Prussia, is not evil through and through. Her mood is *now* evil. But we reap what we have sowed. It is as with a child: if with a sullen, evil soul one provokes an evil mood in the child, there is destruction. But no child is all evil. And Germany is the child of Europe: and senile Europe, with her conventions and arbitrary rules of conduct and life and very being, has provoked Germany into a purely destructive mood. If a mother does this to a child—and it often happens—is she to go on until the child is killed or broken, so that the mother have her way? Is she not rather, at a certain point, to yield to the paroxysm of the child, which passes away *swiftly* when the opposition is removed? And if Prussia for a time imposes her rule on us, let us bear it, as a mother temporarily bears the ugly tyranny of the child, trusting to the ultimate good. The good will not be long in coming, all over Europe, if we can but trust it within ourselves. (This is not yielding to the child—this is knowing beyond the child's knowledge.)

I very much want you to tell me what you think, because it is a question for the *women* of the land now to decide: the men will never see it. I don't know one single man who would give the faintest response to this. But I still have some hope of the women; they should *know* that only love matters, now; that further destruction only means death, universal death, disintegration.

D. H. LAWRENCE.

Garsington Manor, Oxford.
Tuesday (1915).

To Lady Cynthia Asquith.

☆ When I drive across this country, with autumn falling and rustling to pieces, I am so sad, for my country, for this great wave of civilisation, 2,000 years, which is now collapsing, that it is hard to live. So much beauty and pathos of old things passing away and no new things coming: this house —— it is England—my God, it breaks my soul—their England, these shafted windows, the elm-trees, the blue distance—the past, the great past, crumbling down, breaking down, not under the force of the coming birds, but under the weight of many exhausted lovely yellow leaves, that drift over the lawn, and over the pond, like the soldiers, passing away, into winter and the darkness of winter—no, I can't bear it. For the winter stretches ahead, where all vision is lost and all memory dies out.

It has been 2,000 years, the spring and summer of our era. What, then, will the winter be? No, I can't bear it, I can't let it go. Yet who can stop the autumn from falling to pieces, when November has come in? It is almost better to be dead, than to see this awful process finally strangling us to oblivion, like the leaves off the trees.

I want to go to America, to Florida, as soon as I can: as soon as I have enough money to cross with Frieda. My life is ended here. I must go as a seed that falls into new ground. But this, this England, these elm-trees, the grey wind with yellow leaves—it is so awful, the being gone from it altogether, one must be blind henceforth. But better leave a quick of hope in the soul, than all the beauty that fills the eyes.

It sounds very rhapsodic: it is this old house, the beautiful shafted windows, the grey gate-pillars under the elm-trees: really I can't bear it: the past, the past, the falling, perishing, crumbling past, so great, so magnificent.

Come and see us when you are in town. I don't think we shall be here very much longer. My life now is one repeated, tortured, *Vale! Vale! Vale!* . . .

D. H. LAWRENCE.

Higher Tregerthen, Zennor,
St. Ives, Cornwall.

To Catherine Carswell.   *9th July* 1916.

MY DEAR CATHERINE,

I never wrote to tell you that they gave me a complete exemption from all military service, thanks be to God. That was a week ago last Thursday. I had to join the Colours in Penzance, be conveyed to Bodmin (60 miles), spend a night in barracks with all the other men, and then be examined. It was experience enough for me, of soldiering. I am sure I should die in a week, if they kept me. It is the annulling of all one stands for, this militarism, the nipping of the very germ of one's being. I was very much upset. The sense of spiritual disaster everywhere was quite terrifying. One was not sure whether one survived or not. Things are very bad.

Yet I liked the men. They all seemed so *decent*. And yet they all seemed as if they had *chosen wrong*. It was the underlying sense of disaster that overwhelmed me. They are all so brave, to suffer, but none of them brave enough, to reject suffering. They are all so noble, to accept sorrow and hurt, but they can none of them demand happiness. Their manliness all lies in accepting calmly this death, this loss of their integrity. They must stand by their fellow man: that is the motto.

This is what Christ's weeping over Jerusalem has brought us to, a whole Jerusalem offering itself to the Cross. To me, this is infinitely more terrifying than Pharisees and Publicans and Sinners, taking *their* way to death. This is what the love of our neighbour has brought us to, that, because one man dies, we all die.

This is the most terrible madness. And the worst of it all, is, that it is a madness of righteousness. These Cornish are most, most unwarlike, soft, peaceabel, ancient. No men could suffer more than they, at being conscripted—at any rate, those that were with me. Yet they accepted it all: they accepted it, as one of them said to me, with wonderful purity of spirit—I could howl my eyes out over him—because 'they believed first of all in their duty to their fellow man.' There is no falsity about it: they believe in their duty to their fellow man. And what duty is this, which makes us forfeit everything, because Germany invaded Belgium? Is there nothing beyond my fellow man? If not, then there is nothing beyond myself, beyond my own throat, which may be cut, and my own purse, which may be slit: becaue *I* am the fellow man of all the world, my neighbour is but myself in a mirror. So we toil in a circle of pure egoism.

This is what 'love thy neighbour as thyself' comes to. It needs only a little convulsion, to break the mirror, to turn over the coin, and there I have myself, my own purse, I, I, I, we, we, we—like the newspapers to-day: 'Capture the trade — unite the Empire — *à bas les autres.*'

There needs something else besides the love of the neighbour. If all my neighbours chose to go down the slope to Hell, that is no reason why I should go with them. I know in my own soul a truth, a right, and no amount of neighbours can weight it out of the balance. I know that, for me, the war is wrong. I know that if the Germans wanted my little house, I would rather give it them than fight for it: because my little house is not important enough to me. If another man must fight for his house, the more 's the pity. But it is his affair. To fight for possessions, goods, is what my soul *will not* do. Therefore it will not fight for the neighbour who fights for his own goods.

All this war, this talk of nationality, to me is false. I *feel* no nationality, not fundamentally. I feel no passion for my own land, nor my own house, nor my own furniture, nor my own money. Therefore I won't pretend any. Neither will I take part in the scrimmage, to help my neighbour. It is his affair to go in or to stay out, as he wishes. ☆

Middleton.
Sunday, 9th Feb. 1919.

To Katherine Mansfield.

☆ It is marvellous weather—brilliant sunshine on the snow, clear as summer, slightly golden sun, distance lit up. But it is immensely cold—everything frozen solid —milk, mustard, everything. Yesterday I went out for a real walk—I 've had a cold and been in bed. I climbed with my niece to the bare top of the hills. Wonderful it is to see the foot-marks on the snow—beautiful ropes of rabbit-prints, trailing away over the brows; heavy hare-marks; a fox, so sharp and dainty, going over the wall: birds with two feet that hop; very splendid straight advance of a pheasant; wood-pigeons that are clumsy and move in flocks; splendid little leaping marks of weasels, coming along like a necklace chain of berries; odd little filigree of the field-mice; the trail of a mole— it is astonishing what a world of wild creatures one feels round one, on the hills in the snow. From the height it is very beautiful. The upland is naked, white like silver, and moving far into the distance, strange and muscular, with gleams like skin. Only the wind surprises one, invisibly cold; the sun lies bright on a field, like the movement of a sleeper. It is strange how insignificant in all this life seems. Two men, tiny as dots, move from a farm on a snow slope, carrying hay to the beasts. Every moment they seem to melt like insignificant spots of dust; the sheer, living, muscular white of the uplands absorbs everything. Only there is a tiny clump of trees bare on the hill-top—small beeches—writhing like iron in the blue sky.—I wish one could cease to be a human being, and be a demon. *Allzumenschlich.*

My sister Emily is here, with her little girl—whose birthday it is to-day. Emily is cooking treacle rolly and cakes, Frieda is making Peggy a pale grey dress, I am advising and interfering. Pamela is lamenting because the eggs in the pantry have all frozen and burst. I have spent half an hour hacking ice out of the water tub—now I am going out. Peggy, with her marvellous red-gold hair in dangling curl-rags, is darting about sorting the coloured wools and cottons—*scène de famille*. It is beautiful to cross the field to the well for drinking water—such pure sun, and Slaley, the tiny village away across, sunny as Italy in its snow. I expect Willie Hopkin will come to-day.

Well—life itself is life—even the magnificent frost-foliage on the window. While we live, let us live.

D. H. L.

Emily's nickname was Pamela, or *Virtue Rewarded*.

Great Britain Hotel,
Valletta, Malta.

To Martin Secker. *24th May* 1920.

DEAR SECKER,

We came here for two days—kept here for eight by the Sicilian steamer strike.

Land of plenty, land of comfort—Britain, whereso-ever found.

Bacon and eggs for breakfast.

But a horrible island—to me: stone, and bath-brick dust. All the world might come here to sharpen its knives. ☆

Fontana Vecchia,
Taormina, Sicilia.

To Edward Garnett. *10th Nov.* 1921.

DEAR GARNETT,

Thank you for the MS. of the story, which came to-day. I hope it was not a nuisance to you to send it.

No, I won't read Homer, my atom of Greek is too infinitesimal. But if you want to read Homer, I 'll send him you. Somebody made me a gift of him. And then, if you want to read Homer, why, you needn't make the mistake of reading me.

No, my dear Garnett, you are an old critic and I shall always like you, but you are also a tiresome old pontiff and I shan't listen to a word you say, but shall go my own way to the dogs and bitches, just as heretofore. So there.

I ordered *Women in Love* for you from Secker. If he doesn't send it you, go to 5 John St and kill him at once. When you get it, if you get it, and when you read it, if you read it, don't for a moment imagine you are wrestling with the *Iliad*. Just remember that it is your young friend so-and-so, wipe away all your Homeric illusions, and bear nobly on. ☆ *Saluti*,

D. H. LAWRENCE.

R.M.S. Osterley,
Tuesday, 7th March 1922.
Arabian Sea.

To Frau Baronin von Richthofen.

☆ We stopped three hours in Port Said, and it was quite like the Thousand and One Nights. It was 9 o'clock in the morning, and the ladies of Port Said were all abroad shopping: little black waddling heaps of black crêpe and two houri-eyes between veil and mantle. The little peg is comic that stands above the nose and keeps veil and head-cloth together. Then a charabanc came by with twenty black 'women-parcels,' and one of the women threw back her veil and spat at us because we are ugly Christians. But you still see everything — beggars, water-carriers, the scribe who sits with his little table and writes letters, the old one who reads the Koran, the men who smoke their 'chibouks' in the open café and on the pavement. And what people! Beautiful Turks, negroes, Greeks, Levantines, Fellaheen, three Bedouins out of the desert like animals, Arabs—wonderful! We have taken coal on board, and then at midday off again into the Suez Canal. That is very interesting. The canal is eighty-eight miles long, and you can only travel five miles an hour. There you sit on this great ship and you feel really on land, slowly travelling on a still land-ship. The shores are quite near, you can easily throw an orange at the Arabs who work on the shores. Then you see beautifully, wonderfully, the Sahara *wüste* or *desert*—which do you say? The water-way goes narrow and alone through red-yellow sands. From time to time Arabs with camels work on the shores and keep on shouting 'Hallo, hallo' when the big ship passes so slowly. In the distance little sharp sandhills, so red and pink-gold and sharp and the horizon sharp like a knife edge, so clear. Then a few lonely palms, lonely and forlorn in the strong light, small, like people that have not grown very tall. Then again only sand, gold-pink and sharp sand hills, so sharp and defined and clear, not like reality but a dream. Slowly evening came, and we so still that one thought we did not seem to move any more. Sea-gulls flew about like a snowstorm, and a great black bird of prey alone and cruel, so black between thousands of white screaming, quick flying sea-birds. Then we came to the Dead Sea, flat lakes that extend very far, and slowly the sun went down behind the desert with marvellous colours, and as the sun set, then such a sky, like a sword burning green and pink! Beautiful it was, I have never seen anything so superhuman. One felt near to the doors of the old Paradise, I do not know how, but something only half human, something of a heaven with great, proud, overbearing and cruel angels. The palm-trees looked so little, the angels should be much bigger and every one with a sword. Yes, it is a frontier country.

Next morning we were in the Red Sea. There stands Mount Sinai, red like old dried blood, naked like a knife and so sharp, so unnaturally sharp and edged like a dagger that has been dipped in blood and has dried long ago and is a little bit rusty; and always there like something dreadful between man and his lost Paradise. All is Semitic and cruel, naked, sharp. No tree, no leaf, no life: the murderous Will and the Iron of Idea and Ideal—Iron, Will and Ideal. So they stand, these dreadful shores of the Red Sea that is hot like an oven, without air. It is a strange exit through this Red Sea —bitter. Behind lie finally Jerusalem, Greece, Rome and Europe, fulfilled and past—a great dreadful dream. It began with Jews and with Jews it ends. You should see Sinai, then you could know it. The ideal has been wicked against men: and Jehovah is father of the ideal, and Zeus and Jupiter and Christ are only sons. And God be praised Sinai and the Red Sea are passed and consummated. ☆

Originally written in German.

> 'Ardnaree,' Lake View Estate,
> Kandy, Ceylon.
>
> 30th March 1922.

To Robert Pratt Barlow.

DEAR PRATT BARLOW,

We have been here these last 18 days: the heat in the middle of the day rather overwhelming, but morning and evening delicious: the place beautiful, in its way very, the jungle round the house, palms and noisy, scraping and squeaking tropical creatures: good-looking, more or less naked, dark bluey-brown natives. But all a bit extraneous. I feel I don't belong, and never should. I think next week we shall go up higher to Nuwara Eliya.

I wonder what you are doing. This will probably follow you to England. We were at the Perahera here for the Prince of Wales. It was wonderful, gorgeous and barbaric with all the elephants and flames and devil dances in the night. One realises how very barbaric the substratum of Buddhism is. I shrewdly suspect that high-flownness of Buddhism altogether exists mostly on paper: and that its denial of the soul makes it always rather barren, even if philosophically, etc., more perfect. In short, after a slight contact, I draw back and don't like it.

I wonder what you and Cunard thought of the last tirade at your house. Probably nothing. But I do think, still more now I am out here, that we make a mistake forsaking England and moving out into the periphery of life. After all, Taormina, Ceylon, Africa, America—as far as we go, they are only the negation of what we ourselves stand for and are: and we 're rather like Jonahs running away from the place we belong. That is the conclusion that is forced on me. So I am making up my mind to return to England during the course of the summer. I really think that the most living clue of life is in us Englishmen in England, and the great mistake we make is in not uniting together in the strength of this real living clue—religious in the most vital sense—uniting together in England and so carrying the vital spark through. Because as far as we are concerned it is in danger of being quenched. I know now it is a shirking of the issue to look to Buddha or the Hindu or to our own working men, for the impulse to carry through. It is in ourselves, or nowhere, and this looking to the outer masses is only a betrayal. I think too the Roman Catholic Church, as an institution, granted of course some new adjustments to life, might once more be invaluable for saving Europe: but not as a mere political power.

But this I know: the responsibility for England, the living England, rests on men like you and me and Cunard —probably even the Prince of Wales—and to leave it all to Bottomleys, etc., is a worse sin than any sin of commission.

Best wishes from my wife and me.

D. H. LAWRENCE.

Taos, New Mexico,
U.S.A.

To Catherine Carswell.   *29th September* 1922.

MY DEAR CATHERINE,

Your letter from the 'Tinner's Arms' came last night. I always think Cornwall has a lot to give one. But Zennor sounds too much changed.

Taos, in its way, *is* rather thrilling. We have got a *very* pretty adobe house, with furniture made in the village, and Mexican and Navajo rugs, and some lovely pots. It stands just on the edge of the Indian reservation: a brook behind, with trees: in front, the so-called desert, rather like a moor but covered with whitish-grey sage-brush, flowering yellow now: some 5 miles away the mountains rise. On the north—we face east —Taos mountain, the sacred mt. of the Indians, sits massive on the plain—some 8 miles away. The *pueblo* is towards the foot of the mt., 3 miles off: a big, adobe *pueblo* on each side the brook, like two great heaps of earthen boxes, cubes. There the Indians all live together. They are *pueblos*—these houses were here before the Conquest—very old: and they grow grain and have cattle, on the lands bordering the brook, which they can irrigate. We drive across these 'deserts'— white sage-scrub and dark green piñon scrub on the slopes. On Monday we went up a canyon into the Rockies to a deserted gold mine. The aspens are yellow and lovely. We have a pretty busy time, too. I have already learnt to ride one of these Indian ponies, with a Mexican saddle. Like it so much. We gallop off to the *pueblo* or up to one of the canyons. Frieda is learning too. Last night the young Indians came down to dance in the studio, with two drums: and we all joined in. It is fun: and queer. The Indians are much more remote than Negroes. This week-end is the great dance at the *pueblo*, and the Apaches and Navajos come in wagons and on horseback, and the Mexicans troop to Taos village. Taos village is a Mexican sort of *plaza*—piazza—with trees and shops and horses tied up. It lies one mile to the south of us: so four miles from the *pueblo*. We see little of Taos itself. There are some American artists, sort of colony: but not much in contact. The days are hot sunshine: noon very hot, especially riding home across the open. Night is cold. In winter it snows, because we are 7,000 feet above sea-level. But as yet one thinks of midsummer. We are about 30 miles from the tiny railway station: but we motored 100 miles from the main line.

Well, I'm afraid it will all sound very fascinating if you are just feeling cooped up in London. I don't want you to feel envious. Perhaps it is necessary for me to try these places, perhaps it is my destiny to know the world. It only excites the outside of me. The inside it leaves more isolated and stoic than ever. That's how it is. It is all a form of running away from oneself and the great problems: all this wild west and the strange Australia. But I try to keep quite clear. One forms not the faintest inward attachment, especially here in America. America lives by a sort of egoistic *will*, shove and be shoved. Well, one can stand up to that too: but one is quite, quite cold inside. No illusion. I will not shove, and I will *not* be shoved. *Sono io!*

In the spring I think I want to come to England. But I feel England has insulted me, and I stomach that feeling badly. *Però, son sempre inglese.* Remember, if you were here you'd only be hardening your heart and stiffening your neck—it is either that or be walked over, in America.

D. H. L.

In my opinion a 'gentle' life with John Patrick and Don, and a gentle faith in life itself, is far better than these women in breeches and riding-boots and som-breros, and money and motor-cars and wild west. It is all inwardly a hard stone and nothingness. Only the desert has a fascination—to ride alone—in the sun in the forever unpossessed country—away from man. That is a great temptation, because one rather hates mankind nowadays. But *pazienza, sempre pazienza!* I am learning Spanish slowly, too.

D. H. L.

110 Heath St, Hampstead, N.W. 3.
9th Jan. 1924.

To Willard Johnson.

DEAR SPOODLE,

Yesterday came the Horse,[1] capering a trifle woodenly, and to-day a fall of snow. Enough bright white snow on the ground to make a bit of daylight. I've been

---

[1] *The Laughing Horse,* a periodical.

O 958

here exactly a month, in London, and day has never broken all the time. A dull, heavy, mortified half-light that seems to take the place of day in London in winter. I can't stand it.

However, with a bit of snow-brightness in the air, and a bit of a rather wooden neigh from the Horse in my ears, I pick up and write you a London letter.

Dear old Azure Horse, Turquoise Horse, Hobby Horse, Trojan Horse with a few scared heroes in your belly: Horse, laughing your Horse Laugh, you do actually ramp in with a bit of horse sense. I 'm all for horse sense, oh Horse! Come down to it, and it 's the Centaur. Good old Horse, be patted, and be persuaded to grin and to be a Centaur, getting your own back.

Even if you 're only a Hobby Horse, with a wooden head and a Spoodle on your broom-stick flanks, you 're welcome just now. Very welcome. Here 's an apple. Be tempted, like Adam and take it. And for the sake of all horses, be braver than Adam, who only bit a bite out and dropped the main. Eat up the whole gaudy apple, oh Horse. Let 's have the Centaur back.

Dear old Horse, you 'd never be azure or turquoise here in London. Oh, London is awful: so dark, so damp, so yellow-grey, so mouldering piecemeal. With crowds of people going about in a mouldering, damp, half-visible sort of way, as if they were all mouldering bits of rag that had fallen from an old garment. Horse, Horse, be as hobby as you like, but let me get on your back and ride away again to New Mexico. I don't care how frozen it is, how grey the desert, how cold the air, in Taos, in Lobo, in Santa Fé. It isn't choky, it is bright day at daytime, and bright dark night at night. And one isn't wrapped like a mummy in winding-sheet after winding-sheet of yellow, damp, unclean, cloyed, ancient, breathed-to-death so-called air. Oh Horse, Horse, Horse, when you kick your heels you shatter an enclosure every time. And over here the Horse is dead: he 'll kick his heels no more. I don't know whether it 's the pale Galilean who has triumphed, or a paleness paler than the pallor even of Jesus. But a yellow and jaundiced paleness has triumphed over here, the Turquoise Horse has been long dead, and churned into sausages. I find it unbearable.

Let the Horse laugh. I'm all for a horse that laughs. Though I don't care for him when he merely sniggers.

I'm all for a horse. It's not even the Houyhnhnms. They aren't blue enough for me. It's a turquoise Centaur who laughs, who laughs longest and laughs last. I believe in him. I believe he's there, over the desert in the south-west. I believe if you'll cajole him with a bit of proper corn, he'll come down to Santa Fé and bite your noses off and then laugh at you again.

Two-legged man is no good. If he's going to stand steady, he must stand on four feet. Like the Centaur. When Jesus was born, the spirits wailed round the Mediterranean: *Pan is dead*. *Great Pan is dead*. And at the Renaissance the Centaur gave a final groan, and expired. At least, I seem to remember him lamenting and about to expire, in the Uffizi.

It would be a terrible thing if the horse in us died for ever, as he seems to have died in Europe. How awful it would be, if at this present moment I sat in the yellow mummy-swathings of London atmosphere—the snow is melting—inside the dreadful mummy sarcophagus of Europe, and didn't know that the blue horse was still kicking his heels and making a few sparks fly, across the tops of the Rockies. It would be a truly sad case for me.

As it is, I say to myself, Bah! In Lobo, in Taos, in Santa Fé, the Turquoise Horse is waving snow out of his tail, and trotting gaily to the blue mountains of the far distance. And in Mexico his mane is bright yellow on his blue body, so streaming with sun, and he's lashing out again like the devil, till his hoofs are red. Good old Horse!

But talking seriously, Spoodle, man must be Centaur. This two-legged forked radish is going flabby.

The Centaur's lament! Not at all. The Laugh of the Turquoise Man-Horse. Let the forked radish do the lamenting.

In modern symbolism, the Horse is supposed to stand for the passions. Passions be blowed. What does the Centaur stand for, Chiron or any other of that quondam four - footed gentry? Sense! Horse Sense! Sound, powerful, four-footed *sense*, that 's what the Horse stands for. Horse-sense, I tell you. That 's the Centaur. That 's the blue Horse of the ancient Mediterranean, before the pale Galilean or the extra pale German or Nordic gentleman conquered. First of all, Sense, Good Sense, Sound Sense, Horse Sense. And then, a laugh, a loud, sensible Horse Laugh. After that, these same passions, glossy and dangerous in the flanks. And after these again, hoofs, irresistible, splintering hoofs, that can kick the walls of the world down.

Horse-sense, Horse-laughter, Horse-passion, Horse-hoofs: ask the Indians if it is not so.

Tell me the Horse is dead? Tell me the Centaur has died out? It may easily be so, in Europe here, since the Renaissance. But in the wide blue skies of the south-west, and far away south over Mexico: over the grey deserts and the red deserts beneath the Rockies and the Sierra Madre; down the canyons and across the *mesas* and along the depths of the barrancas goes the Turquoise Horse, uneasy, bethinking himself, and just on the point of bursting into a loud laugh, after all, laughing longest and laughing last.

Ask the Indians, if there isn't a little foal born every year, in the *pueblos*, out of the old dark earth-coloured mottled mare. Tell me the Centaur can't beget Centaurs?—Ask the Indian, ask the Navajo, ask the Mexican under his big hat.

It 's no good. I 've GOT to ride on a laughing horse. The forked radish has ceased to perambulate. I 've *got* to ride a laughing horse. And I whistle for him, call him, spread corn for him, and hold out an apple to him, here in England. No go! No good! No answer! The poor devil 's dead and churned into Cambridge sausages. Flabby flaccid forked radishes, sausages, pairs of sausages in forked skins: these seem to drift about in the soup of the London air. There 's no answer.

There's no blue cave to stable the Turquoise Horse, here. There's no dark earth-coloured mare to bear his foals. There's no far-away blue distance for him to roam across. He's dead.

And yet I've *got* to ride, centaur, on a blue stallion.

So, thanks be to the oldest of gods, comes a wooden little Laughing Horse sliding down from the blue air of the Rockies, riding on his hobby stick like a rocket, summoning me to mount and away.

Hurray! Hup-a-là! Up we go! Like a witch on a broomstick, riding west.

D. H. LAWRENCE.

Frau von Richthofen,
Ludwig-Wilhelmstift,
Baden-Baden.

To J. M. Murry.   *7th Feb.* 1924.

DEAR JACK,

We've just got here—all snow on the Black Forest, but down in here only wet.

Europe gives me a *Wehmut*, I tell you. ☆

I don't know if you really want to go to Taos. Mabel Luhan writes she is arranging for it. You seemed to me really very unsure. You resent, *au fond*, my going away from Europe. *C'est mon affaire. Je m'en vais.* But you, in this interval, decide for yourself, and purely for yourself. Don't think you are doing something for me. I don't want that. Move for yourself alone. Decide for yourself, in your backbone. I don't really want any allegiance or anything of that sort. I don't want any pact. I won't have anything of that sort. If you want to go to America, *bien.* Go without making me responsible.

But if you want to go with Frieda and me and Brett —*encore bien!* One can but try, and I'm willing. But a man like you, if he does anything in the name of, or for the sake of, or because of somebody else, is bound to turn like a crazy snake and bite himself and everybody, on account of it.

Let us clear away all nonsense. I don't *need* you. That is not true. I need nobody. Neither do you need me. If you pretend to need me, you will hate me for it.

Your articles in the *Adelphi* always annoy me. Why care so much about your own fishiness or fleshiness? Why make it so important? Can't you focus yourself outside yourself? Not for ever focused on yourself, *ad nauseam*?

☆ You know I don't care a single straw what you think of me. Realize that, once and for all. But when you get to twisting, I dislike you. And I very much dislike any attempt at an intimacy like the one you had with —— —— and others. When you start that, I only feel: For God's sake, let me get clear of him.

I don't care what you think of me, I don't care what you say of me, I don't even care what you do against me, as a writer. Trust yourself, then you can expect me to trust you. Leave off being emotional. Leave off twisting. Leave off having any emotion at all. You haven't any genuine ones, except a certain anger. Cut all that would-be sympathetic stuff out. Then know what you 're after.

I tell you, if you want to go to America as an unemotional man making an adventure, *bien, allons!* If you want to twist yourself into more knots, don't go with me. That 's all. I never had much patience, and I 've none now.

D. H. L.

c/o Del Monte Ranch,
Questa, New Mexico.

To Dr Trigant Burrow.   *6th June* 1925.

DEAR DR BURROW,

I found your letter and the two reprints when I got back here. I am in entire sympathy with your idea of social images. In fact, I feel myself that the Jewish consciousness is now composed entirely of social images: there is no new-starting 'reality' left. Nothing springs alive and new from the blood. All is a chemical reaction, analysis and decomposition and reprecipitation of social images. It is what happens to all old races. They lose the faculty for real experience, and go on decomposing their test-tubes full of social images. One fights and fights for that living something that stirs way down in the blood, and *creates* consciousness. But the world won't have it. To the present human mind, everything is ready-made, and since the sun cannot be new, there can be nothing new under the sun. But to me, the sun, like the rest of the cosmos, is alive, and therefore not ready-made at all. ☆

Yours,
D. H. LAWRENCE.

Villa Mirenda,
San Paolo Mosciano,
Scandicci, Florence, Italy.

To Miss Pearn. 13th May 1926.

DEAR MISS PEARN,

I send you a story, *Two Blue Birds*—probably to be another tribulation to you.

☆ I feel bad about that strike. Italian papers say: 'The Government will maintain an iron resistance.' Since the war, I 've no belief in iron resistances. Flesh and blood and a bit of wisdom can do quite enough resisting and a bit of adjusting into the bargain—and with iron one only hurts oneself and everybody. Damn iron!

Yrs.,
D. H. LAWRENCE.

Villa Mirenda,
Scandicci, Florence, Italy.

To Rolf Gardiner. 11th Oct. 1926.

☆ I think, one day, I shall take a place in the country, somewhere, where perhaps one or two other men might like to settle in the neighbourhood, and we might possibly slowly evolve a new rhythm of life: learn to make the creative pauses, and learn to dance and to sing together, without stunting, and perhaps also publish some little fighting periodical, keeping fully alert and alive to the world, living a different life in the midst of it, not merely apart. You see, one cannot suddenly decapitate oneself. If barren idealism and intellectualism are a curse, it's not the head's fault. The head is really a quite sensible member, which knows what's what: or *must* know. One needs to establish a fuller relationship between oneself and the universe, and between oneself and one's fellow man and fellow woman. It doesn't mean cutting out the 'brothers-in-Christ' business simply: it means expanding it into a full relationship, where there can be also physical and passional meeting, as there used to be in the old dances and rituals. We have to know how to go out and meet one another, upon the third ground, the holy ground. You see, you yourself go out intensely in the spirit, as it were, to meet some fellow men. But another part of yourself, the fighting and the passionate part, never issues—it seems to me—from its shell. I may be all wrong, don't take any notice if I am. We need to come forth and meet in the essential physical self, on some third holy ground. It used to be done in the old rituals, in the old dances, in the old fights between men. It could be done again. But the intelligent soul has to find the way in which to do it: it won't do itself. One had to be most intensely conscious, but not intellectual or ideal.

Let us think about it, and make some sort of start if it becomes possible. No use rushing into anything. If one can be sensible oneself, one will become the focus, or node, of a new sensibility. ☆   D. H. LAWRENCE.

Villa Mirenda, Scandicci,
Florence.

To Dr Trigant Burrow.   *3rd Aug.* 1927.

☆ I believe as you do—one must use words like believe—that it is our being cut off that is our ailment, and out of this ailment everything bad arises. I wish I saw a little clearer how you get over the cut-offness. I must come and be present at your group-analysis work one day, if I may. Myself, I suffer badly from being so cut off. But what is one to do? One can't link up with the social unconscious. At times, one is *forced* to be essentially a hermit. I don't want to be. But anything else is either a personal tussle, or a money tussle: sickening: except, of course, just for ordinary acquaintance, which remains acquaintance. One has no real human relations—that is so devastating.

☆ And then there will *never* be a millennium. There will *never* be a 'true societal flow'—all things are relative. Men were never, in the past, fully societal—and they never will be in the future. But more so, more than now. Now is the time between Good Friday and Easter. We're absolutely in the tomb. If only one saw a chink of light in the tomb door. But your book too is a chink.

☆ And I do think that man is related to the universe in some 'religious' way, even prior to his relation to his fellow man. And I do think that the only way of true relationship between men is to meet in some common 'belief'—if the belief is but physical and not merely mental. I hate religion in its religiosity as much as you do. But you, who like etymologies, look at religion. Monism is the religion of the cut-off, father-worship is the cult of the cut-off: but it's the cut-offness that's to fault. There is a *principle* in the universe, towards which man turns religiously—a *life* of the universe itself. And the hero is he who touches and transmits the life of the universe. The hero is good—your own effort is heroic—how else understand it? It's only this image business which is so hateful. Napoleon was all right: it was the Emperor that was out of gear.

Do you know somebody who said: *On connaît les femmes, ou on les aime ; il n'y a pas de milieu* ? It's Frenchy, but I'm not sure it isn't true. I'm not sure if a mental relation with a woman doesn't make it impossible to love her. To know the *mind* of a woman is to end in hating her. Love means the pre-cognitive flow—neither strictly has a mind—it is the honest state before the apple. Bite the apple, and the love is killed.

Between man and woman it's a question of under-standing *or* love, I am almost convinced.

> Where the apple reddens never pry
> Lest we lose our Edens, you and I—

The Edens are so badly lost, anyhow. But it was the apple, not the Lord, did it. There is a fundamental antagonism between the mental cognitive mode and the naïve or physical or sexual mode of consciousness. As long as time lasts, it will be a battle or a truce between the two. How to prevent suburbia spreading over Eden (too late! it's done)—how to prevent Eden running to a great wild wilderness—there you are. But you're wrong, I *think*, about marriage. Are you married?

How to regain the naïve or innocent soul—how to make it the man within man—your 'societal'; and at the same time keep the cognitive mode for defences and adjustments and 'work'—*voila !*

As for myself, I'm in despair. I've been in bed this last week with bronchial hemorrhages—due, radically, to chagrin—though I was born bronchial—born in chagrin, too. But I'm better—shaky—shaky—and we're going to Austria to-morrow, D.V.—whoever D. may be—to the mountains.

I shall write a review of your book if I can. Probably even then nobody will print it. But it is most in sympathy with me of any book I've read for a long time. Pardon the egoism—what is one to say! I hope we may meet, really.

D. H. LAWRENCE.

Kesselmatte, Gsteig, b. Gstaad.

To A. Huxley.   *Sunday, after Tea.*

☆ For a change, we have E—— and her daughter—and it is really rather suffering—and E——, poor ——, she can't help feeling that ninepence is exactly half as good again as sixpence. If I wearily protest that ninepence is nothing to me unless it's ninepence worth of life, she just looks at me as if I 'd said nothing. How I *hate* the attitude of ordinary people to life. How I loathe ordinariness! How from my soul I abhor nice simple people, with their eternal price-list. It makes my blood boil.

However, they leave next Friday, back safely to England, dear England, with its eternal 'expensive' and 'not at all dear, you know.' The English are *actually* the most materialistic people in the world. They 're deader and pennywiser than any Americans: and I can stand them less.

☆ Here it 's turning to autumn. We had three awful deluge days—then a brilliant morning, brilliant new snow, brilliant new world—and slopes all bubbled over with pink autumn crocuses—very lovely. This evening it 's sulking and trying to thunder: cow-bells ting-ting-ting—very still in all the world, and somehow far. Even our visitors have subsided in comparative stillness.

Am reading again *Chartreuse de Parme* — so good historically, socially and all that—but emotionally rather empty and trashy. Had of course to rescue F.—who is painting autumn crocuses in water, and *naturally* rubbed her paper with milk roll instead of stale bread, to thin off her pencil marks. Of course milk roll is so much better class! nice and greasy.

Night falling—mist on the mountains—stewed rabbit and onions in the kitchen—wish you were here for a party!—D. H. L.

Villa Beau Soleil, Bandol, Var.

To Lady Ottoline Morrell.   *21st Jan.* 1930.

MY DEAR OTTOLINE,

Many thanks for sending me Philip's book[1]—I have begun to read it, and shall enjoy it—nice and fat and human, one can keep on with it pleasantly for many a day. Quite a job worth doing, to make such a book accessible. I must say I like the Englishmen of a hundred years ago. They were still men.

---

[1] *Leaves from the Greville Diary*, edited by Philip Morrell.

All very quiet here—my health been bad this winter
—doctor says perhaps I must go into a sanatorium for
a couple of months. Perhaps I will, I am tired of being
always defeated by bad health. It has been rather
bitter to me, this not being able to get better, for such
a long time. But the body has a strange will of its own,
and nurses its own chagrin.

What a pity we didn't know, when you were at Aix,
so near. It would have been so good to see you again.
I don't know when I shall come to England with my
wretched health, but perhaps you will come south.
With love from us both.

D. H. L.

EVERYMAN'S LIBRARY

By ERNEST RHYS

VICTOR HUGO said a Library was 'an act of faith,' and another writer spoke of one so beautiful, so perfect, so harmonious in all its parts, that he who made it was smitten with a passion. In that faith Everyman's Library was planned out originally on a large scale; and the idea was to make it conform as far as possible to a perfect scheme. However, perfection is a thing to be aimed at and not to be achieved in this difficult world; and since the first volumes appeared there have been many interruptions, chief among them Wars, during which even the City of Books feels the great commotion. But the series always gets back into its old stride.

One of the practical expedients in the original plan was to divide the volumes into separate sections, as Biography, Fiction, History, Belles-lettres, Poetry, Philosophy, Romance, and so forth; with a shelf for Young People. The largest slice of this huge provision of nearly a thousand volumes is, as a matter of course, given to the tyrranous demands of fiction. But in carrying out the scheme, publishers and editors contrived to keep in mind that books, like men and women, have their elective affinities. The present volume, for instance, will be found to have its companion books, both in the same class and not less significantly in other sections. With that idea too, novels like Walter Scott's *Ivanhoe* and *Fortunes of Nigel*, Lytton's *Harold*, and Dickens's *Tale of Two Cities*, have been used as pioneers of history and treated as a sort of holiday history books. For in our day history is tending to grow more documentary and less literary; and 'the historian who is a stylist,' as one of our contributors, the late Thomas Seccombe, said, 'will soon be regarded as a kind of Phoenix.'

As for history, Everyman's Library has been eclectic enough to choose its historians from every school in turn, including Gibbon, Grote, Finlay, Macaulay, Motley, and Prescott, while among earlier books may be found the Venerable Bede and the Anglo-Saxon Chronicle. On the classic shelf too, there is a Livy in an admirable translation by Canon Roberts, and Caesar, Tacitus, Thucydides, and Herodotus are not forgotten.

'You only, O Books,' said Richard de Bury, 'are liberal and independent; you give to all who ask.' The variety of authors old and new, the wisdom and the wit at the disposal of Everyman in his own Library, may even, at times, seem all but embarrassing. In the Essays, for instance, he may turn to Dick Steele in *The Spectator* and learn how Cleomira dances, when the elegance of her motion is unimaginable and 'her eyes are chastised with the simplicity and innocence of her thoughts.' Or he may take *A Century of Essays*, as a key to a whole roomful of the English Essayists, from Bacon to Addison, Elia to Augustine Birrell. These are the golden gossips of literature, the writers who learnt the delightful art of talking on paper. Or again, the reader who has the right spirit and looks on all literature as a great adventure may dive back into the classics, and in Plato's *Phaedrus* read how every soul is divided into three parts (like Caesar's Gaul). The poets next, and he may turn to the finest critic of Victorian times, Matthew Arnold, as their showman, and find in his essay on Maurice de Guerin a clue to the 'magical power of poetry,' as in Shakespeare, with his

> daffodils
> That come before the swallow dares, and take
> The winds of March with beauty.

Hazlitt's *Table Talk* may help us again to discover the relationship of author to author, which is another form of the Friendship of Books. His incomparable essay, 'On Going a Journey,' is a capital prelude to Coleridge's *Biographia Literaria*; and so throughout the long labyrinth of the Library shelves one can follow the magic clue in prose or verse that leads to the hidden treasury. In that way a reader becomes his own critic and Doctor of Letters, and may turn to the Byron review in Macaulay's *Essays* as a prelude to the three volumes of Byron's own poems, remembering that the poet whom Europe loved more than England did was, as Macaulay said, 'the beginning, the middle and the end of all his own poetry.' This brings us to the provoking reflection that it is the obvious authors and the books most easy to reprint which have been the signal successes out of the many hundreds in the series, for Everyman is distinctly proverbial in his tastes. He likes best of all an old author who has worn well or a comparatively new author who has gained something like newspaper notoriety. In attempting to lead him on from the good books that are known to those that are less known, the publishers may have at times been even too adventurous. But the elect reader is or ought to be a party to this conspiracy of books and book-men. He can make it possible, by his help and his co-operative zest, to add still more authors, old and new. 'Infinite riches in a little room,' as the saying is, will be the reward of every citizen who helps year by year to build the City of Books. With such a belief in its possibilities the old Chief (J. M. Dent) threw himself into the enterprise. With the zeal of a true book-lover, he thought that books might be alive and productive as dragons' teeth, which, being 'sown up and down the land, might chance to spring up armed men.' That is a great idea, and it means a fighting campaign in which every new reader who buys a volume, counts as a recruit.

> To him all books which lay
> Their sure foundation in the heart of man . . :
> From Homer the great Thunderer, to the voice
> That roars along the bed of Jewish song . . .
> Shall speak as Powers for ever to be hallowed!

EVERYMAN'S LIBRARY

A CLASSIFIED LIST OF THE 988 VOLUMES

In each of the thirteen classifications in this list (except BIOGRAPHY) the volumes are arranged alphabetically under the *authors' names*, but Anthologies and works by various hands are listed under titles. Where authors appear in more than one section, a cross-reference is given, viz.: (*See also* FICTION). The number at the end of each item is the number of the volume in the series.

BIOGRAPHY

BIOGRAPHY—*continued*

CLASSICAL

ESSAYS AND BELLES-LETTRES

ESSAYS AND BELLES-LETTRES—*continued*

FICTION

FICTION—*continued*

FICTION—*continued*

FICTION—*continued*

FICTION—*continued*

Stevenson's Dr. Jekyll and Mr. Hyde. The Merry Men and Other Tales. 767
,, The Master of Ballantrae and The Black Arrow. 764
,, St. Ives. Introduction by Ernest Rhys. 904
,, Treasure Island and Kidnapped. 763
(*See also* ESSAYS, POETRY, *and* TRAVEL)
Surtees' Jorrocks' Jaunts and Jollities. 817
Swift's Gulliver's Travels. Unabridged Edition, with contemporary maps. Introduction by Harold Williams. 60
Tales of Detection. Edited, with Introduction, by Dorothy L. Sayers. 928
Thackeray's Rose and the Ring and other Stories. Intro. Walter Jerrold.
,, Esmond. Introduction by Walter Jerrold. 73 [359
,, Newcomes. Introduction by Walter Jerrold. 2 vols. 465–6
,, Pendennis. Intro. by Walter Jerrold. 2 vols. 425–6
,, Roundabout Papers. 687
,, Vanity Fair. Introduction by Hon. Whitelaw Reid. 298
,, Virginians. Introduction by Walter Jerrold. 2 vols. 507–8
(*See also* ESSAYS)
Tolstoy's Anna Karenina. Trans. by Rochelle S. Townsend. 2 vols. 612–13
,, Childhood, Boyhood, and Youth. Trans. by C. J. Hogarth. 591
,, Master and Man, and other Parables and Tales. 469
,, War and Peace. 3 vols. 525–7
Trollope's (Anthony) Barchester Towers. 30
,, ,, Dr. Thorne. 360
,, ,, Framley Parsonage. Intro. by Ernest Rhys. 181
,, ,, The Golden Lion of Granpère. Introduction by Sir Hugh Walpole. 761
,, ,, The Last Chronicles of Barset. 2 vols. 391–2
,, ,, Phineas Finn. Intro. by Sir Hugh Walpole. 2 vols.
,, ,, The Small House at Allington. 361 [832–3
,, ,, The Warden. Introduction by Ernest Rhys. 182
Turgenev's Fathers and Sons. Translated by C. J. Hogarth. 742
,, Liza, or A Nest of Nobles. Trans. by W. R. S. Ralston. 677
,, Smoke. Translated by Natalie Duddington. 988
,, Virgin Soil. Translated by Rochelle S. Townsend. 528
Twain's (Mark) Tom Sawyer and Huckleberry Finn. Introduction by Christopher Morley. 976
Voltaire's Candide and Other Tales. 936
Walpole's (Hugh) Mr. Perrin and Mr. Traill. 918
Wells's (H. G.) Ann Veronica. 977
,, The Time Machine and The Wheels of Chance. 915
Whyte-Melville's The Gladiators. Introduction by J. Mavrogordato. 523
Wood's (Mrs. Henry) The Channings. 84
Woolf's (Virginia) To the Lighthouse. Intro. by D. M. Hoare. 949
Yonge's (Charlotte M.) The Dove in the Eagle's Nest. 329
,, ,, The Heir of Redclyffe. Intro. Mrs. Meynell. 362
(*See also* FOR YOUNG PEOPLE)
Zola's (Emile) Germinal. Translated by Havelock Ellis. 897

HISTORY

Anglo-Saxon Chronicle, The. Translated by James Ingram. 624
Bede's Ecclesiastical History, etc. Introduction by Vida D. Scudder. 479
Burnet's History of His Own Times. 85
Carlyle's French Revolution. Introduction by H. Belloc. 2 vols. 31–2
(*See also* BIOGRAPHY *and* ESSAYS) [Brogan, M.A. 965
Chesterton's (Cecil) History of the United States. Edited by Prof. D. W.
Creasy's Fifteen Decisive Battles of the World. Intro. by E. Rhys. 300
De Joinville (*See* Villehardouin)
Duruy's (Jean Victor) A History of France. 2 vols. 737–8
Finlay's Byzantine Empire. 33
,, Greece under the Romans. 185
Froude's Henry VIII. Intro. by Llewellyn Williams, M.P. 3 vols. 372–4
,, Edward VI. Intro. by Llewellyn Williams, M.P., B.C.L. 375
,, Mary Tudor. Intro. by Llewellyn Williams, M.P., B.C.L. 477
,, History of Queen Elizabeth's Reign. 5 vols. Completing Froude's 'History of England,' in 10 vols. 583–7
(*See also* ESSAYS *and* BIOGRAPHY)

HISTORY—continued

ORATORY

PHILOSOPHY AND THEOLOGY

PHILOSOPHY AND THEOLOGY—*continued*

POETRY AND DRAMA

Anglo-Saxon Poetry. Edited by Professor R. K. Gordon. 794
Arnold's (Matthew) Poems. 334
Ballads, A Book of British. Selected by R. B. Johnson. 572
Beaumont and Fletcher, The Select Plays of. Introduction by Professor Baker, of Harvard University. 506
Björnson's Plays. Vol. I. The Newly Married Couple, Leonardo, A Gauntlet. Trans. by R. Farquharson Sharp. 625
„   „   Vol. II. The Editor, The Bankrupt, and The King. Translated by R. Farquharson Sharp. 696
Blake's Poems and Prophecies. Introduction by Max Plowman. 792
Browning's Poems. Vol. I, 1833–44. Introduction by Arthur Waugh. 41
„   „   Vol. II, 1844–64. 42
„   Poems and Plays, Vol. IV, 1871–90. Introduction by M. M. Bozman. 964
„   The Ring and the Book. Intro. by Chas. W. Hodell. 502
Burns's Poems and Songs. Introduction by J. Douglas. 94
Byron's Poetical Works. New edition, reset. 3 vols. 486–8
Calderon: Six Plays, translated by Edward FitzGerald. 819
Chaucer's Canterbury Tales. Edited by Principal Burrell, M.A. 307
Coleridge, Golden Book of. Edited by Stopford A. Brooke. 43
(See also Essays)
Cowper (William), Poems of. Edited by H. I'Anson Fausset. 872
(See also Biography)
Dante's Divine Comedy (Cary's Translation). Specially edited by Edmund Gardner. 308
Donne's Poems. Edited by H. I'Anson Fausset. 867   [Gardner. 308
Dryden's Poems. Edited by Bonamy Dobree. 910
Eighteenth-Century Plays. Edited by John Hampden. 818
Emerson's Poems. Introduction by Professor Bakewell, Yale, U.S.A. 715
English Galaxy of Shorter Poems, The. From pre-Chaucer to A. E. Housman. Chosen and edited by Gerald Bullett. 959
English Religious Verse. Edited by G. Lacey May. 937
Everyman and other Interludes, including eight Miracle Plays. Edited by Ernest Rhys. 381
FitzGerald's (Edward) Omar Khayyám and Six Plays of Calderon. 819
Goethe's Faust. Parts I and II. Trans. and Intro. by A. G. Latham. 335
(See also Essays and Fiction)
Golden Book of Modern English Poetry, The. Edited by Thomas Caldwell. 921
Golden Treasury of Longer Poems, The. Edited by Ernest Rhys. 746
Goldsmith's Poems and Plays. Introduction by Austin Dobson. 415
(See also Essays and Fiction)
Gray's Poems and Letters. Introduction by John Drinkwater. 628
Hebbel's Plays. Translated, with an Introduction, by Dr. C. K. Allen. 694
Heine: Prose and Poetry. 911
Herbert's Temple. Introduction by Edward Thomas. 309
Herrick's Hesperides and Noble Numbers. Intro. by Ernest Rhys. 310
Ibsen's Brand. Translated by F. E. Garrett. 716
„   Ghosts, The Warriors at Helgeland, and An Enemy of the People. Translated by R. Farquharson Sharp. 552
„   Lady Inger of Ostraat, Love's Comedy, and The League of Youth. Translated by R. Farquharson Sharp. 729
„   Peer Gynt. Translated by R. Farquharson Sharp. 747
„   A Doll's House, The Wild Duck, and The Lady from the Sea. Translated by R. Farquharson Sharp. 494
„   The Pretenders, Pillars of Society, and Rosmersholm. Translated by R. Farquharson Sharp. 659
Jonson's (Ben) Plays. Intro. by Professor Schelling. 2 vols. 489–90
Kalidasa: Shakuntala. Translated by Professor A. W. Ryder. 629
Keats's Poems. Revised, reset, with Intro. by the editor, Gerald Bullett. 101
Kingsley's (Charles) Poems. Introduction by Ernest Rhys. 793
(See also Fiction and For Young People)
Langland's (William) Piers Plowman. 571
Lessing's Laocoön, Minna von Barnhelm, and Nathan the Wise. 843
Longfellow's Poems. Introduction by Katherine Tynan. 382
Marlowe's Plays and Poems. Introduction by Edward Thomas. 383

POETRY AND DRAMA—*continued*

REFERENCE

ROMANCE

SCIENCE

TRAVEL AND TOPOGRAPHY

FOR YOUNG PEOPLE

FOR YOUNG PEOPLE—*continued*